# A BOTANIST'S WINDOW
## ON THE
## TWENTIETH CENTURY

# A BOTANIST'S WINDOW
# ON THE
# TWENTIETH CENTURY

## RICHARD H. GOODWIN

HARVARD FOREST / PETERSHAM, MASSACHUSETTS
HARVARD UNIVERSITY
2002

# TO ESTHER

My loving partner and support in this life's rewarding adventure.

# CONTENTS

1  Ancestors / 1

2  Growing Up / 15

3  The Harvard Years / 27

4  Letters From Africa / 49

5  The Web of Research / 99

6  War and the Uneasy Atom / 123

7  Wilderness / 135

8  Land Saving Action / 153

9  Dolbia Hill and the Burnham Brook Preserve / 185

10  The Conservation and Research Foundation / 213

11  Sunset Rambles / 249

12  Philosophy and Motivation / 299

   Appendix: Wartime Letters from Old Scouts / 307

   Notes / 325

   Index / 331

# ACKNOWLEDGMENTS

First I would like to express my gratitude to the many wonderful people who have made this book possible — devoted family, warm friends, stimulating students, creative colleagues, and dedicated environmental activists. For a preliminary editorial review of most of the manuscript, I would like to thank my daughter-in-law Judith Bell. Robert Braunfield provided seven of the sketches that appear under chapter headings; Allen T. Carroll and Julie Zickefoose, two additional drawings. For design and production, I am indebted to my editor, Susan Hayes. Sponsorhip of the book by the Harvard Forest, Harvard University, was arranged through the good offices of its Director, David R. Foster, to whom I am duly grateful.

# A BOTANIST'S WINDOW
## ON THE
## TWENTIETH CENTURY

# I

# ANCESTORS

I was born on the fourteenth of December 1910, in Brookline, Massachusetts, in my parents' house on Tappan Street, just around the corner from Beacon Street. When I was two, my family bought an English-style plaster-and-beam house, that was built about 1880 at the corner of Walnut and Warren Streets overlooking the Old Reservoir and a little triangular park in front of the First Parish Church (Unitarian) of Brookline. In that house I was brought up as an only child, and Mother was still living in it when she died sixty-one years later at the age of 102. Despite the tremendous growth that has taken place in the metropolitan area of Boston, the attractive neighborhood around the house has experienced remarkably little change.

My father, Harry Manley Goodwin, was professor of electrochemistry at the Massachusetts Institute of Technology (MIT). Born in 1870, he grew up in West Roxbury, Massachusetts, in my grandfather's house. When he was almost six, he and his younger sister, Florence, lost their mother, who died of consumption. The two children were raised by my grandfather's first cousin, Ruth Dinsmore. According to my father, "Aunt Ruth" was somewhat of a harridan. Dad attended MIT, graduated at the age of twenty, and then, with the exception of two years studying for his doctorate in Leipzig, Germany, was continuously on the staff of that institution for fifty-two years. Having been a foreign student himself, he was always most caring of the graduate students from abroad and served as their informal advisor for many years before MIT created the position of Dean of the Graduate School — a post he filled until his retirement in 1940. We were told that when students got in trouble or needed assistance they were advised, "Go see Maw."

As a young adult Dad was a confirmed bachelor. He was very fond of the theatre and spent many summers traveling abroad and hiking through the Alps. One year he rode horseback through Yellowstone Park. It was not until he was thirty-five, that he finally met my mother and married her the following year, 1906. He had a very warm personality, worshiped Mother, and became a doting parent.

Dad always had a lively concern for the quality of teaching and worried that overemphasis on research at MIT might have a detrimental effect on faculty instruction. One of his significant contributions was the publication in 1908 of a little book entitled *Precision of Measurements and Graphical Methods*, which served as the text for a course he gave on that subject. His students frequently commented that this was the most valuable course they had taken at MIT.

Dad died in his sleep af a heart attack in his eightieth year. It was a wonderful way to go. Mother and I endowed the Goodwin Medal at MIT in his memory. It is awarded annually to the graduate student, who is judged, on the basis of student evaluations, to be the most outstanding teacher. One of the first Goodwin medalist was Kenneth R. Wadleigh, who later became Dean of the Graduate School and then the Vice President of the Institute. A more recent recipient was Frank E. Perkins, who also became Dean of the Graduate School.

Dad's sister, Aunt Florence, was a generous, warm-hearted woman,

*Clockwise from left:* Grandfather Richard D. Goodwin, father, Harry M. Goodwin, and Richard H. Goodwin, 1911.

but not at all practical. She married Richard Marcy, and they lived in Lincoln, Massachusetts, in a huge house modeled after an Irish castle. She and Uncle Dick, who was thin as a rail, nearly killed themselves each fall attempting to harvest and dispose of the apples produced in their orchard. After father acquired our first car around 1915, we used to drive out to Lincoln from time to time to visit. It was on one those trips, when I was still a small child, that we discovered a woodcock's nest with four eggs in it. On a second visit a few days later I patted the mother bird while she was brooding her fledglings.

My grandfather, Richard D. Goodwin, was eighty when I was born. I remember him as a portly, kindly old gentleman with a flowing white beard. We occasionally visited him in his substantial house on Town-send Street in West Roxbury. It had a massive mahogany bannister on the stairway in the front hall and a front parlor crowded with Victorian furniture. On the third floor was a pool table.

Grandfather was brought up in central New Hampshire. His father, Samuel, was a carpenter-builder, reported to have constructed the church in Charlestown, New Hampshire. As a young man, Grandfather came to Boston and soon started working for a clothing manufacturing firm, the first to develop mass production methods for cutting many layers of cloth with a patterning machine. After a few years Grandfather became a partner. He met my grandmother, Sarah Clisby, in Boston, where she was taking singing lessons. She was also from New Hampshire. Until just before his death Grandfather regularly walked the three miles from his home in West Roxbury to work in downtown Boston. At eighty-five he broke his hip and died of pleurisy as a result of being immobilized. He was buried beside his wife in the Goodwin plot in Forest Hills Cemetery in Jamaica Plain, Massachusetts. Aunt Florence, Uncle Dick, and my parents are also interred there.

My mother, Mary Blanchard Linder, was born in Newton, Massachusetts, one of five children. As a young woman she was considered delicate, and for this reason never attended college; but being of a scholarly bent, with a very retentive memory, she became better educated than most college graduates. She was especially interested in languages and developed a proficiency in French, Italian, German, and Latin. Languages were never my strong point, and I can remember my feelings of frustration when Mother would pick up Virgil and toss off a translation without having looked at the language for forty years. She became a member of the Circolo Italiano in Boston, and after World War I she developed a contact through this group with an Italian boy in Italy, giving him financial assistance . When she was in her eighties she went on a Boston Museum of Fine Arts tour of Spain and Italy. At one of the villas in Italy it was she who was able to carry on a gracious conversation with the owner of the establishment. When Mother was ninety, my wife and I took her to Greece, a country she had always wanted to visit. In preparation, she arranged to have an instructor from Boston College come to her home to tutor her in modern Greek. On the trip she managed to converse in a limited way in Greek with people she met.

Mary B. Goodwin and Richard H. Goodwin, 1911.

The dictionary was the vade mecum in our household. Hardly a day would go by without consulting it for the derivation of a word, its exact meaning, its pronunciation, or its spelling. It was Mother who upgraded the family performance in the use of our native tongue.

Mother survived my father by more than twenty-two years, dying in 1973 in her house in Brookline at the age of 102. One of the goodies that turned up in her incredibly tidy desk was a small bundle of Christmas cards that Mother couldn't bear to discard. These beautiful cards were from Oakes and Blanche Ames. They were etchings that Mrs. Ames had made of some of her husband's orchids. Professor Ames, by the way, was a member of the Harvard faculty who served on the committee administering my undergraduate honors exam in 1933. Mother and Mrs. Ames became friends when they served together as officers of the Massachusetts Birth Control League, in the days before its headquarters were raided by the police. The organization had to go underground and change its name to Planned Parenthood. We were

Great-great-grandfather Captain William Linder.

wondering what to do with these cards, when it was announced that Blanche's grandson, Oakes Ames, had been selected to become president of Connecticut College. I turned the cards over to the college librarian and they were subsequently reproduced to good effect in some of the college's publications.

Mother was brought up in her parent's house on Cotton Street in Newton. Grandfather George Linder II was in the business of importing chemicals. His father and a German named Meyer had established the company in Boston in 1848. I have no remembrance of Grandfather Linder; he died when I was only two, of a creeping paralysis following a fall on the ice. He was a sportsman and owned a camp on Moosehead Lake in Maine, which Mother used to visit.

The Linders were of English extraction. My great-great-grandfather Captain William Linder was a resourceful and dynamic person. In 1797 England found herself in a precarious situation, fearing invasion by Napoleon and facing a domestic crisis with inadequate gold to stabilize the currency. To make matters worse, repressive treatment of sailors in the British Fleet had resulted in revolts on a number of the fleet's vessels, which were blockading the Thames River estuary. Captain Linder, in command of a merchant vessel, managed by clever and courageous navigation, to elude the blockade of the mutinous fleet. He sailed to Rotterdam and took on a heavy cargo of gold, which he hid under a thick layer of potatoes. He again slipped by the blockade and came safely to port in London. I do not know how significant it was in bolstering the English economy, but for this exploit he was presented with a gold watch at the behest of the Admiralty. The testimonial document that accompanied it is said to be on deposit at the British Museum. That Captain Linder was a man of spirit and decision is further attested by a family report that a King's sheriff once boarded his ship to serve him papers, whereupon the Captain seized the man and tossed him overboard.[1]

Another family anecdote is told about Captain Linder's son, George A. Linder, my great-grandfather. One day in a crowd in London he felt his pocket being picked. According to the story, he grabbed the thief by the wrist, held the pilfering hand up above the crowd with the wallet still in it, and announced in a loud voice, "This fellow has just picked my pocket!" He then laid the thief out with his other fist.

Grandmother, Mary Frances Linder, was a remarkable woman. Although in delicate health for years, she had many devoted friends — as demonstrated by her correspondence with them and by the condolence letters that poured in after her death. Mother, before she was married, travelled abroad with Grandmother Linder and helped take care of her at home. After my parents moved to Walnut Street, Grandmother moved into a large house overlooking ours. In the basement of this house I attended a kindergarten that was run for some of the neighborhood children. I learned to count by tens, using bundles of colored toothpicks.

Grandmother was a discerning collector with infallible judgment. She collected silver, furniture, old lace, porcelain, and, during a sojourn in the southwest, Indian baskets and other artifacts. Many of these

Portrait of maternal grandmother Mary Frances Linder, hanging in the
front hall of my family's home in Brookline, Massachusetts.

items found their way into museums and some to our house. Grandmother gave her Indian artifacts to the Peabody Museum at Harvard. A handsome inlaid corner cabinet filled with rare English china and carved ivories, which adorned my mother's reception room, was later given to the Lyman Allyn Art Museum in New London, Connecticut.

Grandmother's most notable piece of furniture was an early American Chippendale block-front secretary desk. She bought it for $200 from the Jones family, who were running the Golden Ball Tavern in Weston, Massachusetts. It was solid mahogany but covered with paint. Scraped down and restored, it stood in the corner of our living room, serving as Mother's desk until the time of her death. In her estate it was appraised at more than everything else in the house put together. By that time, a group of antiquarians has acquired the tavern from the Jones family and were restoring it as a museum. They discovered that we had inherited the desk and were very anxious to recover it for the tavern. After some negotiations we gave the desk to the Golden Ball Tavern Trust — a very nice charitable deduction for us —and they in turn made some substantial charitable gifts to a number of philanthropic enterprises of our choosing.

Grandmother Linder's father, John Smith Farlow, came to America as a penniless young man from a small town in northern Ireland and eventually made a fortune in railroads. He lived on his Nonantum Hill estate in Newton and during his life gave the town a library and a park. Grandmother had five brothers, one of whom was William Gilson Farlow, who became the father of cryptogamic botany in this country. Great Uncle Will was a small man with a full moustache and bushy eyebrows. Relatively late in life he married Lilian Horseford, who, by contrast, was a large woman, very active in the development of Radcliffe College. I remember, when I was six, going with my parents to their home for Easter dinner. They lived on Quincy Street in Cambridge, Massachusetts, now the approximate site of the Harvard Faculty Club. We were shown the fireproof wing that housed Uncle Will's rare books and herbarium. His outstanding collection of algae and fungi now

Great uncle William Gilson Farlow.

forms the core of the Farlow Herbarium at Harvard. On that visit I admired a handsome little metal chest that had a trick way of opening. The Farlows generously gave it to me.

They had a summer cottage in Chocorua, New Hampshire, referred to as "Saint Chads." It was on the north side of a hill overlooking the lakes and had a picture-postcard view of Mount Chocorua. My family spent two summers there — when I was four and again when I was eight. I learned how to fish for perch and sunfish from the boathouse on Little Chocorua Lake, and I discovered other wonders of the natural world, such as the frog that dwelt in the rain barrel at the corner of the house and the snake I extracted by the tail from a stone wall. Those were anxious days of the First World War, and I recall sitting on my father's lap and being told about the Battle of Verdun.

Of my mother's siblings, George was the oldest. He married and moved to Seattle. Mother took care of his first daughter, Muriel, for a while and kept contact with this branch of the family through correspondence.

Her second brother, my Uncle John, lived in Canton, Massachusetts, and carried on the chemical import business in Boston established by his grandfather. He had four children. Two of the boys, Jack and Bob, stayed in the Linder family busines with their father. A third son, David Linder, became a cryptogamic botanist, following in his great-uncle's footsteps. When he was employed at the Missouri Botanical Garden, he married a botanist, Elinor Alberts, who discovered how to germinate the minute seeds of *Cattleya* orchids by inoculating them with a fungus. The discovery was commercially significant because flowers of this genus are much prized for corsages. When David came East to assume the directorship of the Farlow Herbarium, he and his wife brought with them a larger number of her little orchid seedlings, but it was a difficult time financially because the plants had to be grown for about seven years before coming into bloom and generating some income.

Uncle John's youngest child was Mary F. Linder, born in 1905. She became a friend of Ruth Bemis, my wife's older sister.

Aunt Ethie, Mother's younger sister, was a beautiful woman. She married Dwight Prouty and they had one son, Dwight, Jr.

Mother always referred to her youngest brother, Hosmer, as the star of the family. He was an excellent student headed for a medical career. While an undergraduate at Harvard he was tragically killed by a blow to the temple while boxing in the gym. Grandmother established a medical fellowship in his memory and also made an anonymous gift to the Harvard Medical School in support of medical research. She received the following letters from Dr. George B. Magrath and Dr. Councilman, both on the staff of the medical school, thanking her for the research grant.[2]

On April 21 1903, Dr. Magrath wrote:

> Once more my dear Mrs. Linder let me thank you on behalf of all who are engaged in the research for furnishing us so freely with the sinews of war in our campaign. And now let me tell you what will be publicly announced at a meeting of the Boston Society of Medical Sciences, next Tuesday night, that we have identified beyond doubt the organism which is the cause of small pox. The last link in a lengthening chain of evidence came into our hands only yesterday, although for some little time past we have felt very sure that we were very close to important discoveries. . . . (I) will now merely add that the importance of the results of the work is such that we can hardly realize that we have actually accomplished what we have been striving for; one thing, however, we realize fully, namely that it is you who have made it all possible.

On May 12, 1904, Dr. W. Councilman wrote:

> My dear Madam: From my position I necessarily became aware of your generous contribution to the research on smallpox and vaccinia which was conducted by the pathological laboratory of the Harvard Medical School. Your gift came at a time when without it the work must have ceased. The money was expended through the University in the purchase of apparatus and supplies. The example of your anonymous contribution led to other gifts for the expenses of publication, and for an expedition to Manilla where unequalled opportunities for the experimental study of the disease on monkeys are found. Here the study has been completed and I send you by todays mail a copy of the report. The work contains a description of the changes in the tissues produced by the disease and of the parasite which is the cause. The parasite is the same in both small pox and vaccinia, the difference being that in the milder

disease vaccinia the parasite does not reach full development. There are many details in our knowledge of the disease and of the parasite which are still incomplete and which we hope to have in part completed by the work now being done in Manilla. In justice it must also be claimed for the work that it has led to the discovery of the cause of scarlet fever, a parasite of somewhat similar character having been discovered by Prof. Mallory of our laboratory in that disease. I am also quite sure that the knowledge which we have acquired in these diseases will throw light on other infectious diseases and with the light of knowledge will come, slowly it may be but surely, means to prevent and to relieve.

This was surely a highly catalytic investment!

How rapidly we lose track of our ancestors. This brief account fairly well covers what I know about mine. However, I do have the documentation for mother's election to the Massachusetts Society of the Colonial Dames of America. It traces her lineage through her maternal grandmother, Nancy Wight Blanchard, back another six generations to Francis Peabody of Topsfield, Massachusetts, who was born in England about 1613. Nancy Wight was a niece of John Hancock, whose ornate signature appears on the Declaration of Independence. Through her we have inherited a Federal tea caddy and a set of celadon plates.

# 2

# GROWING UP

My childhood was marred by illness. I was born healthy but at the age of three contracted influenza and whooping cough simultaneously. Had it not been for Mother's devoted care I would not have pulled through. This experience followed by a bout with tubercular glands in my neck, which was caused by contaminated milk and were surgically removed, left me underweight and in delicate health with a tendency toward asthma and bronchitis for the next nine years. I also had hearing loss as a result of perforated eardrums acquired at the time I had the whooping cough. Mother arranged to have me take lessons in lipreading. These clearly had good and bad effects; I always had better comprehension in lectures when I could see the speaker, but keeping a eye on the leturer had an adverse impact on the quality of my lecture notes when I got to college.

In the early twentieth century households still employed servants.

My folks had a cook and a housemaid who lived in the maid's quarters on the third floor, and, while I was little, a nurse. In addition there was a laundress who came once a week, a seamstress who came occasionally, and William Kidd, the Irish choreman, who tended the coal furnace and took care of the grounds. Our house, having been built before the day of autos, had no garage, and no stable that could be converted into one, so when we acquired our first car in 1915, father arranged for the use of a stall in a neighbor's garage, located on the back side of our block. Grandmother had a chauffeur named David who drove her Pierce Arrow, which we referred to as the Fierce Sparrow. It had big brass lanterns on the sides.

My nearest playmates were Tim Rhodes and Rich Prouty. Tim's house was next to Grandmother's and could be reached by climbing a long flight of stone stairs. He was the middle sibling in a family of seven children. His mother was English. Not long after the last child was born his father deserted the family to live in Europe. Tim was always welcome at our house. In those days there was a Sunday comic strip entitled "The Tuggles." The son was an urchin named Elmer Tuggle who got into scrapes with his friend Tim Early. My parents used to refer to my friend as Tim Early, and Tim to them as Ma and Pa Tugs. One of Tim's and my Sunday morning rites consisted of freezing the ice cream, first at my house on Walnut Street and then at Tim's on Welch Road. The freezer had to be cranked in a bucket of salted ice, and then the dasher removed and licked. For us this procedure greatly reduced the urgency of Sunday dinner.

Rich Prouty and his older sister Jane lived across the park in an ample, square colonial. We had a great time playing in their old stable situated down in back. There were hay chutes, a loft, and a roof onto which we were not supposed to climb, but did. There were splendid cherry trees from which we could pitch fruits at the straw hat of Graham, the Prouty's hired man, while he was working in the garden. When we were really little, Rich and I undertook a grandiose project to connect our two yards with a secret tunnel. At my end the excavation attained a depth of about one foot. The tool, a tin fish mold.

Thus, the problem of how to engineer the meeting of the two ends of the tunnel somewhere under the park never had to be confronted. Later Mr. Prouty gave his son a radio set and I remember adjusting a little wire onto a crystal to bring in a station. It was a bit of magic.

When I was seven my family took me to Wilton, New Hampshire, where we boarded at the Burton Farm. It was a time when the gypsy moth was spreading, and at lunch one day I called attention to one of the woolly caterpillars crawling on a corner of the stove. To my astonishment, two spinster boarders fled the room, napkins to their mouths. Mother took the occasion to instruct me in matters of social discretion.

From Wilton we took the train to Haines Landing at the northern end of Lake Mooselookmeguntic in northwestern Maine — my first taste of the north woods. There was no ragweed pollen and I was free of hay fever. We discovered "The Birches," a family camp run by Captain Barker on an island halfway down the lake and serviced daily by his steamboat. We spent four summers there, commencing in 1920. That is where I learned to swim, coached by one of the lady boarders, and to row a boat. Mother and I explored the beauties of the boreal forest and became entranced by the ledges covered with verdant blankets of mosses and lichens dotted with ferns and mushrooms. I and some of the other kids at the camp built a raft of four long logs and navigated the rocky shores using poles and a square sail. Tim Rhodes and some of his family visited there at least two of those summers. It was during our stay in 1922 that Grandmother Linder died of cancer. Mother went down to Brookline to be with her during the last days, and Father was left to cope with me. According to letters he wrote to Mother, he found me to be a bit of a brat.

My first five years of schooling were at Park School, which was then in a brown shingled building on a road below the Proutys' house. I remember my mortification at being the slowest in my class at arithmatic and a horrid little girl who sat behind me and prodded my backside with a ruler. In my twelfth year I began attending The Country

The author, behind the sail, navigating the shores of Lake Mooselookmeguntic
in Maine, on a raft constructed of four logs lashed together.
Tim Rhodes is at the rear.

Day School, which was located on my great-grandfather Farlow's estate
in Newton. My devoted father drove me, adding six miles to his trip
to work.

At about this time my health began to pick up, but I was still underweight so team sports were not my dish. Oh, the joys of football —
my bare knuckles on frozen ground and face stepped on by a cleated
boot! But at Country Day I began to get into shape through tennis,
squash, and cross-country running.

My class was small — about twelve to fifteen students — but
academic competition was keen, with Albie Pratt, Oliver Garceau, and
Jack Ratcliff often edging me out of the top slots. I have particularly
warm memories of a couple of the teachers. One was Austin Chute,
who taught Latin and also coached the hockey squad. He was a perfect
shot with a piece of chalk when someone was misbehaving in the back
row. He could make a difficult subject tolerable through patience and

good humor. I can still recall some of his jokes, for example a student's translation of "post equitem sedit atra cura" as "after horseback riding the dark lady sits down with care." Homer Boyer, a kindly older man, taught us French. Garceau irreverently refered to him as "homard," the French for lobster.

The First Parish Church is an attractive stone structure fronting on the little park across from our house. It has had an interesting history. It was indeed the first church in Brookline, at a time when it served political as well as religious functions. Then came the separation of church and state, followed by a succession of split-offs for the various Christian denominations. What was finally left became a Unitarian Church; but as can well be imagined, with so much history behind it, the parish retained many conservative traditions. Mother was an active member of the church. Father, on the other hand, being an agnostic, only accompanied mother for social reasons at Christmas and Easter. I attended the Sunday School with other neighborhood kids.

When I and eleven of my friends were just turning twelve years old, we formed the Boy Scout Troop 4, Brookline — a most significant development. We had home base in a room at the parish hall of the church. Robert Schacht, who was studying for the ministry at Harvard and later became minister of the Unitarian Church in Providence, Rhode Island, was our scoutmaster. Under his leadership we became a close-knit group; six of us were still in touch after seventy years! The outdoor skills I learned as a scout have always been an asset. We were most fortunate in getting permission from Amelia Peabody to use a little cabin next to a couple of millponds on her estate in Dover, Massachusetts. Bob Schacht acquired an old Ford Model T truck for transportation.

The chestnut blight had just reached central Massachusetts at this time, and we had permission to cut any infected trees for firewood and construction projects. Chestnut has a beautiful straight grain, and long logs can be neatly split in half — ideal for making bridges, benches, and tables. I became quite handy with an axe.

One of our troup, Eddie Andrews, was headed for Yale; all the rest of us for Harvard. The outhouse at camp very shortly became referred to as the Yale Bowl.

One day Tim Rhodes and I bicycled out to Dover to visit the camp. We discovered it had burned to the ground; nothing was left but the stone chimney and a few scorched trees. Gone was not only the structure, but of course also our canoes, tents, and other gear. It was a strange experience. I found myself unable to come to grips with reality. It was like the loss a close relative. Shortly after this disaster our parents chipped in and had the old camp replaced. But for me the new structure lacked the flavor of the old one, which had been constructed from pieces of old freight cars. Some of the railroad hardware was still attached, and I remember sleeping on a brake rod on the floor of the open loft.

At home there was always the atmosphere of interest in science. We usually shared Thanksgivings and Christmases with foreign graduate students from MIT. It was an opportunity for them to learn about our customs, and they added a cosmopolitan atmosphere to the holidays.

For quite a few years Dad was in charge of the free popular science lectures given at MIT, some of which he delivered himself. He often took me to them. His interest in the advancement of the frontiers of knowledge, especially in the physical sciences, was an important factor in conditioning my own attitudes toward basic research.

Dad's most intimate friend was the astronomer George Ellery Hale, from whom I received my middle name. Their relationship was a remarkable one, dating back to 1885 when they entered MIT as freshmen. When my family spoke of him to me, he was always referred to as "Uncle George." He was a genius, and my father, who must have had a premonition of his greatness, saved every letter he ever received from Hale. There were at least 160 of them, almost all inscribed longhand, some running to twelve sheets written on both sides. The salutation was usually "My dear Old Boy." I inherited these letters and had them microfilmed before placing the originals in the Huntington Library in Pasadena, California, where Hale lived during the later years of his life.*

---

*About twelve of these letters were of such a personal nature that they were sequestered in my safe-deposit box for a number of years before they were released.

Boy Scout Troop 4, Brookline, Massachusetts, 1925.
(*See Appendix for full caption.*)

One of the earliest of these letters, written from his family's home in Chicago in the summer of 1888, between his junior and senior year at MIT, describes the concept of the spectroheliograph, an instrument he invented for photographing the hydrogen prominences on the sun.

This is what Hale wrote to my father on August 5, 1889:

> Of scientific work I have accomplished but one thing this summer, and even that did not involve much labor. It is a scheme for photographing the prominences, and after a good deal of thought I can see no reason why it will not work. The idea occurred to me when I was coming home from uptown the other day, and amounts to this. Stop the clock of the equatorial, and let the sun transit across the slit, which is placed radial to the limb. Bring H (in the blue) into the field of the observing telescope, and replace the eye-piece by a plate-holder, held in a suitable frame, and drawn by clock-work across the field at the same rate as the sun

crosses the slit. As the H line lengthens and shortens — as
it will do with the variable height of the prominences. . . . I
have studied it out in detail, and designed a travelling plate
holder, which I will have Brashear make. . . . I have great
hopes that the thing will be a success. If it is, new chances
for work on the prominences will be opened.

Later Hale told father the idea came to him as his horse-drawn
trolley was passing a picket fence and he observed objects behind the
fence being scanned by the slits.

Uncle George usually stayed with us on his infrequent visits to the
East Coast, and when I was little he would tell me stories and "play
bear" with me on his hands and knees behind the sofa. Later on he gave
me copies of his favorite books by Harry Castleman about the Wild
West adventures of Frank Nelson.

Hale was one of the first astronomers to develop the field of astro-
physics, and his special research interest was the sun. He was a man of
great charm and a fantastic fundraiser. He found the resources to construct not only some of the country's major observatories — the
Yerkes, the Mount Wilson, and the Mount Palomar — but also the
splendid home of the National Academy of Sciences on the Mall in
the nation's capital. The latter building was completed in 1922, and our
family was invited to attend the dedication. We went to an elegant dinner in Washington the night preceding the ceremony. There were twelve
at our table — Uncle George and his wife, Aunt Evelina; their two children, Bill and Margaret; Hale's sister, Mrs. Hart, and her daughter,
Cynthia, who was about my age; Dr. James H. Breasted, historian of the
ancient world, his wife and daughter, Astrid; and my parents and I.

The event took place very shortly after the opening of Tutan-
khamen's tomb in Egypt's Valley of the Kings. I remember sitting on
the edge of my chair as Dr. Breasted recounted the excitement of
breaking through the untouched wall that sealed off the final burial
chamber. It was very rare to find such a tomb that had escaped the des-
ecration of grave robbers. The person who first peered through the

George Ellery Hale in the rotunda of the
National Academy of Sciences Buidling at the time of its dedication in 1922.

aperture beheld two full-size golden statues guarding the sarcophagus; as the beam of the torch illuminated one of these figures, the statue winked! A small fleck of gold leaf, caught on a spider's thread hanging right in front of the statue's eye, had been stirred by a breath of air from the new opening.

In 1925, on a summer trip out West, we stopped to visit the Hales in Santa Barbara. It was right after a severe earthquake that had peeled off the outer walls of some of the apartment buildings, which had the appearance of doll houses, the furniture in place and pictures still hanging on the inner walls. I recall my complete disgust at learning I had slept right through a minor aftershock while we were there.

In Pasadena we visited Uncle George's private lab, where he was making models of vortices in a tank of water to help him interpret the cyclical storms observed on the sun. He took us to meet Mr. Henry E. Huntington, who was sitting at an enormous desk looking over the latest treasures that had been collected in Europe for his library. One of these was a document signed by Queen Elizabeth I of England.

The final excitement of the visit was driving to the observatory at the summit of Mount Wilson, where we were shown the telescopes, including the 100-inch refelector and the tower telescope, the top of which we reached in an open bucket.

When Hale died, the following obituary by J. H. Jeans was published in the March 19, 1938 edition of *Nature*:

> Anyone meeting George Ellery Hale must, I think, have felt at once that he was somewhat out of the ordinary run of scientific men. We knew he was a great figure in science, but felt that he could have been equally great at almost anything else. For Nature had not only endowed him with those qualities that make for success in science — a powerful and acute intellect, a reflective mind, imagination, patience and perseverence — but also in ample measure with qualities which make for success in other walks of life — a capacity for forming rapid and accurate judgments of men, of situations, and of plans of action; a habit of looking to the future, and thinking always in terms of improvements and extensions; a driving-power which was given no rest until it had brought his plans and schemes to fruition; eagerness, enthusiasm, and above all a sympathetic personality of great charm.

Back home Dad gave me a compound microscope and a camera lucida, with which I made drawings of mites and other fascinating objects. Mother always leaned toward natural history and spoke of birding trips that she had taken with Charles J. Maynard, author of the Directory to the Birds of Eastern North America. We were always observing the birds nesting around the yard in Brookline — robins, catbirds, red-eyed verios, yellow warblers, and rose-breasted grosbeaks

— and she took me on bird walks during the warbler migration and on canoe trips on the Charles River.

In the early twentieth century, summers could be real vacations for those in academia, and Dad made the most of them. Commencing in 1923 we made six wonderful excursions through the western states, staying at dude ranches and visiting national parks. Travel in those days was by train and then by ranch or park vehicle. The first ranch we stayed at was Eaton's Ranch near Sheridan, Wyoming, the earliest enterprise of this sort in the country. Later we spent several summers at the JY Ranch in Jackson Hole, Wyoming, just east of Grand Teton National Park. The JY Ranch, run at the time by a member of the DuPont family, was later acquired by the Rockefellers. We visited national parks, which including Yellowstone, Glacier, Rocky Mountain, Mount Rainier, Yosemite, Grand Canyon, Bryce and Zion Canyons, and Mesa Verde, as well as several of the national monuments and Indian pueblos in the southwest.

The JY Ranch in Jackson Hole, Wyoming, looking west up Phelps Lake to Death Canyon, a deep defile cutting into the Tetons.

By the end of the sixth western trip I was pretty handy at handling a horse and felt more at home in the Rocky Mountain states than I did in New England. I was at the JY Ranch in the summer of 1929 when I learned that I had been admitted to Harvard.

# 3

# THE HARVARD YEARS

I came to Harvard in the fall of 1929 with a somewhat nebulous idea that I might become a forester. I loved the outdoors and wild places and had the thought that by entering this field I might be able to contribute to the rehabilitation of devastated country. Five years earlier I had had an experience that strongly influenced this motivation. That summer I was traveling west with my family, first by train to Buffalo, New York, from there by boat through the Great Lakes to Duluth, Minnesota, and thence via the Great Northern Railroad to Seattle, Washington. What I recall most vividly from this trip was traveling by train for an entire day through the bleak, burned forests of Minnesota. The sight was deeply engraved upon my memory.

As a freshman I signed up to take the introductory course in zoology, followed by the one in botany. Prof. George H. Parker gave the lectures in zoology, which I found fascinating and I admired them for their elegance. It made a great impression on me to learn that even then, near the end of his long teaching career he was nervous just before his lectures, a tension no doubt produced by a striving for perfection. I also have a vivid memory of my first laboratory exercise — a study of the amoeba. After struggling for a good part of the period to draw what I saw under the microscope, I was informed that I had been depicting a piece of gunk. This experience stood me in good stead later during my years of teaching. A sympathetic check of students' preparations early in the lab period pays off.

In those days each student had a whole lobster to dissect, as a generous example of the *Arthropoda*. To this day, whenever I encounter one on my dinner plate, I am reminded of my dissatisfaction with the mush I discovered within the shell of the unfortunate creature that found its way onto my dissecting tray in the old laboratory on Oxford Street.

In the second semester I took botany. Prof. Ralph H. Wetmore gave the lectures, and G. Ledyard Stebbins was the teaching assistant in the laboratory. I enjoyed this course, and it launched me in my profession. One detail that I recall very clearly was anything but academic. Ledyard was an earnest fellow who did his best to help us find what we were supposed to see under the microscope. Some of the athletes in the class would attach test tube clamps to the tail of his coat as he was leaning over someone's microscope. It would have served them right if they had had to carry on over the Bunsen burner without these useful little gadgets. Surely none of us imagined that this young graduate student would become one of the world's outstanding evolutionary biologists.

The only A I received as a freshman was in mathematics. I found the subject difficult and worked hard to keep on top of it. However, it was clear to me that the computer I had above the ears was not built to deal with mathematical problems of much greater complexity than the calculus.

That first year I roomed with my childhood friend, Tim Rhodes. The adjacent room was inhabited by our classmate Charlie Fowler. We had good times together, including a ski trip during Christmas vacation, which Charlie arranged with three Canadian debutantes. A bus took us all to a little country inn about twenty-five miles from Ottawa. I had rented skis and boots, and it was a pleasant skiing on the gentle hills. The weather was clear and cold, mostly below zero. When it came time to leave, the nearest bus left from a town ten miles away. We had to ski through a foot of fresh snow and took turns breaking the trail. We made it in good time, but when I removed my boots I discovered I had lost the skin on both heels.

Fred White, one of Charlie's friends, used to visit him and borrow his phone for hour-long conversations with his girl friend in Sudbury, Massachusetts. He had the habit of saying "Oh!" with his mouth open. One day Charlie got a large gob of peanut butter on a knife, sneaked up behind Fred and neatly inserted it in Fred's mouth during an "Oh!" It would have been interesting to know just what Betty heard in Sudbury. In Cambridge we were scraping peanut butter off the walls and ceiling of Gore Hall.

One of the graduation requirements at Harvard was the ability to swim. When I took the test, which I passed with ease, I found to my disgust that I was a bit out of breath. The coach encouraged me to join the swimming team and advised me to do some exercises to build up my shoulder and back muscles. So I took a ten-pound dumbbell through Europe the next summer, 1930, when I went abroad with my parents.

On that trip I was able to do some serious rock climbing with a guide in Cortina d'Ampezzo in the Italian Alps. He started me out with some training on the Cinque Torri. We then climbed the Becco di Mezzadi and ended up ascending the face of the Punta Fiammes, which involved a traverse across a sheer rock wall. Dad underwrote the expense of the guide, and I have always been grateful to him for allowing me this challenging opportunity.

In my sophomore year at Harvard I swam the 200-yard breast-stroke on the varsity team. Although I never distinguished myself in competition, I learned a great deal about swimming from the coaches and passed the senior lifesaving course. Academically that year was a

The Punta Fiammes in Cortina, Italy,
the face of which I climbed in the summer of 1930.

new scientific ballpark. The second-level courses in botany — taxonomy with Prof. Merritt L. Fernald and plant anatomy with Prof. E. C.
Jeffrey — were predominantly filled with graduate students. The pace
was stiff, but the stimulus of working with mature students on congenial materials gave me a great feeling of accomplishment.

Fernald's course, in particular strongly developed my interest in
plants. His lectures were somewhat rambling, but packed with interesting bits of folklore, natural history, economic botany, and phyto-
geography. The lab part of the course consisted of drawing specimens
of representative species belonging to the important families, which
gave me some proficiency with a drawing pen. But it was in the field
that Fernald's teaching really caught fire. He was short and stocky, but
could maintain a vigorous pace. When he spotted an interesting plant
on terra firma he would recline on the ground beside it, point out its
characteristics, and expound on whatever was of particular interest.

Aquatics were a vital part of the flora for Fernald. At the first stop, he usually led us into a swamp where the water came right over our boot tops. For the rest of the day we had no inhibitions about sloshing through wetlands. Sometimes Fernald's enthusiasm got him into trouble. Once he was standing at the end of a small dam where an interesting plant emerged from a solid sheet of floating duckweed. Stepping forth to collect it in his usual way, he plopped in over his head. Fernald could not swim. A football player, who fortunately was standing beside him on the dam, reached over and pulled him out. The story goes that this student had been doing poorly in the course, but passed it with flying colors.

The author in the field circa 1936.

The field trips were memorable — to Cape Cod for plants of the coastal plain, to the rich calcarious hills of Vermont for the spring wild flowers. I was astonished to find the prickly pear cactus, a plant with which I was familiar in the arid Southwest, smothered by grasses on the sand dunes of the Cape and excited to encounter eighty species of wild flowers simultaneously in bloom in May on the slopes of Mt. Equinox in Vermont. Later I participated in forays to poorly collected counties in Vermont to help round out the collections of the New England Botanical Club, which I joined as its youngest member in 1931. Club meetings were held in Boston at the home of the American Academy of Arts and Sciences on Newbury Street. They were attended by a distinguished group of enthusiastic and well-informed amateurs — men who, in the days before automobiles, had spent their weekends walking from railroad stations and trolley lines through the countryside in the tradition of botanist Asa Gray. These amateurs far outnumbered the professionals, but Fernald played a leading role in ordering the agenda. It is fascinating that up to that time more copies of *Gray's Manual of Botany* had been sold in the United States than any other book except the Bible.

A number of the biologists on the Harvard faculty were prima donnas and hated one another with a passion. Fernald and Jeffrey had no use for each other, and neither one could abide Professor William J. Crozier, the physiologist. There was also a schism between the staff at Harvard's Arnold Arboretum in Jamaica Plain and the university botanists in Cambridge, which years later was to erupt into a full-scale war. It was an example of behaviors that Harvard graduate students could well learn to avoid.

The summer of 1931, between my sophomore and junior years, was spent out West. I took a six-week course in geology with Professor Samuel H. "Doc" Knight at the University of Wyoming. Home base was the university's camp located in the Snowy Range a few miles west of Laramie at an altitude of about 10,000 feet. During the last ten days of the course we covered quite a bit of the state in a fleet of old air-cooled Franklin touring cars, all more or less on their last wheels. At the end of the trip Doc stood by the roadside laughing as one by one these vehicles limped into Laramie. Sixty-nine years later I was delighted to see that the university had recognized this outstanding teacher as Wyoming's Citizen of the Century.

The rock formations in Wyoming are easily distinguished by their color, texture, and fossil content, and are only thinly disguised by the vegetation — so different from New England, where the bedrock is mostly concealed by forests and recent glacial deposits. I found the subject and the Wyoming terrain completely fascinating.

At one point during the course, a forest fire broke out near where we were camping. Our group joined the firefighters and we managed collectively to contain the blaze. At the end of the day the U.S. Forest Service issued government checks for our labors. Mine was for fifty cents. I would have kept it as a souvenir had it not been for the fact that it was incorrectly made out to Richard Goodman.

One of our camps on the tour was at Whisky Gap, so named for an event that took place there on an early military expedition. The commanding officer, discovering that his men had smuggled a barrel of whisky onto the commissary wagon and concerned about their sobriety in Indian country, ordered the barrel's contents to be dumped on the ground. Whereupon the men dug their heels into the prairie, creating dents that caught enough of the spilled liquor for them to get roaring drunk.

At this spot a small stream flowed from a lovely spring located in a trough between two steep-sloping sandstone ridges. The stream had eroded a sharp break through one of the ridges and beyond that it meandered quietly through the prairie, where it was at least a foot deep and a foot or two wide, with overhanging banks. Walking along the edge this stream Dick Stoiber and I, who were about the only two east-erners taking the course, noticed large trout darting away under the banks. Carefully exploring the underwater cavities with our hands, we were able to feel the fish, which we managed to grasp and extricate from their hiding places. We brought two large cutthroat trout back to camp. The first people we encountered were some Wyoming girls who were taking the course. They asked us where we got the fish. When we explained the operation, they put their noses in the air and comment-ed that "no good sport would do a thing like that!" When their Wyoming boyfriends asked the same question, their response was, "Gee! Let's try to get some more!" — which they did. Nineteen years later I revisited this spot with my wife and children. It was a bitter dis-appointment. In the intervening years the area had been overgrazed by cattle, which had trampled down the overhanging stream banks. The watercourse had become eight to ten feet wide and was running shal-low over a stony bed. My son and I managed, after considerable effort, to catch a couple of rainbows under small rocks. Gone were the native cutthroats.

After the geology course I joined my parents for a few days at the JY

Ranch in Jackson Hole and then spent a fabulous three weeks at a camp in Waterton Lakes Park in Alberta, Canada, run by the Marquis degli Albizzi. The previous winter I had stayed at a ski lodge run by the marquis in the Laurentians at St. Sauveur des Monts. That was where I learned about his summer operation, which he advertised as his "Nomad Camp, from the glaciers of Canada to the sands of New Mexico." Our group that summer consisted of the marquis; his cousin Duke Dmitri von Leuchtenberg, a Hungarian wrangler; Mary Bird, who was one of my special girlfriends, Mary's friend Pussy Reid; and myself.

The camp was located on an open sagebrush flat reached by kayak across the outlet to the Waterton Lakes. The marquis' mother had been a member of the Russian royal family and his father an Italian noble-man. The marquis had ridden with the Russian Cossacks and later with the Italian cavalry. His horses at the camp were beautifully trained. He could jump one of them over a chair in the middle of a field without a bridle. He gave us intensive riding instruction, and we rode through the rough country on English saddles. We explored by kayak, did a lot of mountain climbing — about 40,000 feet of ascent, including Mt. Cleveland, the highest mountain in Glacier Park — and hiked for four days in a remote section of the Rockies where there were no trails.

Around the campfire the marquis regaled us with the unbelievable story of his life, which was better than fiction. He was like a cat with nine lives. According to what he told us he must have already lost at least six of them. He survived the purge of the nobility during the Russian Revolution by escaping across Siberia. Eventually reaching Italy, he joined the Italian army during World War I and was put in command of men who had just been released from prison. In one action in the Italian Alps, his battalion was given the assignment of storming an impregnable mountain position. On the ascent the Germans wiped out the assaulters with a rock barrage. The only sur-vivor was the marquis who, characteristically, was ascending by the most difficult route and was under an overhang. He continued alone and, by surprise, took the position single-handed. After the war he fought with the White Russians in the Ukraine. Later he married an Italian woman. While sailing with her on Lake Maggiore, their boat capsized in a sudden storm. His wife drowned, but the marquis was rescued. Shortly thereafter he migrated to the United States, his only assets being some jewels with which he had escaped through Siberia. He settled in Colorado, where he started a new life teaching Russian, riding, skiing, and flying. After surviving a plane crash, he moved to the East. In Lake Placid in the Adirondaks he broke his neck on a ski jump, then later established his ski lodge in St. Sauveur. By the time I came to know him he had a stiff neck!

At the end of our stay at Nomad Camp, Mary and I took the boat to the south end of Waterton Lake and hiked for two days through Glacier Park. We passed through the tunnel in the Ptarmigan Wall and arrived at Many Glacier Hotel in time to catch the bus for the railroad station.

Although Harvard never allowed me any academic credit for the Wyoming summer course, I found the Geology Department very happy to accept it as a prerequisite for Kirk Bryan's upper-level field course in New Mexico, which I took the following summer. This time I drove west with my Troop 4 chum Charlie Denny, who was majoring in geology. With the exception of mineralogy, I found myself better prepared to interpret the landscape than the students who had had their introductory training at Harvard. Bryan's course was another enriching experience. We explored a lot of glorious backcountry and visited a number of Indian ruins and pueblos. My nickname on this trip was "Beetle." I was collecting these insects on the side, and my fellow students would say "beetle!" to call my attention to specimens. Soon the word was being used just to get my attention.

Geology kept us very busy for six days of the week. The seventh we had off, but the management kept us out of mischief by arranging special events. One was a tour in the field-trip truck through the Valle Grande, the very beautiful floor of a large extinct caldera located just west of Los Alamos. In the middle of the caldera rises Redondo Peak,

The Volcanic Plug, Cabazon, New Mexico.

a relatively recent volcanic cone. After driving around the valley, we left it by driving on a narrow track straight up the very steep slope of the crater rim. We all piled out of the truck and pushed it up the grade a few feet at a time while the driver repeatedly revved up the motor and gunned the vehicle until it stalled. Shortly after cresting the rim, the track led between two huge ponderosa pines spaced just a little too close to permit the truck to pass. Our driver had a good eye. He charged the "gate," taking about half an inch of bark off each tree. Our route then took us down through the backyard of a ranch, and you should have seen the looks of astonishment on the faces of the folks on the porch!

It is heartening to know that this magnificent sweep of country — nearly ninety thousand acres lying embedded in the Santa Fe National Forest — will be permanently preserved. Previously known as the Baca Ranch, it was acquired in 2000 by the federal government and established as the Valles Caldera National Preserve, to be managed by a special nine-member board of trustees.

On another day, an incident occurred that I will never forget. We were camped below a volcanic plug called Cabazon, and a number of us decided to climb it. It was several hundred feet high, with perpen-

dicular walls of basalt. The vertical, columnar components tended to
fracture transversely, but at a slight angle. On one side of the plug the
fractures sloped inward, making them stable; on the opposite side it
was the reverse. I started up the wrong side. Fairly near the top, one of
my footholds gave way, starting a small avalanche. I looked down the
dizzying cliff to find the route I had followed was gone. To continue
upward would be to court disaster. I was on my toes, and my foot began
to tremble. I managed to get this under control by establishing my heel
on a little bit of ledge and then cooled off with a swig from my can-
teen. The descent was hairy, but fortunately proved possible.

As a junior back at Harvard, I started an independent study project
with Professor Wetmore. He had been working on the cytogenetics of
goldenrods and asters and called my attention to a goldenrod (*Solidago
asperula*) that was thought to be a hybrid between *S. rugosa*, a very common and widely distributed species and the salt marsh goldenrod, *S.
sempervirens*, that is restricted to sand dunes, salt marshes, and rocky
headlands at the edge of the sea. He suggested that I attempt to cross
the two putative parental types and compare the progeny with *S. asperula*. This I proceeded to do, submitting the results as an honors thesis in
the spring of my senior year. The project involved collecting the
parental species, bringing them into flower in the greenhouse, confirm-
ing their self-sterility by attempts at self-pollination, and then cross-
pollinating them. Seeds derived from these crosses then had to be ger-
minated and grown in the greenhouse. I soon discovered that young
seedlings require tender loving care on a daily basis; the fellow in charge
of the greenhouse could not be depended upon to water tiny pots, nor
to watch for the first signs of insect damage. This kind of experience
is simply not obtained from conventional academic courses.

The germination of the few precious hybrid seeds became a matter of concern. Seeds were placed to germinate on moist filter paper in
petri dishes and subjected to a regime of freezing and thawing. This
was unsuccessful in breaking dormancy. One day I observed nearly 100
percent germination in some test dishes left on my laboratory table in

full sunlight. Thus I discovered, more or less by accident, that germination was triggered by the rather high temperature of 100°F. This seemed odd, as I had observed good germination in the field in early spring when the air temperature was around 40°F. However, those

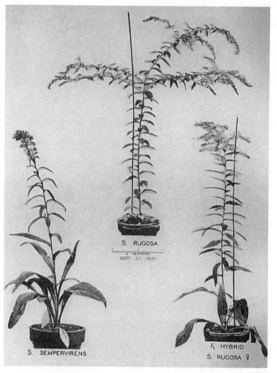

S. RUGOSA
SEPT. 21, 1935

S. SEMPERVIRENS

F₁ HYBRID
S. RUGOSA ♀

seeds were germinating on bare black soil, and when I measured the temperature of the soil surface on such cold spring days, sure enough, it was around 100°F.

The flowering of goldenrods is photoperiodically controlled by the onset of short days, normally in the fall. Thus it takes at least a year to produce a generation, unless the process can be artificially speeded up — most desirable if genetic experiments are to be carried out. I found that by germinating seeds shortly after maturation in the fall and growing the seedlings under glass during the winter, it was possible to induce the plants to flower during the short days of spring. Several years later I was able to present my fiancée with a goldenrod bouquet at the June party announcing our engagement.

I continued the goldenrod research as a graduate student at Harvard for the next four years and it provided the basis for my doctoral dissertation.[1] The study had a number of facets. I established chromosome numbers for the parental species and the hybrids, determined their meiotic behavior, made second-generation hybrids and back-crosses, compared these with natural populations where hybridization was taking place, and finally investigated the role of plant hormones in making the leaves of the two parental species so different in size and shape. It was a great project. It required me to become somewhat proficient in a number of different fields — genetics, cytology, and hormone physiology — to say nothing of the practical experience growing plants. Wetmore was a wonderful graduate advisor, always generous with his time, thoroughly familiar with the literature, ever ready to give advice and criticism, and always asking the interesting and significant questions but not knowing the answers or exactly how to get at them. After each conference it was back to the lab or greenhouse to work things out.

Some of my hybrid seedlings were peculiar, looking very much like the maternal parent, *S. sempervirens.* At one point I had a consultation with plant geneticist E. M. East, a man with whom I had never studied. He asked a number of penetrating questions about my techniques, and I went away feeling very insecure about drawing conclusions from my limited data. It could have been that my plants represented an interesting case of maternal inheritance.

I also benefited from another member of the faculty, Professor Kenneth V. Thimann, who had just come to Harvard from the California Institute of Technology. He advised me regarding the plant hormone studies. He had a very sharp, analytical mind and would lay out a logical sequence of experiments, which only needed to be carried out. I learned much from him about an exciting new field that was just beginning to open up, but not as much as I learned from Wetmore in terms of independent resourcefulness.

I came especially to admire Professor Irving W. Bailey. Although I never took a course with him, he was always warm and friendly, and I had numerous opportunities to visit him in his lab and observe his research in progress. The thoroughness of his approach to botanical problems, the elegance of his techniques, and the clarity of his publications were models to emulate.

Graduate work seemed easy. It was in a field that was congenial to me, and when I observed the struggles of some of my fellow graduate students who had come from other institutions, I realized that I had become accustomed to Harvard's high standards.

Much of what is learned in graduate school is from fellow students. One of my special friends was Ralph Emerson, a direct descendant of Ralph Waldo Emerson. Ralph later became one of the country's outstanding mycologists. I followed the progress of his research on the water mold *Allomyces* with fascination. This fungus could be induced to perform the sex act — the production of gametes, fertilization and early development of the new generation — on demand.* I later made use of *Allomyces* to demonstrate these processes — which would take place within less that two hours — as a laboratory exercise.

Ralph's mentor was Professor William H. Weston. We all called him Cap. He was a delightful character as well as being a respected scientist and an excellent teacher. He always had a twinkle in his eye and had a wonderful sense of humor. The Harvard Botanical Club, the membership of which consisting mostly of graduate students, had as its principal function, an annual dinner. This event was also attended by some of the faculty, and one year Cap served as toastmaster. His speech started off with some awful puns, good for groans, but pretty soon one or two of them started the members laughing. From then on we were kept in stitches. I still remember one bon mot. It was just at the time of King Edward's abdication in order to marry the commoner Wallace Simpson. Cap twisted the motto of the Order of the Garter, *"Honi soit qui mal y pense,"* into *"Honey soit qui Wally pense."*

\* \* \*

*Allomyces is a water mold that grows in ponds and ditches on suitable substrates such as seeds. It can be collected from nature by suspending hemp seeds above soil samples in jars of water. If present in the sample, a motile stage will swim up and infect the seed. The fungus can then be cultured on agar plates, on the dry surface of which it produces sex organs — orange male and colorless female gametangia. By scraping these structures off and placing them in a drop of water on a microscope slide, one can, within a two hour lab period, observe the production and emergence of the small male and larger female gametes, which are both motile, and their subsequent fusion and germination into a zygote.

In 1934 I drove west in my model A Ford roadster with my fellow graduate student Paul Vestal, who later became a professor of biology at Rollins College in Florida. Shortly after crossing the Mississippi River the paved highway became a dusty washboard traversing unfenced prairie. It was extremely hot. My companion was on the verge of heat prostration, so we drove without stopping until we reached the Snowy Mountains of Wyoming, where we camped briefly. I dropped Paul off at his home in Colorado and drove on to New Mexico, where I collected plants while camping with friends from the previous summer who were working on their doctoral dissertations.

One of these was Harold Smith, who later became a professor of geology at the University of Kansas. Another was Robert Nichols, who later became a professor of geology at Tufts University. The latter had with him a couple of undergraduate assistants to whom he had promised a visit to the Grand Canyon. We took them there and then Bob and I embarked on a dramatic little adventure hiking in to Rainbow Bridge. Our starting point was Rainbow Lodge, reached at that time by about a hundred miles of very rough desert track leading north from Tuba City, Arizona. We arrived at the lodge late in the afternoon and, as our time was limited, immediately set out on foot for the bridge. We managed to cross two canyons and begin to descend the head of a third

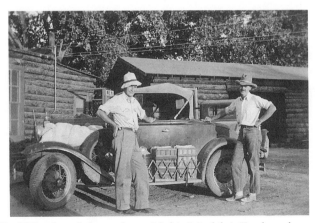

Paul Vestal, and the author with his Model A Ford roadster
in Colorado Springs, Colorado, summer of 1934.

Geology graduate students with whom I camped in New Mexico:
Robert L. Nichols (*left*) and Harold T. U. Smith.

before darkness fell. Flashes of lightning from a nearby thunderstorm brilliantly illuminated the beetling cliffs, which rose ever higher as we descended, and the thunder rolled and reverberated against the canyon walls. We finally reached a spring at the foot of a great sandstone wall and slept on the sand. The next day a narrow cleft in the vertical canyon wall, called Red Bud Pass, gave us access to Bridge Canyon. As we neared the Rainbow Bridge we came upon a deep pool in the canyon floor. I was in the lead and commented, as I scrambled up the far side, that one had to take care because the rock was slippery. Bob, who at that time was carrying my old Graflex camera, proceeded to fall in over his head. Despite this catastrophe the films came out well. We reached the spectacular stone arch by mid-morning.*

*Today the visitor can almost reach this natural wonder by boat from Lake Powell, formed by the construction of the Glen Canyon Dam, completed in 1962.

Looking downstream.

Looking up the canyon.

From above.

Rainbow Bridge.

On our return we got caught in another thunderstorm, fortunately at the crest of the divide in Red Bud Pass. The nearly vertical walls were about six feet apart. Everywhere water poured off the thousand-foot cliffs in blood-red waterfalls, some of it right on our heads. Flash floods came pounding down both the adjacent canyons. It was about an hour before the floodwaters subsided and we could proceed.

We had to buy gas at Rainbow Lodge. I thought we were at the end of the world: The price was fifty cents a gallon! It was about five times what we were used to paying.

At the end of the summer I picked up Paul, and we drove east via the coasts of Texas and Florida, collecting salt marsh goldenrods, and then north through the Great Smoky Mountains. We carried two spare tires and a tire repair kit. Our normal procedure was to wait until we had three flats before stopping to repair all three. One night we had a flat on a dirt road in the coastal swamps of Texas. The mosquitoes came at us in clouds. We fortunately had one last good spare, and I think we must have made the change in about one minute! As we resumed our way a black cow loomed up right in front of us. We managed to skid side wise to a stop without landing in one of the deep water-filled ditches lining the roadway. Our first thought was the tires! Fortunately they were intact.

In the summer of 1935 my fellow graduate student Albert Delisle and I were privileged to spent six weeks in Cuba at the Atkins Institution of the Arnold Arboretum, a botanical garden established in 1900 by Edwin A. Atkins of Boston. It was situated in the middle of a sugar plantation at Soledad, a town just north of Cienfuegos on the south shore of the island. We stayed at Casa Harvard, the laboratory and sleeping quarters provided for visiting scientists and serviced by Filipe, the house attendant. He brought us horses each day for our ride down an impressive avenue of royal palms to the extensive collection of tropical trees and shrubs that had been assembled by Mr. Grey, the plantation's resident horticulturist. His main job was breeding improved varieties of sugar cane. It is heartening to learn that more that sixty-five years after our visit this great tropical botanical garden has survived repatriation and bad hurricanes.* It is now known as the Cienfuegos Jardin Botanico. Hopefully its maintenance will be continued long into the new century.

Neither Albert nor I was at all proficient in Spanish, but Felipe instructed us with a vocabulary liberally sprinkled with words and phrases that should not be repeated in polite society. The lab at Casa Harvard was in need of house cleaning, and we pitched in and discarded old reagents left by previous visitors. One evening we left our plant press on the wooden laboratory table. In the morning we discovered that the press had been invaded by termites, which had already reduced the table to a shell. The industrious little creatures had sealed off the openings in the sheets of corrugated cardboard and were going to work on the contents of the press.

We were most hospitably treated during our stay at the plantation. Mrs. Atkins was in residence at the hacienda, and, among other things, we were invited to her seventy-fifth birthday party. After the strong cocktails I wondered whether the double door to the dining room was going to be wide enough for me. Mrs. Atkins was known on the plantation as Dona Katerina and was much loved by the local women. She taught them needlework skills, which allowed them to embroider linens for sale to supplement their family incomes. I bought a lovely tablecloth and matching napkins. The plantation was a sort of feudal system, in which Cubans provided the labor to produce the cane and process it at the mill.

During our visit we were told a lovely story about zoologist Thomas Barbour of Harvard's Museum of Comparative Zoology. He was collecting reptiles during a visit to the plantation and had offered a reward to anyone bringing in live specimens. On the last day of his stay, after all his collections had been packed and shipped, a local brought in a lovely eight-foot boa constrictor. Tom couldn't bear to lose this specimen, so he packed it up in a cardboard suit box, hand

*Personal communication from a member of the Atkins family.

carried it to Havana by train and to Miami by boat. On the Pullman sleeper to Boston he took the snake to bed with him in an upper bunk. In the middle of the night he awoke to discover the suit box very light. Poking his head out between the green curtains, he beheld the snake making its way down the central aisle. According to the tale, Tom discreetly withdrew his head, rolled over, and went to sleep. We never learned whether the serpent was headed for the men's end of the car, where the porter would have been snoozing, or toward the women's facility.

During our stay in Cuba we made a four-day horseback foray with Filipe into the Trinidad Mountains just north of the plantation. We stayed two nights at little coffee fincas and one very noisy night on cots set up in a barber shop. The latter facility was one of four adjacent rooms opening onto a roofed cobblestone patio. In the middle of the night we were awakened by a horrible racket. Goats had come in and were polishing their horns by rubbing them up and down on the corrugated sheet-iron shutters that served as the door.

Our hosts started us off in the morning with a demitasse of very strong coffee followed by a regular-size cup of café au lait. They would then go out to work in the cool of the morning, returning for a big meal and siesta around eleven. But for us those two cups were all we had until we reached our next destination around three or four in the afternoon, by which time we were faint with hunger. The trails were so steep in places that we had to dismount and lead our horses. Although the terrain was very rough, we found only small patches of relatively undisturbed vegetation.

After Cuba Albert and I proceeded by boat to Panama, where we spent about two weeks exploring Barro Colorado, an island preserve managed by the Smithsonian Institution. It was isolated from the surrounding forest by Gatun Lake, formed during the construction of the Panama Canal. This was my first introduction to the sounds and sights of a tropical rain forest. Exploring the preserve on our own was an unforgettable experience. Under the closed canopy of the mature forest, the understory is often sparse, allowing easy passage, but along the shores the vegetation becomes very dense right to the ground. One day we were on a trail leading to the shore. It was like a dimly lit tunnel leading to a brilliant spot of water. Suddenly the light winked out. The black hull of a large freighter was passing just a few feet off the shore.

Upon my return to the States I made a fateful weekend trip to Waterville Valley in the White Mountains of New Hampshire with Mary Bird and Pussy Reid. There I met Esther Bemis climbing Mt. Osceola. For years the old Waterville Inn, where we were staying, had been a favorite vacation resort for the Bemis family, and Esther, who had been caring for her mother after her father's death, was taking a well-deserved break. After that weekend we started dating. She accompanied me on a collecting trip to Ipswich. I took her to the Harvard-Yale game. We went skiing together. By spring we were engaged. Professor Wetmore, when I told him, asked, "Where did you find the time for this?" The wedding took place the following fall in 1936, immediately after I passed my oral examination for the doctorate. Our honeymoon in Vermont was very brief, and we set up housekeeping in a fourth-floor walk-up apartment in Cambridge.

An amusing incident occurred during the spring of my final year at Harvard. Esther and I had spent a morning on a meadow along the Charles River within sight of the Harvard Stadium making mass collections of goldenrod plants. Formerly a brackish marsh under tidal influence, this area had gradually lost its salinity after the basin had been dammed, but there still were pockets occupied by stands of the saltmarsh goldenrod. The rest of the area had been invaded by the upland species, creating an ideal place for natural hybridization. While I was collecting the plants, Esther was sitting on a blanket making tags and placing the specimens in a vasculum — a white metal box about eighteen inches long and eight deep.

The next day it was raining. Late in the morning we were preparing to leave our fourth floor walk-up to go out to my parent's house in Brookline, as we were feeling the effects of typhoid shots taken in preparation for our imminent trip to Africa. The doorbell rang and a voice came up through the speaker,

"This is Officer O'Learty. Is Mr. Goodwin there?"

I responded, "Yes Officer, come right up." I began to review my immediate past. Could I be getting a ticket for speeding? Presently a uniformed policeman and a man in plain clothes appeared at the door.

"Were you up along the river yesterday?" says O'Learty.

"Yes. I was up there collecting plants with my wife." At that point Esther put in an appearance from the back room. The two men exchanged glances and began to grin.

"We had a report that you were burying something. We've had a posse of men up there digging all morning."

An Italian who had been picking over a nearby dump had observed our peculiar activity and reported the license plate number of our car to the police. What do you suppose would have happened if the police had found an empty apartment and had caught up with us as we were embarking for Europe on the *Queen Mary*?

# 4

# LETTERS FROM
# AFRICA

Some time after the announcement of our engagement in June 1936 we received a letter from my cousin Mary Linder Putnam from Africa inviting us to visit her on our honeymoon. She and her husband, Patrick Tracy Lowell Putnam, were operating a camp on the Epilu River in the Ituri Forest of the Belgian Congo (now Republic of the Congo) — the heart of the pigmy country. It was an exciting prospect. Our actual honeymoon consisted of a four-day trip through the hills of Vermont, but the following winter, while I was busy completing my doctoral dissertation, we were laying plans for an expedition to Africa.

My cousin suggested we take a boat to Dakar on the western bulge of the continent and then drive some 3,000 miles across subsaharan French West Africa, Nigeria, French Equtorial Africa, and the Belgian Congo to reach her camp. It would have been an exotic adventure for a couple of greenhorns. My father wisely squashed it. Meanwhile we began to visit with people who had traveled on the "dark continent." Among these were Tom Barbour, of boa constricter fame, Henry S. Hall, Jr., who had climbed the Ruenzori Range, and Arthur Loveridge, a herpetologist at Harvard's Museum of Comparative Zoology. Mr. Loveridge was especially helpful in providing letters of introduction and a detailed inventory of what we would need for our expedition, which was set for the summer of 1937.

We planned to go by boat to Mombasa on the east coast of Kenya, from there by rail to Kampala, Uganda, and then by car to the Congo. In the spring of 1937, we learned that the Putnams were returning to the States, but we were all set to go and merely modified our itinerary to make the most of the country through which we would be traveling. We learned later of Mary's untimely death from pneumonia after she had arrived back home.

We sailed on June 9 from New York on the Queen Mary, arriving five days later in Cherbourg. We crossed France by train and, after waiting three days in Genoa for the boat, sailed June 20 on the British freighter *SS Llandaff Castle* for East Africa. We disembarked at Tanga, Tanganyika on July 11.

Our stay in Africa can be broken down into five episodes: a week at the East African Agricultural Experiment Station in the Usambara Hills about fifty miles inland; nine days climbing Mt. Kilimanjaro; a five-day auto safari out of Arusha to visit the Jaida Swamp; a week climbing Mt. Elgon in Uganda; and a week driving to and through the eastern edge of the Congo. Then, on the first of September we flew via Imperial Airways from Lake Victoria to Southhampton, England — a four-day trip in those days.

From Southampton we went on to Denmark, where we spent the winter and I did research at the Plant Physiology Laboratory of the University of Copenhagen.

The following letters, written to our parents back home, have been slightly edited. They describe our experiences on the trip. Mr. Loveridge wrote to us afterward, "I have never heard of anyone making better use of their time."

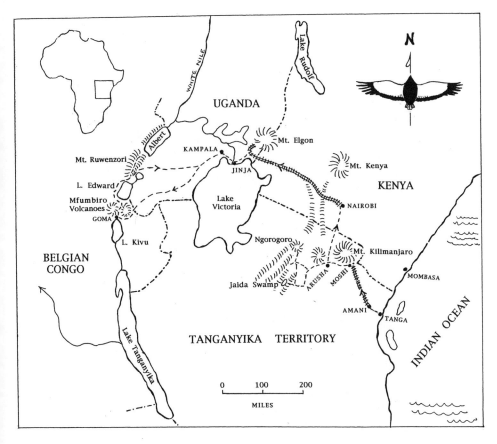

Route of the expedition.

Amani Guest House July 19, 1937
East African Agricultual Experiment Station
Amani, Tanganyika Territory

Dear Family:

Here we are, really embarked on our African wander-
ings. We put in at Mombasa on July 8. The town  is on an
island cut off from the mainland on either side by a narrow
passage. The docks are behind the island at Kilindene Port.

Our gear crate being unloaded at Tanga, Tanganyika.

Mombasa is very small considering it is the port of British East Africa, but it is obviously prosperous and growing rapidly. The business section of the town is straggled out over a mile or so of road, while the native quarters and white residential sections lie on either side.

While we were in port, we had very little time for conventional sightseeing. E and I spent most of our time going to or from the town — a matter of I.5 miles from the dock — by bus, taxi or foot, waiting to be waited on and haggling with the Indian shopkeepers. It was a fearfully expensive place to buy things, and we have thanked heaven numerous times that we brought as much gear from the States as we did.

We went to see the District Officer about hiring boys. He advised us to wait until we arrived at Tanga, because engaging boys in Mombasa would entail getting a permit to take them into Tanganyika. So we postponed that bit of business for another couple of days.

An important part of the ship's cargo for Kenya was cement, which was carried off the ship in bags by black stevedores. Our schedule was slowed down by frequent showers that necessitated battening down the hatches almost every half hour.

On one of the days in port the passengers were taken on a tea picnic in some of the ship's lifeboats to a swimming beach. The handling of the boats by the ship's crew was such a landlubberly performance that we were very gratefeul that we had had no crisis at sea. The heavy lifeboats were beached at high tide and in the course of the afternoon became throughly stranded. It took a native who happened along to organize the manpower to shove the boats clear. The crew then proceeded to foul the propeller of the power launch with the painter, and the passengers managed to row the boats back to the ship, arriving late for dinner.

The ship left for Tanga on July 11, arriving in the midafternoon. Mr. Malcolm Ross, with whom I had previously corresponded, had arranged for a Mr. Thomas to meet us at the boat. The latter is the head of a booking and shipping company — a dear old gent — who smoothed all the rough spots with the customs, etc. We had to pay 20 percent duty on all the canned food we brought with us. We spent the night at the Tanga Hotel, where we were royally treated, but not without paying for it, and there we met Mr. Ross himself. He is a real estate agent, auctioneer, and general factotum. He apparently eats habitually at the hotel and we had the next three meals with him.

The next morning we interviewed our boys, or rather Mr. Ross was kind enough to do this for us. They are natives from Nyassaland. The general servant, David, is quite young and can speak just a little English. He wants 30 shillings a month. The cook's name is Benson Kaula. He speaks no English and wants 40 shillings. They have so far proved to be a good-natured crew and seem to be reasonably clean and willing. It has taken us both a bit of time to get accustomed to running them about and to find out how to get milk, meat, eggs, vegetables, etc. at Amani. It has been a most interesting experience, and one which an American going on an "arranged" safari would never have. We are trying to learn Swahili.

That afternoon, having obtained light leather mosquito boots, kerosene, butter, and bread in Tanga, we set out on the 52 mile drive to Amani on the front seat of a flat-bed lorry. The road was beautiful for the first half mile, which was as far as the Tanga Golf Club. Then the pavement gave out and the bumps began. Each native along the way is supposed to fix his bit of road, and some of them must have been "out of town" for some time. The boys and all our gear bumped along behind. Our luggage now consists of 4 duffle bags, 2 suitcases, 2 holdalls, 2 kerosene tins, 1 knapsack, 1 metal table, 2 boxes of food, and the plant press.

The road passed through fields of sisal, little native villages, and patches of jungle and fruit trees. We followed the railroad for the first 25 miles to Muhesa, where we stopped at a native market to buy oranges, bananas, and mangoes. The oranges were only a quarter of a cent apiece. The bananas were about three inches long and rather tasteless. From Muhesa it was up into the Usambara Hills, which are covered with a beautiful rain forest. They rise to 3,500 feet in our part of the range. At Amani we are at 3,000 feet. The western hills go up to 7,000 feet.

We arrived at the Station just at nightfall, and the ornithologist, Mr. R. E. Moreau and his wife were kind enough to have us for dinner, after which we were conducted next door to the guesthouse, where we managed to settle in without undue difficulty.

This was our first night on our camp cots under mos-

Tree ferns.

quito netting. At dawn the next morning we were greeted with, "Chi Memsahib," by David, who brought us piping hot cups of tea.

Later on, we introduced ourselves at the Research Station and the Director, Dr. H. H. Storey, who is also the plant pathologist, showed us all about. The Station, which operated under the British Colonial Office and is funded in part by the Imperial Treasury and in part by contributions from the various African Colonies, is very up-to-date and has an excellent library and good herbarium. The buildings are of stone and are landscaped with plantings of roses — a nostalgic touch of Old England. The houses for the staff are well separated for privacy.

We then went for a walk in the forest. The trees are magnificent, being between 150 and 200 feet high and all festooned with vines and aeroids. Beautiful tree fern are in the understory. Birds are abundant here, but few mammals are in evidence. Esther caught a glimpse of a bushbuck and we have seen several very familiar looking little squirrels. I took a short walk with the botanist, Mr. Greenway, this morning, who reeled off the names of numerous native plants, many of which I have managed to forget.

One evening, while returning from a walk, we noticed something moving in a large piece of dung. It was a big scarab beetle cutting out a perfect ball, over an inch in diameter, which she then proceeded to roll to a burrow as food for her offspring.

This week has been spent exploring the Station and its environs, collecting and pressing plants, organizing our equpment, and constructing two chuck boxes for storage, which will also serve as seats in our future camps.

Getting fresh meat here is an interesting operation. An animal is slaughtered in the early morning, and the boys from all the various households are present to hack off whatever they can get. Benson has done the best he could, but is probably at the bottom of the peck order. Since we have no refrigeration, the meat is stewed at once. We find curry greatly enhances the flavor. Esther went out to the cook house to give Benson some instructions and found him squatting on the floor with all our cooking utensils spread out on the ground around him. She decided right then that it was best to leave him to his own devices.

We have been royally entertained. I suppose a couple of young foreigners must bring a little novelty to this isolated community. We had a "sundowner" at the Director's, dinners at Mr. Greenway's and Mr. Worsley's, and tea at the Milne's. The Moreau's came to our house for tea and we had Mr. Glover, the plant physiologist, for dinner. We are much amused by the boys, who wait on us in flowing white "nightgowns," red fezzes, and scuffing bare feet.

Tomorrow we take off for Moshi and, hopefully, Mt. Kilimanjaro!

With much love,<br>
R and E

Kilimanjaro Hotel July 31, 1937
New Moshi, Tanganyika Territory

Dear Family,

Last night we arrived here around eleven o'clock after our successful ascent of Mt. Kilimanjaro. Here is what has transpired since our last letter.

July 20. We left Amani in the Experiment Station lorry and drove down to Muhesa, where we caught the train for New Moshi at 9 a.m. From Muhesa our route skirted the southern flanks of the Usambara and Pares Mountains, passed through many old and new sisal plantations and then traversed a desolate thorn country. Before reaching Mombo the area became very arid. Thick stands of thorn trees, completely devoid of leaves, gave the landscape a steel gray appearance. Later on we saw ostrich, bushbuck, and Thompson's gazelles, and the euphorbias and aloes were in flower.

Late in the afternoon, as we were approaching New Moshi, a fellow passenger suggested we look out the window to see the mountain. He laughed at our puzzled faces and said, "You are not looking in the right direction. Look up there!" And there it was, a snow-capped dome floating among the puffy clouds, 18,000 feet about the surrounding plain.

Upon our arrival at New Moshi we established our base at the Kilimanjaro Hotel and had a long chat with Major Perkins, the proprietor, who is also president of the East African Mountain Club. His fatherly advice and assistance with the necessary arrangements were most important to the success of our climb.

The hotel is a delightfully rambling structure. Its large cool veranda serves as office, breakfast room, and general lounge. Just beyond a screen of potted plants is the hot and dusty road, where swarms of barefoot native laborers have been trooping by. The main house opens on this porch.

Except for the dining room, its contents are a mystery to us. The bedroom cubbyholes are in an adjoining house, connected to the main building by the veranda. There is a German atmosphere about the place harking back to the pre-war days, an impression heightened by the delicious food prepared by a German cook.

July 21. Major Perkins is an important person around these parts. This morning he took us to his real estate office, where he showed us some of his superb photographs of Kilimanjaro of which he is justly proud. He then conducted us across the street to introduce us to Mr. Ungerer, the manager of the store in New Moshi and treasurer of the Mountain Club. He is a stocky Alsatian in his middle forties, who, after following the sea for many ears, has settled down in this frontier environment. While we were in his store I heard him speaking fluently in four different languages: English, French, German, and Swahili. From Mr. Ungerer I obtained keys to the three club huts on the mountain; a list of rules concerning their use; and provisions, including food for the porters. Climbers are required to take a guide and a minimum number of registered porters, whose rations and pay are stipulated.

It seems strange to be so dependent upon our black boys. Both took a self-appointed holiday today, so Esther had to go to get her boots, which were being cobbled by the Indian shoemaker just around the corner. Most of his equipment and all his numerous family were spread about on the porch around him, while he sat cross-legged on the floor, hard at work. He insisted on sending his own African servant back with her to carry her boots, showing clear disapproval of her unescorted state. Thus one learns the customs of the country.

It was midnight before we had sorted out all our necessary equipment and finished making up our ten loads. Four were food for the boys; two, boxes of food for ourselves; three, duffle bags of warm clothes, bedding, medical supplies, electric torches, collecting equipment; and one the plant press plus our axe, panga, and saw. The small heavy objects were juggled around until each load stretched the spring of our little Sears Roebuck balance to forty pounds.

July 22. At 7:30 we set out in an Indian lorry for Old Moshi, situated on the lower slopes of the mountain. There we were met by our guide, Kirandeny, and a swarm of other Wachaga natives who clustered around hopefully. From these, ten stalwart chaps were selected. Meanwhile the grinning Indian, well pleased with his pay, had vanished down the road in a cloud of dust, leaving us to our own devices. After bickering for a large leg of beef for the porters, the men were lined up with the loads parcelled out. With a jubilant "Safari" we were off, Swahili dictionary in hand.

The following description of "Kili" may help you to follow our upward progress from day to day. In the midst of an arid, thorn tree plain, from an altitude of 2,000 feet, rises the enormous volcanic mass. European cultivation of the lower slopes gives way higher up to the more numerous native banana and coffee shambas of the Wachaga. Above this, between 5,000 and 9,000 feet, a girdling band of excessively moss-covered cloud forest clothes the steep, dissected mountain sides. Clouds hang at this level most of the time. At 9,000 feet the forest opens out into an immense, gently sloping plateau of savanna, where the contours of the underlying lava flows are plainly revealed. Dominating the plateau are jagged Mt. Mawenzi, about 17,300 feet, and snow-capped Kibo, about 19,700 feet. They are connected by five miles of saddle at about 14,500 feet. Mawenzi is the eroded core of a formerly active volcano. Kibo is a much more recent cone within which is the larger crater. At first we followed a grassy road up which we found later the Indian should have driven us. Almost at once we were enveloped in clouds, and it began to drizzle. Although the porters were out of sight, we could hear them shouting to one another and to friends in the nearby shambas. In an hour we arrived at the beginning of the forest trail, where our porters were waiting for us. After a short rest we started on. One by one the blacks were swallowed up in the murky gloom.

The forest is prehistoric, totally different from anything I have ever seen. Instead of the lofty gothic naves of the Usambara Hills, we traversed an endless crypt. Huge low-spreading limbs, festooned with dripping moss and laden with orchids, ferns, and vines, arched over our heads from distorted, buttressed trunks. Among the fascinating epiphytes were a long pendulous Lycopodium and feathery selaginellas. Climbing begonias were blooming above us.

The slippery path led up along a ridge, which sloped off precipitously on either side, giving mysterious vistas into the steaming depths below. Soon our guide whispered, "Tembo!" pointing to a recently uprooted tree. There could be no doubt about it. Elephant had been by. Pools of muddy water nearly two feet across stood as mute evidence of the animals' tread. Wide trails had been smashed through the undergrowth in every direction. Huge piles of dung, the old ones covered with mushrooms, lay about. In one place a polished, muddy slide dove straight down a very steep slope. Esther said it looked as if the old boys had been slithering down on their tails. Farther on, the bark of a tree had been torn away by an old fellow polishing his tusks. The guide encouraged us with, "Tembo mbale sana," which meant elephant a long way off, but the glances of the porters were far from reassuring.

Along the trail we saw other signs of game, spoor of buffalo and leopard, and tracks of other animals we did not know. We encountered several caved-in native game pits. A Wachaga irrigation ditch for conducting water to shambas on the dryer lower slopes, eroded in places to a miniature chasm fifteen feet deep, followed one side of the ridge. We crossed it from time to time on short poles covered with slippery moss.

After several hours the sun began to burn through the clouds, We were entering a more open forest composed largely of giant heaths, trees at least fifty feet high with

Esther beside senecios.

trunks a foot in diameter. Here the ground was covered with a lush vegetation of ferns and wildflowers, even the trail being carpeted here and there with a trailing vine-like violet.

Suddenly we emerged onto the open grasslands of the plateau and saw in the distance Johannes Hut at 9,000 feet, a dirt-floored shack of corrugated sheet iron with wooden bunks and a small stove.

July 23. We were up before daybreak to see the moon set. Looking at Kibo with the binoculars, we discovered the

lanterns of the English party that was climbing the mountain ahead of us. They were making their final ascent and we
were able to follow their progress along the eastern slope
until they disappeared behind a ridge. Then, as we stood
shivering in almost complete darkness, the first rays of the
sun tinged the summit of Kibo with a rosy glow, nearly an
hour before we ourselves saw the sunrise.

This day we spent a number of fascinating hours
exploring the nearby forest and collecting plants, while
waiting for the English party to evacuate the higher huts.
During the night Esther had been awakened by a sniffing
which she thought might be a leopard. She turned on the
flashlight full in the face of a rat! After watching it foraging
about, she went after it with our one weapon of defense, the
panga, and nearly removed its tail. The following night, at
her suggestion, the window of the cabin was closed. I slept
peacefully through this episode, but at four a.m. was awaked
by elephants trumpeting in the forest below, one of the most
thrilling sounds I have ever heard.

July 24. On this day we had an easy walk across gently
sloping lava flows, covered with grasses and low shrubs, to
Peters Hut at an altitude of 12,500 feet. In the more protected valleys are found the giant senecios and lobelias,
weird arborescent representatives of prevailingly herbaceous
families endemic to the high mountains of Africa. They may
attain a height of 20 feet or more.

We passed the four Englishmen on the trail. They were
in rather poor shape. One actually looked a little green.
Three had failed to reach the summit, having had to turn
back due to altitude sickness. The two days they had taken
in getting to the highest hut were insufficient for acclimati-
zation.

Peters Hut was relatively luxurious, with wooden floor,
bunks, stove, tables, and benches. It overlooks the plateau,
which appears to float like an island on a sea of clouds.

July 25. This day was spent acclimatizing and collecting
plants, while the porters made a trip to our highest camp

with wood and water. Last night the water froze in our petrol tin. David came running into the hut this morning holding the tin upside down and laughing like a small child. Ice and no Frigidaire machine to make it! To the natives a natural phenomenon is, strangely enough, a wonder, while such things as radios and airplanes are taken as a matter of course.

Benson is upset. He cannot understand why he must boil potatoes twice as long at this altitude as he used to down in Tanga. We are afraid Esther's explanation was a bit over his woolly head. Both boys have been suffering from the cold at night, despite the extra coats and blankets we have given them. The porters keep a fire going all night, but hog the warmest places for themselves. Every evening before settling down they sing. Occasionally we recognize a hymn. At the close comes the "Lord's Prayer." chanted by the guide and ending with a fervent chorus of amens.

In the afternoon a slight personnel crisis took place. I told Kirandeny to send four porters down, in accordance with our original plans. If they remained we would run short of food. Forthwith Kirandeny burst into a lengthy harangue in Swahilik, delivered with an intense scowling face. All sorts of possible troubles crossed our minds as we anxiously awaited David's translation. With exasperating slowness he boiled it down to one laconic sentence, "Kirandeny says boys stay here." After I counted out the loads before Kirandeny's very eyes, he reluctantly gave in. Bwana was not as much of a greenhorn as he looked.

Esther described another incident as follows. "For several days now David has been slipping. Plainly he disapproves of safaris at high altitudes in the Goodwin manner. His attitude has become more and more sulky and lazy. Instructions have to be repeated several times, and yesterday he ordered a porter to do one of his jobs. Today he blamed Benson for the filthy condition inside the hut, obviously the houseboy's job and not the cook's. Rich boiled over, and such a blowing-up as he administered! I quaked in my boots.

Mt. Mawenzi.

It was just what David needed, and it ought to improve matters considerably."

July 26. We continued the ascent to the very foot of Mawenzi at about 14,500 feet, where we had magnificent views of both peaks, but especially of Kibo's dome across the saddle. The saddle is a stony, windswept waste looking just the way I always imagined portions of the Gobi. Here sparse tufts of grass and other plants manage to survive. Although we kept a sharp lookout on our way across the saddle to the highest hut on the slopes of Kibo, we saw only hoofprints of the herd of eland that inhabit this desolate region. The other tracks were impressions of tire treads made by the sandals of our porters, which had been improvised from discarded tires.

Kibo hut is at 16,500 feet. The altitude was beginning to tell on poor Benson, who appeared from the boy's quarters shortly after we arrived, with a ribbon tied tightly around his head. We gathered that he was afraid it would split open and dismissed him for the day with an aspirin, which, being dreadfully mountain sick, he promptly lost. We prepared a large supper of corned beef hash, tomatoes, and pineapple which, contrary to the predictions of Major Perkins, we devoured with gusto. We felt no ill effects from the altitude until after we had gone to bed. Then both of us developed headaches. Our clock was given to David who was instructed not to go to sleep until he called us at one a.m.

July 27. We were already awake at one when David came to call us, on time for once. Our plan was to make the climb independently, Rich to head for the summit with Kirandeny, Esther to see how far she could go with Elhemso. So we will describe our experiences separately, first Rich's, then Esther's.

Shortly after getting up my headache cleared, but I could eat little breakfast. I started the ascent of Kibo at two with Kirandeny. The moon was three days beyond the full and shining brightly, so we carried no lights. From two to four the ascent was slow and steady through sliding scree. Always above shone a gleam of silvery snow. By four we were up about 18,000 feet, judging from the summit of Mawenzi, which appeared to be below us. The cold was bitter, even through mittens, ski pants, flannel shirt, leather jacket, and parka. My head was throbbing and a rest was necessary after every fifteen steps. By this time I decided to stop following the guide, who was interminably backsliding in the loose cinders, and climb a ridge of solid lava. At 6:00 we reached Gillman's Point by the only rocky approach to the crater rim, just in time to see the sunrise.

Several hundred feet below us stretched a wide expanse of the snow-bound crater floor, roughly a mile in diameter. Long shadows on the walls of wind-carved ice were beyond description. I tried to take a photograph, but the shutter of my Rolleiflex was frozen fast! Not a single exposure on this day's climb. Although rather exhausted, the grandeur of the scene and a swig of cold whisky and tea refreshed me.

The record box that was supposed to be on Gillman's Point was not to be found. It must have been buried in the snow. We proceeded along the crater rim on wind-packed snow over Bismarck Towers to Stella Point, where I registered, and thence to the very top, Kaiser Wilhelm Spitze.

It is not surprising that so many people setting out from Kibo Hut fail to reach the true summit. Although we had beautiful clear conditions, it took me an hour and a half to cover this final mile. I reached Hans Meyer Point in a very debilitated state, thinking it was the top. Kirandeny pointed on across a slight dip to the real summit some three hundred yards away. It took me ten minutes to rally my strength before I could decide to go on. I made it at last at 7:45.

The view from the summit was in some ways rather disappointing. To the east is a marvelous view of Mawenzi, standing out as a fine jagged series of pinnacles. To the north is the crater, the rim at this point rising as a sheer thousand feet of cliff. Southward a snowfield feeding the Ratzel Glacier undulates out of sight, and beyond, all that could be seen was a boundless, cottony sea of clouds about 10,000 feet below. Above this, at about 14,000 feet, appeared the sharply delineated top of a dense bank of haze.

In the record box I found a Bible and many scraps of paper with the names of previous climbers. I had little inclination to read them. The cold was intensified by a strong wind. My blood was thin and I was shaking like a leaf. It was all I could do to write my name and date on a slip of paper that had already been used by someone else. My writing was probably illegible.

I greatly admired Kirandeny hunched in his blanket, a

scanty supplement to his flimsy clothes. Here we were in a rugged situation and our relationship was as man to man. We shared a few lumps of sugar and a handful of raisins and started down.

The snow was hard and icy, sculptured by the wind into extraordinary ridges — about the dimensions of two by eight beams — which were spaced about two inches apart and set an oblique angle to the slope. This made the first part of the descent slow and tedious. I arrived back at Kibo Hut at eleven with just enough energy to roll onto a bunk and fall asleep.

Here is Esther's account: After an almost untouched breakfast Rich departed on the dot of two. At 2:20 my headache had improved and I decided to start. I routed out my boy in spite of his protests that it was much too early. He then claimed he must have some shoes, and David generously donated his battered black oxfords. Finally, he had no dark glasses. I only had my own and a broken pair which I stored in my pocket hoping that he would not need them.

It was bitterly cold and windy. We went very slowly, resting briefly about every fifteen minutes The talus was not so bad where the slope was gentle, but before long it became steeper and the tracks zigzagged back and forth. The rests became more frequent. Then Elhemso's shoelace broke and got lost. I produced string from my supply pocket. Finally the sole of one of his shoes came loose. This was also tied with string, but it was clear that he would never reach the crater rim. It seemed foolish to start back before seeing the sunrise, and we dared not stop for fear of getting too cold. It was then nearly five o'clock, and the sun rises at six. So we climbed on, munching lump sugar during out frequent rests. I rarely remember an hour which has passed so slowly. The scenery always seemed the same, always talus, clumps of shadowy rocks and the snow glittering in the moonlight tantalizingly above. Then the dawn came and almost immediately the sun rose just behind Mawenzi.

I will never forget my feeling of complete isolation at that moment — of being withdrawn from the world of men. Below, nothing of the real world showed, only haze, and to the east, jutting into the clear upper air, Mawenzi's pinnacles outlined against a brilliant sun.

Elhemso spoke, asking for his glasses, and urgently handed me my sun helmet. The glasses he hardly tried. He thought them utterly useless because the frame was broken. This time I had no remedy. I knew he would not go up where we would soon reach large patches of blinding snow, so I pointed to a sunny sheltered place among the rocks and asked if he would wait there while I went on. At this he became eager. The top was only a little way. "Huko Mem-sahib," he said, pointing. So on I went, and he was last seen curled in a wee ball under his blanket.

At first I was relieved to be alone. When I came to the snow, I decided to walk on that instead of the rubble. I continued quite happily, neglecting to rest in my eagerness to get on. Quite suddenly I became tired and my head began to ache. I stopped and ate raisins. At eight o'clock I was on the edge of a snowfield which seemed to rise continuously to the crater rim and which looked very near. I took an extra long rest in the warm sun and fell asleep. When I awoke it was 8:30 and my headache was worse. Three steps upward convinced me that I was finished, and I tentatively stepped down three to see if that would ease my head, as I had been told. But no relief did I have until I reached the hut below.

I went down, sliding a yard or more with each step, covering in fifteen minutes the distance it had taken me two hours to climb. When I reached Elhemso's shelter I began calling for him. For several minutes he did not answer. He had been so sound asleep he nearly missed me. He was crest-fallen when I told him I had not reached the crater rim or signed in any book.

The rest of the descent was pure grind. My head seemed to split with each jarring step. We reached the hut at 10:30 completely done in. Benson removed by boots as I

Esther with David, Benson, and Kirandeny at the end of the climb.

lay on the bunk. I must have dozed for twenty minutes. Suddenly I came back to life and remembered Rich. I had seen his guide as I came by the porter's hut and had been told that Bwana was coming. I got to my feet just as Rich opened the cabin door. Without a word I helped him pull off his parka and removed his boots, Three hours later we both awoke refreshed, and I learned that he had reached the summit. We descended to Peters Hut that afternoon.

July 28. This morning we slept until 7:30, a special indulgence, as we usually get up at five. I collected plants around the hut, including *Protea kilimandscharica*, some shrubby helichrysums and pieces of the woody stems of *Senecio cottonii*. I was disappointed to find that we were out of season for the senecio. Although I had scoured the valleys I found none in flower. You can imagine my delight when Dowdy, one of the porters, brought in a specimen in full bud. A half-day's extra pay was apparently ample inducement to spur him into activity. The succulent shoot will be most difficult to dry. We spent the morning trying to dry out the wet blotters of the plant press. In the afternoon we descended to Johannes Hut, which we could just see at the edge of the sea of clouds.

July 29. We completed the descent from Johannes Hut to the road, a beautiful but uneventful walk through the forest. The lorry which was supposed to meet us never showed up. The trek to New Moshi, which we had previously done by lorry, seemed a long one to our weary limbs, so we dispatched a porter with a note for Major Perkins and then prepared to camp by the roadside, as prospects for transportation that night seemed very poor. The other porters were dismissed after they had brought us wood and water.

The sun set blood red shortly before six and the clouds around Kibo cleared. It seemed unbelievably high, looking quite unapproachable in the rosy glow. Benson cooked a supper of oatmeal — the only provender left — and we sat sociably around the campfire with our boys until 8:30. Just as we were rolling out the beds we hear a car, which had been sent by Major Perkins grinding up the hill. Except for a flat tire which took an hour to repair, because the Indian had no wrench with which to remove the wheel, we arrived uneventfully at New Moshi about 11:00, quite ready to hit the hay.

Tomorrow we drive to Arusha by box-body car. Beyond that our plans are nebulous. We hope to arrange a trip to the Ngorogoro Crater, but whatever happens we expect to see game.

And now in our best Swahili, "Kwa heri" (=farewell).

Much love from

R and E

In the years since this letter was written New Moshi has grown from a little town to a bustling city and the burgeoning native population is having a significant environmental impact. Recent visitors report that illegal timber extraction from the cloud forest is severely reducing the flow of water from the mountain, so vital to the agricultural economy of the adjacent slopes and plain.

We now have a lovely painting of Kilimanjaro hanging on our walls. It shows Kibo floating above clouds bathed in a pink glow. In the foreground are the black silhouettes of three giraffes near an acacia tree. It is a gift from our good friend Craig O. Vine, Horticultural Assistant at the Connecticut College Arboretum, which we received at a celebration held in our honor at Connecticut College almost sixty-one years after the preceding letter was written. The following note came with it:

> To Richard and Esther Goodwin. Late in 1972 as I was relating my recent experiences in East Africa, in particular a late afternoon glimpse of Kilimanjaro as the cloud cover broke, Dick informed me that he and Esther had climbed to the Kibo summit on their honeymoon trip to East Africa. As this statement sunk in, I thought what a magnificent, exhilarating experience this was for a young couple to share as they embarked on life together! In appreciation for their friendship through the years, their great contribution to the educational experience and to the conservation of our natural resources, I offer them this painting of "Kili" more recently referred to as Uhuru (Freedom) Summit, as viewed from Masai Amboseli Game Reserve in Kenya. May the Light ever shine in your lives!

New Arusha Hotel
Arusha, Tanganyike Territory
August 8, 1937

Dear Family:

I am now writing in the lobby of this hotel, a most amazing structure, combining features of a rustic New England roadhouse with those of a Californian villa built in Spanish style. The two-storied dining hall, however, besides being able to boast a sumptuous cuisine, claims the unusual distinction of having its wall thoroughly plastered with huge frescoes of Tanganyika's scenic wonders executed by an itinerant artist of somewhat mediocre talent. The hotel is flanked by a luxuriant tropical garden from which we have seen the top of Mt. Meru, a 14,900 foot volcano, through an occasional break in the clouds.

We have hired a car to drive us to Nairobi early tomorrow morning. Since we still have much of our equipment to repack, including the plant press, the blotters of which are spread out all over the place to dry, and David's railroad ticket to buy, as his month is up and we are sending him back to Tanga, including his sour face, there seems to be little hope of my ever getting caught up on all the exciting things that have happened since my letter from New Moshi.

We arrived here eight days ago after a hot and dusty drive across the Sanya Plains on the weekend of a bank holiday. The hotel was overflowing into tents with people from Nairobi and the neighboring coffee plantations. We were fitted into a storeroom which was cleared for us in a house across the street.

The following morning we had a great stroke of good luck. I had asked Mr. Ray Ulyate, the hotel proprietor, about ways and means of getting to the Ngorogoro Crater. He said that he and his son Ken were planning a reconnaissance trip into some very wild country west of Arusha to map out a future route for their big game safaris, and offered to take us along as far as the Crater. Half an hour later one of his black boys came over with the message, "Bwana wants to see you." The upshot was an invitation for us to join his safari for a whole week, bringing our own boys, our food and bedding and paying 20 pounds (=-$100) towards expenses! We learned later that the charge for this same trip for the next party, all pre-arranged would be $10,000! We set out two days later. In spite of the fact that the expedition was pursued by a jinx, from our point of view it was a howling success.

August 3. The outfit consisted of the Ulyates and ourselves in a box-body car, which at home would be called a station wagon. Our food, equipment, extra fuel, and nine boys were in a big lorry.

Shortly after leaving Arusha we had the thrill of seeing the first herd of giraffe, six adults and one suckling "toto," browsing in an open Acacia grove. It is amazing how the weird shape and striking coloration of these animals blends harmoniously into their environment. Since they have no reputation for ferocity, present the hunter with no attractive trophy, and enjoy government protection, these animals are locally abundant,. We have seen many of them during the past five days.

The drive first took us westward through vast open grasslands baked to a golden brown. The broad erosion surfaces leading to blue mountains in the hazy distance continually reminded us of our own southwest. Except for numerous flocks of colorful birds, these plains appeared lifeless and still, depopulated by the promiscuous potshots of the people from Arusha. We skirted the eastern shore of Lake Manyara and then drove south to the northern end of Lake Babati, where we turned westward to reach the foot of Mt. Hanang, 140 miles from Arusha. There we were initiated into the mysteries of camping on the veldt Ulyate style.

The truck disgorged its nine occupants, seven of whom were galvanized into activity by a glance from Mr. Ulyate, who was ensconced by this time in a comfortable camp chair. The position of the tents was fixed with a wave of the finger, while further details needed little guidance Only our boys, who were gaping at this animated scene, required the additional prod of some well-chosen epithets in Swahili. We had had just enough experience with the natives to begin to appreciate the years of training required to attain such efficiency. At the magic command, "Ticalosh-bin-ticidum!" evidently coined by Mr. Ulyate, a steaming meal, including all sorts of delicacies from the Arusha garden, appeared from the cook's fire behind a clump of bushes. As we retired we were cautioned to leave a lantern burning outside to keep the hyenas, which were already howling, at a distance.

August 4–5. The following day we ascended our first rift wall, a long regular fault escarpment very characteristic of this part of Africa, and drove across an extensive, open plateau country. This is inhabited by the semi-nomadic Wambulus that are depended upon a cattle and corn culture. These rather handsome black people are a mixed race with some Somali blood. They live in low, flat-roofed houses half excavated from the hillsides. By noon we had descended the other side of the plateau via a tortuous makeshift of a road at the end of which a small coffee plantation had been carved out of a thorny wilderness by a German pioneer. We were at the end of the Jaida Swamp, where Mr. Ulyate had hoped to obtain movies of buffalo and rhino in their unmolested state.

The owner, Herr Nichols, came out to meet us through a swarm of hungry tsetse flies. He informed us in good English that a hunting part of four Americans, a man and his wife and their two teenaged boys, had preceded us by three days.

This was indeed a misfortune for us, as we were soon to discover. Guns had been emptied at everything in sight, and naturally all the big game had retreated into the dense bush. This convergence of trails was not without its educational value, however. Esther and I had a splendid opportunity to witness firsthand the process of ruthless destruction which has been and still is rapidly sweeping away the remnants of the African game, and we were ashamed to realize the large role our fellow Americans are playing. The hunting party, organized by Safariland Limited, consisted of five vehicles, two white hunters, a mechanic, a cook, personal boys, and about a hundred natives hired locally. Although our contact with the outfit was for the most part indirect, we were for the next two days almost constantly aware of its presence. There were no roads in the valley, but automobile tracks were everywhere. Here and there clumps of trees were black with vultures and marabou storks satiated by the excess of rotting meat from the kills. We actually observed at least

A baobob tree (*Adansonia digitata*) on the floor of a rift valley in Tanzania.

eight animals, including zebra, wildebeest, hartebeest, and an eland cow and calf, hanging by their feet from trees as bait for lions. How many more there were we have no idea. When hanging this way the vultures cannot strip the carcasses and they remain intact for some time. We heard that at last two lions, logy from gorging on these kills, had been shot. Shortly after we left Herr Nichols, we encountered four natives, one with blood caked to his lower arms. That morning he had been skinning a rhino. We came upon the skeleton later in the day. Divested of head, feet, and hide by human hands, the birds had done the rest.

The Jaida Swamp lies in a basin between two up-thrust land masses. Once it must have been a lake, but now it has become silted in and choked with grass and reeds. During the wet season it takes on the aspect of a lake again, but at this time of year much of the valley floor is dried rock-hard, affording, especially at the periphery, an easy surface on which to drive. Toward the center, bright green patches of tall reeds indicated residual water — a wonderful congregating place for game. At the edge of the swamp, on the alluvial fans, grow open acacia forests, which in turn, give way to thick thorn and bush, interspersed with scattered baobabs on the more arid, steeper slopes. The baobab is an incredible tree, not very tall, but with enormously thick trunks and spreading branches.

The valley was evidently teeming with game. Fresh spoor was everywhere in evidence, and game trails ran in all directions, but especially from the hills toward the middle of the swamp. Despite the hunting party, we saw during the next two days herds of giraffe, zebra, wildebeest, hartebeest, impala, eland, Thompson's and Grant's gazelles grazing on the flats, jackals, badgers, a bat-eared fox, and a serval cat at the edge of the acacia forest, and higher up on the escarpment, duikers and one klipspringer, which the Ulyates told us was rather rare. We had our biggest thrill in the afternoon of the first day, when we sighted two elephants returning to the hills from a drink in the swamp. We followed them slowly for about a quarter of a mile along the edge of the swamp until they disappeared among the trees. A little later we saw a cheetah bounding into the tall grass. We camped that night near a wallow, marked with fresh rhino tracks, from which we flushed a large flock of ducks. Shortly after dark began the hyena chorus.

The big ground birds so characteristic of the African plains were as interesting as they were abundant. The ostriches were a nuisance, because we were continually mistaking the black bodies of the males for more exciting game. We passed two nests of the snake-eating secretary bird — , huge bundles of sticks 20 feet up in the tops of low thorn trees. The owners, disturbed by our presence, finally bounded off and ran away with long elastic strides. Other spectacular species included frankolins, greater and lesser bustards, giant ground hornbills, golden-crested and saddle-backed cranes, and flocks of guinea fowl.

Distances were most deceptive. The open swamp must be at least five miles wide by fifteen miles long. We circum-navigated it in the car in the hopes of finding portions unvisited by the hunting party. At the southern end we left the fringe of trees and cut directly across through the tall grass, which was over ten feet high. Ken climbed onto the roof through a trap door designed for the purpose and stood there, cocked elephant gun in hand. At any moment we might have bumped into a herd of buffalo enraged by previous molestation. Everything was fine until we hit some old, well-dried elephant tracks running in every direction. Each footprint was six inches to a foot in depth and com-pletely concealed by the grass. Why we didn't break all the springs I will never know.

August 6. On the third day, unsuccessful in our quest for buffalo and live rhino, we left the swamp to the Americans and the vultures. En route we met the mechanic of the other party in a truck. His mission, over eighty miles of one of the rougher roads I ever hope to see, had been fresh eggs. His success had only been moderate. He had found six. We wondered whether they had arrived in camp intact or scrambled.

Above the Jaida Swamp escarpment we had a flat tire near a Wambulu village. The natives flocked around and three of the younger women discovered their reflections in the rear window of our car. They at once started to dance to a chant which was reminiscent of our American Indians. Now advancing, now retreating, and sometimes turning around, they enhanced the effect by lifting their blouses to expose their bouncing breasts before the glass.

Driving north and west we arrived on the slopes of Mt. Oldeani, where we inquired the way into Lake Eyasi of some charming German coffee planters. Coffee thrives in this locality. We pitched camp nearby.

August 7. The following morning we started in  toward the northern end of Lake Eyasi, when our car became mired in an irrigation ditch. In our efforts to get extricated, Mr. Ulyate was stricken with a fainting spell, and we were afraid that it might be a heart attack or a shock. We tried to make him comfortable on an improved bed in the back of the box-body and started to return to Arusha. Fortunately he soon revived.

To compensate us for returning a day early, we were driven on a side trip to the rim of Ngorogoro Crater, where we were able to observe some of the game on the vast open floor of the crater through the binoculars. Later on, just before we descended the escarpment north of Lake Manyara, we paused to examine the valley several hundred feet below. There, in a clearing, we saw what appeared to be a large boulder. Through the glasses it turned out to be a rhino taking a dust bath. A gunshot brought the animal to his feet ready to charge. Finding no enemy, he wheeled and vanished into a thicket. This was the only live rhino we have seen on the trip thus far.

We look forward to getting mail from you tomorrow in Nairobi.

Lots of love,<br>R and E

Rest House
Budadiri, Uganda
August 22, 1937

Dear Family:

Here we are at the foot of Mt. Elgon. Today we are catching up after a delightful eight-day safari on the mountain. We will probably mail this in Kampala when we arrive there the day after tomorrow.

We left Arusha on August 9  and drove north to Nairobi, skirting the east slope of Mt. Meru and crossing plains to the Kenya border at Longito. We then crossed a game reserve in the hills and the Athi Plains. Big game was plentiful. We saw numerous herds of giraffe, zebra, Grant's and Thompson's gazelles, impala, hartebeest, wildebeest, as well as a serval cat, wild dogs, jackals, and a mongoose. Rhino spoor was in evidence along the road.

Our two days in Nairobi were busy ones. We picked up our four letters from you, four from Mother Bemis, and one from Cousin Mary mailed in Stanleyville en route to the States. We visited the Coryndon Museum and, during the second afternoon, drove out to the eastern escarpment of the Great Rift Valley. It was very hazy and the view disappointing. I collected some bull thorn acacias, the swollen thorns of which are inhabited by stinging ants that protect the tree from at least some types of herbivores.

At 10:30 a.m. on the 12th we boarded a train for a 25-hour trip to Mbale. We had a second class compartment for four all to ourselves, and economized "six bob" ($1.50) by using our own bedding, a system apparently quite generally used in Africa. Meanwhile Benson was segregated in third class at the front-end of the train. This was the through train to Kampala. Early in the morning we got off at Tororo, which is situated at the foot of a volcanic plug similar to Cabazon, the one I climbed in New Mexico. There we boarded a dinky, semi-freight train for the 30-mile run to Mbale. Mbale in Swahili means far away.

The station at Mbale was about two miles from town. I phoned the District Commissioner, who suggested that I come up to see him. A lorry was procured to move us and our luggage and the D.C. was duly visited. He looked at us askance as if to say, "more d—— Americans! I wonder what these will do?" When I informed him that we wished to climb Mt. Elgon, he said, "That's no place to take a woman in the rainy season!" And then, after commenting that the paths were slippery, that the "porters hate to go up now" and that one must hurry the trip so the porters won't get fevers, etc., crashed through with a letter to the Chief at Budadiri, the location of the lowest Rest House.

We then hired a lorry and, after buying necessary supplies, drove out 25 miles to Budadiri where we ensconced ourselves in the Rest House. It is a large square building of adobe with a thatched roof and doors and windows that can only be closed with bamboo screens. These houses are built and maintained by the natives primarily for the periodic visits of the D.C., at which times he takes care of administrative matters and adjudicates any tribal disputes. When not in official use they are available to visitors free of charge. There are additional separate buildings for the kitchen, the boys' quarters, and the outhouse, but none are provided with furniture, plumbing, or lighting of any kind.

In the afternoon we were visited by the Chief, a young-looking black man dressed in a brown sun helmet, immaculate white shirt, tie and swank pin, blue jacket, gabardine shorts, calf-length stockings with yellow garter tassels, worn-out sports shoes, a cane, and a Parker fountain pen in his coat pocket. We also discovered he owns a swanky sports car. He could speak no English, but with the aid of the Indian who drove the lorry we made our wants understood. We arranged for nine porters and a guide for the following day. Most of the natives here speak only their own tongue. Benson has felt a bit lonesome, I think, because Swahili is understood only occasionally.

A native came by late in the day with a scrawny chicken for sale. We bought it, thinking it would be a nice change. Benson cooked it for us. It was just like rubber, so tough we couldn't get our teeth into it.

Mt. Elgon is a huge, very old volcano lying right on the border between Kenya and Uganda. We are on the western, Uganda side. Its diameter at the base is about 50 miles and the volume of volcanic material that has been extruded onto the plain must be in excess of 800 cubic miles. The crater is several miles across and 2,000 feet deep. Our

Our porters. The second in line carries the plant press.

objective was Jackson's Summit, the highest portion of the rim in Uganda, a little over 14,000 feet.

This year the rainy season has been late and it is still going on. Mornings have always been clear, but it has rained hard every afternoon, commencing sometime between noon and three and clearing between four and five. We have always had spectacular sunsets, occasionally with rainbows. The sun goes down red due to the large amount of smoke from grass fires in the atmosphere.

In view of the weather pattern, we planned our travel in the mornings as far as possible, so we could enjoy the shelter of the rest houses during the afternoon downpours. The first two days we only ascended about 4,000 feet, the nights being spent at Butandiga and Bulambuli.

Esther with a native child.

We had a new set of nine porters for each day we moved from one rest house to the next. Wages had been established for each day's distance and ranged between 12 and 20 cents a day in U.S. currency. The guide's wages were $2.50 for eight days. We had a small holdall loaded with copper coins to pay the porters. In East Africa these are made with a hole in the center. One of our loads consisted of our folding metal table and this small money bag. The porters would often scramble for this load, thinking it would be a light one, and it was amusing to see their expressions of disgust when they found that it was exactly the same weight as the others.

At the end of the first day, when the porters lined up to receive their pay, an unusually tall lad held out his hand with the money in it, his disgruntled expression indicating that I hadn't given him enough. I took the money back and went on down the line paying all the others the proper amount. There was a lot of laughter among the porters at this fellow's expense. He returned about an hour later with a very long face and I paid him about 10% short of the standard amount. We never had any further difficulties with the porters.

The lower slopes of Mt. Elgon are rather densely populated. The Bawambisi appear to be a healthy and prosperous people who have completely occupied the lower slopes of the mountain above Budadiri. There is virtually no original vegetation left, except on the steep cliffs. The natives have extensive, flourishing banana plantations and small plots of coffee and maize. Their houses are all round structures with conical, thatched roofs and adobe walls constructed on a framework of poles supplemented with bamboo lattice. The adobe is protected by the overhanging roof and, on the windward side, by an additional fence of thatch. The latrine, in a separate building, consists of a pit covered except for a small hole.

We found these people very friendly, They speak no Swahili, but they almost always say "mirambe" instead of "jambo," when met on the trail. Loads are carried on the head and are often huge, for instance three large bunches of bananas one on top of another. They sometimes weave a little pad from a banana leaf to cushion the load. One woman was very curious about the way we were doing things and squatted outside our house for a long time peering at us as she nursed her baby.

On the third day we left Bulambuli shortly after six with our guide and one porter to climb the remaining four or five thousand feet to Jackson's Summit. The 12-mile ascent took us 4.5 hours and the weather held fair until a few minutes before we reached the top.

Above 9,000 feet we found bamboo forest that gave way to vegetation quite similar to that encountered on Mt. Kilimanjaro. Here were giant branching senecios, some over 30 feet tall, gladioli, and terrestrial orchids. Still higher up, the open slopes were interspersed with tree heaths, shorter senecios, and shrubby helichrysums. Here also were woody lobelias, their six-foot flowering spikes with hundreds of

Esther on the crater rim of Mt. Elgon.

purple flowers hidden amid a forest of green ciliate bracts. In this open country we found several huts of pastoral Masai who were living with their cattle.

It was a gentle incline to the base of Jackson's Summit and then a steep scramble through clouds to the top. We did manage to get glimpses of the crater during our lunch hour. The temperature was cool, but well above freezing. Our return took four hours. Of course we got soaked in the afternoon downpour, which lasted about an hour, and were slowed in the descent by the very slippery condition of the trail.

When we arrived back at the rest house wet and muddy, we discovered we had company. An English couple, Mr. and Mrs. Arthur Williams, had arrived that afternoon. We had tea with them and enjoyed a glorious sunset in which Lake Victoria and Lake Kioga could be seen shining in the distance. That evening we hung a blanket in the middle of the room for privacy.

We had gotten such a kick out of our independent life on the mountain that we decided to prolong the safari for three more days with an excursion northward along the flanks of the mountain to Sipi, where there was a lovely 400 foot waterfall. This part of the mountain was somewhat less densely inhabited and we went through patches of forest, where I collected a beautiful climbing gloriosa lily with deep brownish-red and yellow flowers and we saw quite a few interesting birds. Here we encountered the Bagishu who appeared to be less friendly. The men were clothed solely with a blanket knotted over the shoulder, which very poorly concealed the body. The women were more modest and usually covered their breasts as we passed. The babies are carried slung to the back or sometimes at the front.

At Sipi we met seven missionaries one of whom was from Texas. He had been out here for six years and said we were the first Americans he had met during this period.

Upon our return to Budadiri we had another visit from the Chief, this time in a magenta shirt and blue serge trousers. Today being Sunday has been a day of rest and let-ter writing. Benson has been busy washing our sheets in the muddy river across the road, and a number of woman have gathered there to wash and primp for church. Each one is wearing a large number of brightly colored skirts of purple, red, and yellow, often checkered or with large polka dots. These are wrapped double below the waist to form a bustle, with a contrasting sash tied with a loop knot low in front. The upper part of the body is wrapped snugly below the arms, leaving the shoulders bare. There were also a group of boys busily scrubbing their legs with stones.

Tomorrow we have chartered a taxi-bus to take us back to civilization. We go first to Jinja on Lake Victoria and then to Kampala. It doesn't seem possible that we have been gone nearly two and a half months. I will now sign off with much love.

As always,
R and E

Imperial Hotel
Kampala, Uganda
August 31, 1937

Dear Family:

We are now back in Kampala after a great six-day trip
by car into the eastern edge of the Belgian Congo. We are all
packed and weighed in at Imperial Airways, have taken our
safari equipment to an auctioneer, paid our faithful Benson
and bought him a railroad ticket back to Mombasa. So we
are all set for our flight tomorrow.

On August 23 we took a taxi-bus from Budadiri to
Jinja, a small city located at the outlet to Lake Victoria, the
headwaters of the White Nile. There we put up at the Ibis
Hotel overlooking the lake. After lunch we walked to Ripon
Falls, a drop of about 25 feet, and watched the hippos
cavorting in the river. Fish were trying to leap the falls.

In the evening we went down onto the golf course,
which borders the river, to see the hippos. At night they
come out to graze, and this course may be the only one in
the world where hippo footprints are legitimate golf hazards. The moon was bright, so we didn't take flashlights. Just
as we arrived at the top of the steep river bank a cloud
obscured the moon and a stentorian bellow and snort arose
from the river. Esther beat a hasty retreat, having been
warned never to get between a hippo and his aquatic habitat. We only saw one shadowy form of a hippo on land.

The following day we chartered a 1936 4-door Ply-
mouth sedan and native driver to take us on a seven day trip
to the Belgian Congo at a rate in our exchange of $2.50 per
day plus 12.5 cents a mile. The first lap of the journey was
a 58-mile drive to Kampala, where we checked in with
Imperial Airways and got organized for the rest of the trip.

On August 25th we started out, Esther and I on the
front seat with the driver; Benson squeezed in back with all

the food and bedding. Before we had been seven miles we had had two blowouts. This gave us an opportunity to see some of the natives, who materialized out of seemingly uninhabited country and offered to assist us without expecting any remuneration for their labors. They pumped up our tires with a bicycle pump.

Our route took us west of Lake Victoria through arid plains that were being grazed by long-horned cattle. No game was seen. Southwest of Mbarara the road followed papyrus-choked valleys between grassy hills, many of which had been burnt or were still in flames.

Shorly after dark we arrived at a rest house 25 miles north of Kibale and some 246 miles out of Kampala. Inspection by flashlight revealed the facility to be in a very tumbled-down condition, so we slept outside under a somewhat cloudy moon.

The following day a 140-mile drive took us through Kibale and thence on a winding mountain road over a 8,000-foot pass to the Belgian border at Kigoro and then south on a little-used road to Goma on the north shore of Lake Kivu. We picnicked at the edge of a jungle thicket close to the outlet of Lake Bunyonyi, where we collected a 12-foot tall lobelia. The boys claimed they saw a lion across the valley.

At Kigoro we were given a permit to enter Belgian territory and a few miles later we arrived at the border, where we were stopped by a wooden barrier. The black man on duty disappeared into his little guard house as we arrived and reappeared shortly dressed in puttees, blue uniform, and red-lined cape. He ceremoniously unlocked the bar and lifted it for us to pass. It was clear that no car had been through for some time, as the only sign of use on the dusty road was a well-worn footpath that wandered down the right-of-way.

As we drove along, we soon came to a place where the road had been built across a deep gully. The fill consisted of chunks of sharp lava rock surfaced with pumice or weathered volcanic tuff. In the middle of this gully we startled a

Benson with the lobelia.

group of barefoot natives, who ran down the road ahead of us and then leapt off, landing on the lava rocks of the steep embankment many feet below and then turned to grin at us. The soles of their feet must have been as tough as rhinoceros horn!

This area is really overpopulated. There seemed to be a native behind every bush. The Watuzi are tall with splendid physiques. Clothing is scanty, often of skins. Jewelry consists of copper wire wound in bulky rolls about the ankles, and the hair is often shaved in patterns or combed into peculiar crescents. The steep hillsides are under intense cultivation and the colorful fields gave us the impression of a painting by van Gogh. As we drove south we could just barely discern the outlines of the lofty Mufumbiro volcanoes which were nearly obscured by smoke.

That night we put up at the Hotel des Volcanes and after dinner walked down to the edge of the lake on a deserted path through an avenue of tall trees, no doubt planted in the early days of colonial settlement.

The next day we drove 45 miles north through the Mufumbiro volcanoes to Rutchuru, where we purchased permits to visit Parc Nacional Albert, and then on another 25 miles to Ruindi Camp within the park. There we enlisted a native guide, which was included in the permit fee, and took a late afternoon drive on a side road toward Lake Edward, covering about 40 miles. The road was really only a jungle track, but was in excellent condition. The guide stood on the running board next to our driver. We first caught a glimpse of the back and ears of an elephant standing close to the track in very tall grass. Soon afterward we saw several herds of elephant below us, also in tall grass, and finally we came to a group of five which crossed the road right in front of us. We also saw baboons and topi.

That night we had a bit of excitement. When Esther went to use the outhouse, her flashlight beam illuminated a nine-foot black mamba coiled up in the middle of the facility. When she returned to report this, the natives at the camp dashed out just in time to see the last few feet of the snake disappearing down the hole The mamba is one of the most poisonous snakes in Africa. Needless to say the building was not used that night.

August 28 was our banner day for big game. We started at 5:40 on our second route through the park. We saw our first lions, two females and a male. They got up lazily and walked away as we drove up. We then proceded on toward the lake, where we saw in rapid succession herds of topi, three hippos completing their morning browse, a distant herd of elephant, and then two more lions. The guide directed our driver to turn off the road toward the retreating lions, which quickly disappeared. In the distance, however, three elephant appeared, one a huge bull. As they were to windward and the grass short, we waited. The bull retired behind a euphorbia tree to rub his itching back, while the others continued toward us in leisurely fashion. One came to within less than 100 feet before the wind changed. Up came his trunk which immediately zeroed in on us. As soon as he spotted us he turned in discreet retreat, much to my relief, as I was standing outside the car snapping pictures. It shows what poor eyesight these beasts have, as I was in full sunlight with a white helmet on. We continued to the bank of the Rutchuru River, where we found a herd of hippos wallowing in the muddy water. While we watched them we saw several fights between belligerent males and two tardy chaps waddling down the opposite bank for their matutinal ablutions. Esther was just saying, "Now we have seen everything but buffalo," when we spotted a buffalo bull close to the track. He was one of the nastiest looking animals I have ever seen.

It was noon by the time we had returned to Ruindi Camp, and a 128-mile drive lay ahead, first up a steep escarpment and then north along the western side of Lake Edward over the longest, continuously curvy mountain road I have yet seen. One drives to the right in Belgian territory and this added a bit of tension to the trip, as we wondered how our driver, used to passing on the left, would react to a car coming at us around a blind curve. However, I don't recall encountering a single car on the road that day. We did meet and have a brief chat in French with a judge who was making his rounds through the back country in a chair carried by eight natives.

Arriving at Lubero, we were "encouraged" by the attendant at the gas station, who told us that from there it was a week's drive to Kampala! We then pushed on to the Butembo Rest Camp, arriving after dark. The proprietor was away in Kampala, having left his black boys in charge. It took them forever to get us and an English party, which was

Ferry across the Semliki River.

also stopping there, some dinner.

The next day was our longest one. We left Butembo at 8:00 and drove to Beni, where we tried unsuccessfully to pick up a spare inner tube, and thence to a stream-propelled ferry crossing the Semliki River, which flows north from Lake Edward to Lake Albert. In the Semliki valley we saw numerous almost stark naked pygmies, some of the women with heavy baskets carried on their backs with a tumpline across the forehead. More hippos were in the river. Just before arriving at the Uganda barrier we encountered three buffalo very close to the road. Beyond, we saw large flocks of flamingos appearing as a pink strip along the margins of a small crater lake.

Passing the turn-off where parties drive in to climb the Ruwenzori Range, we were lucky enough to get a magnificent view of the snow-hung peaks through a break in the clouds, the first glimpse anyone had had for days.

Just before reaching Fort Portal we ran into a swarm of four-inch grasshoppers. From a distance it appeared as a light gray cloud, filling the whole valley. When we drove down through it, the insects darkened the sky. We were reminded of the Biblical plagues.

East of Fort Portal we were caught in a very heavy thunderstorm which required us to wait until it had passed. The delay meant that we had to drive after dark in order to reach the Kygegwa Rest House where we were to spend the night. It is dangerous to drive in this country after dark, as animals may be on the road. On a curve with steep banks on either side we encountered a huge bull buffalo in the middle of the road. He was facing away from us, but his head was lowered and he was pawing the ground. Our driver, who was accustomed to hippos, suggested blowing the horn, but I indicated in sign language to shove into reverse and back up. We did this twice. As the lights swung off the animal, he fortunately jumped off the road. Meanwhile we discovered that Benson had disappeared underneath the luggage on the back seat and we could hear his teeth chattering for some time thereafter. He knew what we learned later, that buffalo charge lights!

Out last day was uneventful. We arrived at Kampala a few minutes before 2:00, just in time to get into the bank before it closed. The round trip had come to 1,067 miles, the last thousand of which were without a spare tire. Weren't we lucky not to have had another flat!

Lots of love,
R and E

Our flight to England was an expensive present from my family, making it possible for us to reach Denmark in time to begin my postdoctoral fellowship. It cost $1,037 for the two of us — almost as much as did our seven week's sojourn in Africa.

Piccadilly Hotel
London, England
September 5, 1937

Dear Family:

We hope you received the cable announcing our safe
arrival in England.

The flight was a fascinating experience, but we would
love to have been able to stop over for a little sightseeing in
Egypt and Greece. As it happened, we were most fortunate
to be on the flight at all, since Imperial Airways has just
begun to carry all the first class mail between the British
Colonies and England. Our flight was the very first to do
this from South Africa and the change in policy necessitated halving the normal passenger load to make room for the
mail. Thus travellers with more recent reservations were
bumped from the flight and stopovers are now out of the
question.

Our plane, the *Capella*, was a Sunderland flying boat,
which is only able to land on water. It has a passenger capacity of 24, each passenger and his luggage being limited to
100 kilos. The fact that we both lost ten pounds sailing
down the Red Sea made it possible for us to bring our plant
press with us without paying excess baggage charges, and we
have now sent our collections, some of them still wet, back
to the Gray Herbarium by air mail.

We only flew during daylight hours, covering 1,000 to
1,200 miles a day at the speed of between 140 and 165
miles per hour. The altimeter in our compartment indicated
that we were flying somewhere between 5,000 and 9,000
feet, depending upon the terrain. Here is what we jotted
down day by day.

September 1. Up at 6:00. Left by car for Port Bell on
Lake Victoria by 7:00. Into the huge aircraft at 7:30 and off
in a cloud of spray. This first day of the flight doesn't seem

*Capella*, the Imperial Airways flying boat in which we flew from
Lake Victoria to Southampton in 1937.

real. We have a compartment with two easy chairs on the
starboard side right underneath the wing. On the other side
is a bed made up for anyone who wants to take a nap. To the
rear are two more compartments larger than ours, one with
a "promenade" on one side. Forward are two toilets, a kitch-
enette, and the baggage. Above us are the cockpit and the
mail.

Today we are flying so high that game and other details
are difficult to make out. E. saw an elephant and I, several
hippos. The ship drones through the air so smoothly that it
seems as though we were floating among the fluffy clouds on
a magic carpet while the world slides by underneath. After
crossing the land to the northern end of Lake Albert, where
we stopped at Butiaba, we have been passing over the Sudans
— flat as a pancake from our elevation. The monotony is
broken only by the silvery Nile and its muddy tributaries
winding their way through vast expanses of swampy
papyrus, referred to as the sudd.

We came down at noon to fuel at Malakal. The river was in flood, and the main channel was partially obstructed with large floating islands of papyrus. The Imperial Airways motor launch had been busy for over an hour prior to our arrival, pushing these islands to one side to give us a clear stretch of water on which to land. As it was we did a little weaving to get in between them. The passengers always leave the plane during a refueling operation. On shore we saw tall, naked Shilluks with their long spears, standing on one foot or paddling about in dugouts. Their hair is dyed red with a mixture of red clay and manure and their brows are marked with rows of scarifications.

There was an interesting transition from the excessively wet northern section of the Sudan to the arid desert region surrounding Khartoum, which we reached at 4:00. The city lies at the junction of the White Nile and the Blue Nile, the latter originating in Abyssinia. At the Grand Hotel it is very hot, even after dark. Being the only couple on the plane, we have been assigned the bridal suite, a huge room with ceiling fan and cool tiled floor.

September 2. Called at 5:15. Off on a five-mile bus ride to the mooring at 6:00. Take-off at 6:45. Just outside Khartoum the desert began. At first there was some sparse vegetation of grass and scattered trees, but soon it was absolutely barren, with stretches of wind packed sand and bare rock, interspersed with cinder cones and dikes. We saw one camel caravan and occasional oases consisting of two or more palm trees in the sandy washes. We went over some barren mountains, where the valleys were choked with drifts of sand. The Nile makes a big bend out of sight to the east and then another one to the west. We crossed it at Karima. At our altitude it appeared as a fine silver ribbon, far too narrow to land on. We came down at Wadi Halfa in an eight-knot current. The temperature was 115°F. After refueling we took off again on the second try and arrived in Cairo about 3:00. The pilot dipped his wing over the pyramids to give us a splendid view of them before landing. We

then had the inevitable British tea on a houseboat in the
river. One hour more and we landed in the harbor of
Alexandria.

Alexandria is a fascinating cosmopolitan city. We
walked about before dinner visiting shops and listening to
the proprietors conversing with the customers in all the
Mediterranean tongues — Egyptian, Arabic, Greek, Italian,
French, and English.

September 3. Out from Alexandria at 6:00, taking off
amidst a squadron of British destroyers and an aircraft car-
rier. We flew low across the clear blue sea at about 500 feet
to a gap in the mountains at the eastern end of Crete, landing in the Gulf of Merabelle. I and two other male passengers went off behind a rock for a skinny dip, while the plane
refueled. Esther and another lady, with much dissatisfaction,
went wading. By the time we reached Greece we had
obtained permission to get access to our bags and were all
set in bathing suits for a proper swim, which five us took off
the pier at Piraeus.

We had a brief glimpse of the Acropolis at Athens as
the plane circled the port. We then flew across the Gulf of
Corinth and over the Island of Corfu to Brindisi on the heel
of Italy. As we were crossing the Adriatic I observed something fall off one of the starboard engines, which was then
turned off. As a result we flew the sea route to Rome on
three engines, incidentally avoiding a storm over the
Apennines. As we flew across the Gulf of Taranto between
the heel and the toe of Italy we observed the Italian Navy
doing maneuvers. We landed on Lake Bracciano just north
of Rome and went ashore on a wet sandy beach, where
Italian officials kept us standing around until nearly dark
before giving us clearance to be bused into the city. It was a
little taste of the international tension that has built up
between Great Britain and the Mussolini regime. We were
taken to the four star Hotel de la Russe, where we had an
elegant meal al fresco in the hotel's beautiful garden just
below the Villa de Medici. Again we had a regal suite with a

huge bathroom, which was in use most of the night. What a mistake we made to go swimming in the polluted harbor of Piraeus!

September 4. Up before dawn to return to Lake Bracciano for an early take-off. Our route took us over Corsica to Marseilles. On this leg the first mate showed us around the flight deck. Just as we were reboarding at Marseilles we observed history in the making. Our sister ship was arriving from England on the first scheduled mail flight to India.

The final leg of our flight took us over the farms and chateaux of France and the English Channel to South-ampton, where we landed at 3:00. A train was waiting for us. Major Dyke, with whom we have become very friendly, sat in the compartment with us and was highly amused by our failure to pronounce correctly a single station on the way into London.

After settling in at the Piccadilly and having a quiet sup-per we strolled down to Buckingham Palace for the chang-ing of the Guards and so back to bed, tired but happy to have successfully pulled off our African adventure.

Our next letters will be from Copenhagen.

Much love from
R and E

As a closing note it will be apparent from these letters that Esther and I managed to stay healthy during our entire eight weeks in Africa. This was not entirely due to good luck. We had lived carefully and had taken precautions. One exception. About two weeks after arriving in Copenhagen I noticed what I thought was dirt under the nail of one of my big toes. I soon discovered it was dried blood and then dislodged a chigger. It is probable I had acquired this mite in Khartoum. There I had walked barefoot on the cool white-tiled floors of our bridal suite.

It is not always thus. Someone told me that the Harvard Medical School used to schedule their course in tropical medicine on years when Arthur Loveridge was returning from extended collecting expeditions to Africa. He usually provided fresh examples of health hazards, which he had acquired in the country.

Kibo, the summit of Mt. Kilimanjaro, from above
Johannes Hut at about 9,000 feet.

# 5

# THE WEB OF
# RESEARCH

SCOPOLETIN

E sther and I spent academic year 1937–1938 in Denmark, where I
was an American-Scandinavian Fellow and guest investigator in the
plant physiology laboratory of the University of Copenhagen, under
the direction of Prof. P. Boysen-Jensen. BJ, as he was often referred to,
was one of the pioneer researchers in the new field of plant hormones
and was the author of a book, *Growth Hormones in Plants*, that had been
translated into English by George S. Avery, Jr., and his colleagues at
Connecticut College. I was familiar with Avery's work and had visited
his laboratory in 1933, when Connecticut College hosted a summer
meeting of the Botanical Society of America. I was interested in learning BJ's techniques for assaying these growth hormones, which were
somewhat different from those of Kenneth Thimann at Harvard. I
hoped to investigate the production and distribution of these substances in plants.

I learned about the fellowship through my father, who was a good friend of the Danish naval architect Professor Hofgaard, who had recently retired from the faculty at MIT. This contact may well have been helpful in getting favorable action for me by the American-Scandinavian Foundation's fellowship committee. Before going abroad, Esther and I had a delightful visit with the old gentleman at his apartment in Brooklyn. The fellowship stipend was $1,000, which enabled the two of us to live abroad quite comfortably for a year, including trips to Austria and Norway to ski, and to Germany, Holland, and England for professional contacts.

The building that housed BJ's laboratory was situated in a corner of the university's botanical garden. The front door opened on a spacious atrium. To the left was the entrance to Professor Boysen-Jensen's living quarters, to the right was the home of the professor of algology, and straight ahead was the door to the laboratory.

My first few days in Copenhagen were spent editing one of BJ's papers, which the professor had written in English. His birthplace was Schleswig-Holstein, where German was the native tongue. His sentences were in the German style, long and convoluted. He was happy with all my editorial changes except for a minor suggestion of a substantive nature.

After an initial indoctrination in his methods of bioassay, I set out to determine whether growth hormones, also called auxins, could be produced by plants grown in total darkness. I started by incubating pieces of dandelion roots in the darkroom until they had regenerated stems and leaves, then extracted these etiolated tissues. The extracts, when tested for their growth-promoting properties using BJ's technique, turned out to inhibit growth rather than promoting it. This upset the professor, as his bioassay would no longer work. He correctly surmised that there was a substance in the extract that was "interfering" with the action of the auxin and suggested that I try to separate the two by differential rates of diffusion, on the assumption that the inhibitor had a larger molecular size than the auxin. His assumption was correct, the method worked, and the activity of the growth hormone, when separated from the inhibiting substance, could be measured. Upon further investigation I found that inhibiting substances were also present in other species of plants. The paper that I wrote as a result of my stay in Copenhagen described the presence of growth inhibiting compounds in plants and discussed their significance to methods of auxin bioassay.[1]

This concept of plant growth inhibitors was a new one. As soon as I had left for home, BJ's laboratory turned to an investigation of these substances. Upon my return to the United States, I discussed my results with a well-known plant physiologist. Less that a month later, I found that he had managed to get a brief note on a growth inhibitor published in *Science* — several months before my paper appeared in print. This was my first brush with the fiercely competitive nature of scientific research.

During my year abroad I was impressed by the difference between the way research was carried out in Europe as compared to the way it was in the United States. Equipment was much more modest; experiments were thoughtfully planned and then very carefully executed on a smaller scale. This was true in England and Holland as well as in Denmark.

The winter days in Copenhagen were short and dark. There was a spell of about six weeks when we saw the sun only once for a few minutes at high noon. I got a photo of a bicycle standing at the curb at midday, casting a shadow all the way across ten feet of sidewalk. People at the lab came late to work, and after dark the city took on a cozy, intimate air, alive with shoppers and illuminated softly with twinkling Christmas lights.

We were invited by the Boysen-Jensens to attend a Christmas Eve service. Esther didn't have a hat, so we fabricated an adequate one out of a velvet scarf. Then on to the professor's house for dinner with BJ and his attractive daughter. The latter had modeled a clay elephant as a table decoration in honor of our recent African expedition. It was contrived that Esther got the almond in the rice pudding, the significance of which was that she should get her wish. After dinner we all joined hands and sang carols around the fifteen-foot Christmas tree lit by candles. When the candles had burned low, the professor produced a six-foot-long glass tube with an atomizer bulb at one end with which to snuff them out. After a brief demonstration he handed it to me with a twinkle in his eye. I found the device required a very steady hand and good coordination.

During our stay we lived at Pension Mejløv, just a few blocks from the lab. It was run by a Norwegian lady with two teenaged daughters. Most of the inhabitants were elderly and we sat for meals at a long narrow table. Communication was sometimes a problem, and we soon gained some expertise with the boardinghouse reach. One of our favorite people was Dr. Djorup, a man in his eighties, who would come in on cold damp days carrying a hot dog in each hand to warm his fingers.

There were very few cars in town. Almost everyone had a bicycle. Carpenters rode by with ladders on their shoulders, and deliveries were made with all sorts of pedaled contraptions. At rush hour there were traffic jams, during which people often kept their balance by placing a hand on a neighbor's shoulder. Much of the time the streets were wet from mist, and the bicycles wheels sprayed shoes with a fine spray of muddy water.

Of course Esther and I had bicycles, which we used on weekends to tour the countryside, often on special bicycle paths. One day in dappled sunlight I had the misfortune to hit a rock on one of these trails. My spill resulted in a broken collarbone, and I had an opportunity to experience socialized medicine. This type of injury was obviously a common occurrence. I was taped up at the hospital without an X-ray and, when I inquired how much I owed, was informed that the service was completely covered by taxes.

At Easter we made a delightful excursion to the picturesque Danish island of Bornholm, an overnight boat trip east off the southern coast of Sweden. The thatched houses were all old, of plaster and beam construction, painted in pastel hues with violets in bloom on their roofs. We bicycled around the island, spending the nights in youth hostels. The first day we literally blew across the island in a stiff west wind.

While still in Copenhagen and just as I was beginning to wonder what I would be doing the following year, I received by cable an offer from the University of Rochester of an instructorship in botany at an annual salary of $2,200. In 1938 this was a good starting salary. Our friends in the pension were curious to know exactly where Rochester was and were amazed to discover that I was a bit vague as to its exact size and location. In their little country they are familiar not only with every town but also with each noteworthy tree and monument.

That summer my parents joined us in Copenhagen and all four of us made a tour through Sweden and Norway. One of the stops was at the lovely old fortified town of Visby on the Island of Gotland. Esther and I took off for the south end of the island on bicycles and spent the night in a pasture. When two very friendly horses started visiting us after dark, we decided to move with our bikes to the other side of the fence. The next morning we found we were sleeping on a bed of orchids! We knocked on the door of the neighboring farmhouse to see if we could get some breakfast and were cordially greeted in perfect English. The proprietor had served for twenty-four years as pastor of a church in Minnesota and proceeded to show us pictures of his flock.

Later on as we were going by train to Trondheim, we stopped off at Åre near the Norwegian border and I spent three days climbing Sylarna, the highest mountain in Sweden. A memorable evening was enjoyed in a mountain hut with a friendly group of Swedish climbers. They sang songs for about two hours, and not a single tune was familiar to me.

Upon returning to the States, Esther went to visit her mother in Chestnut Hill, while I drove to Rochester to look for a place to live. Shortly after I left Boston the 1938 hurricane hit New England. For more than a week there was no communication between the two cities. Finally a telegram came through to me via Canada indicating that all members of the family were safe.

My first teaching assignments kept me pretty busy that fall. But while I was cutting thin sections of living tree trunks for my class in plant structure, my colleague and department chair, David Goddard, whose special field of research was plant respiration, suggested that I measure the metabolic rate of the various layers of the stems — bark, cambium, and wood — using the Warburg respirometers that were available in his lab. The investigation developed into a joint paper, written the following summer while I was a guest of the Carnegie Institution of Washington at its Division of Plant Biology at Stanford, California.[2] As the senior author, I presented the results of this study orally at the 1940 meetings of the American Institute of Biological Sciences. When the chairman of the section announced our paper he said, "Goodwin and Goddard, the Respiration of Woody Tissues. Good God this must be good!"

Just being at the Carnegie laboratory was an exciting and educational experience. I came to know some of the staff and to learn about the research going on there. Jens Clausen, David Keck, and William Heisey were in the midst of writing up their now classic studies on experimental taxonomy, and some of their plants were growing in the garden outside the window. Physiologist Hermann Spoehr was the director, and Robert Emerson, an older brother of my friend Ralph, was conducting his landmark experiments on photosynthesis. Irving Bailey and Ralph Wetmore were also there as guests, and I learned more about Bailey's innovative studies on the structure of the cell wall. In the frenetic, world of "publish or perish," the scientific pace at this institution was, and still is, an exception. The research is meticulous, and time is taken to produce really significant contributions. Exposure to this intellectual climate was important to me at this formative stage in my career.

Esther and I had a delightful stay on the Stanford University campus that summer of 1939. We lived in a little one-room apartment in Kingscote Gardens. Esther was pregnant and enjoyed visiting Ruth Peabody Rossbach who was in the same condition. I had known Ruth in Cambridge before she married my classmate George Rossbach, who was also a botanist. Ruth was at Radcliffe, and she and I had taken an advanced taxonomy course together under Professor Fernald. Three women signed up for this course, and I was the only male registrant. Fernald understandably arranged to give the course just once for the four of us. I doubt that there had been any consultation with the Dean's office. Perhaps this was Harvard's very first integrated offering. The Goodwins and the Rossbachs went on a number of weekend forays together into the California hills. We stayed in touch with Ruth and forty-nine years later were invited to accompany her and her second husband, Ian Berendsen, on a trip to New Zealand. Ian had just retired from his position at the United Nations and was returning to his native land. He took us to visit some of his favorite places.

Back in Rochester our first excitement was the advent of our little daughter, born on September 12, just two days after her mother's birthday. We named her Mary Linder after her grandmother. Twenty months later her brother Richard Hale, Jr. arrived. As soon as he started talking he contracted his sister's name to Minda, and this nickname has stayed with her ever since. Grandpa Goodwin immediately dubbed his grandson Dicko, but the "o" was dropped as soon as my son started school.

At Rochester my colleague Donald R. Charles, a mathematical geneticist and student of Sewall Wright, was interested in what everyone was doing in the Biology Division and most generously offered to share his mathematical expertise with anyone who was disposed to accept it. The goldenrod material I brought from Cambridge included genetic data on the first- and second-generation hybrids that would lend themselves to analysis. Don worked up a new formula that permitted a calculation of the minimum number of genes differentiating the two parental species. This resulted in joint papers that showed the two species were differentiated by quite a few separate genes.[3]

The method also permitted me to pursue the inheritance of flowering time within strains of the salt marsh species that had been collected at different latitudes along the Atlantic Coast. Early frosts in the north have eliminated late flowering strains, whereas lack of these frosts in the south has permitted plants in Florida to flower on shorter

Mary ("Minda") and Richard, Jr. ("Dick"), Christmas 1942.

photoperiods. At the latitude of Rochester, by mid-October the south-ern strains were growing through the ventilators at the top of the greenhouse before coming into flower. In order to obtain crosses between the early-flowering northern plants and the late-flowering southern ones, it was necessary to shorten the photoperiod under which the southern strains were growing by daily removing the plants to a dark room. In this way simultaneous flowering was achieved. It turned out that even within the same species many genes are involved in controlling when flowering begins and how rapidly the buds devel-op, once they are initiated.[4]

I also studied the effects of light on the growth of oat seedlings. The first internode, the bit of stem that develops between the nutritive material in the seed and the growing point that produces the developing leaves, is enormously sensitive to light. In complete darkness it grows very long. When a seed germinates in the soil, this structure serves to bring the growing point and young leaves to the surface of the ground. It has been shown that the minute amount of light required to bring about an inhibition can reach the internode through the tissues of the plant once the protective coleoptile tip breaks the soil surface. My first series of experiments was designed to determine how much light was required to inhibit the growth of the internode. A second series was designed to find out what wavelengths were effective.[5] In this way, it is possible to get information about the absorption spectrum of the pigment involved in the light reaction.

In a study of the structure of the first internode, I found that elongating dark-grown stems contained no thick-walled water-conducting cells, which are incapable of further elongation. But plants exposed to light immediately developed enlarged, thick-walled vessels that could no longer grow in length.[6]

In order to carry on these experiments it was necessary to grow the seedlings in a growth chamber under carefully controlled conditions of temperature and humidity. No such chamber was commercially available at that time, so I built one for $200. My colleagues jokingly referred to the contraption as "Goodwin's Rube Goldberg."

An incidental observation made in the course of these studies had significant consequences later: The roots of the oat seedlings, when irradiated with ultraviolet light, exhibited a brilliant blue fluorescence. Dave Goddard was on leave at the time, and a microbiologist, Kavanagh, Frederick, was filling in as his replacement. Fred was interested in fluorescent compounds and had designed a fluorimeter for their quantitative measurement. With his encouragement I acquired one of these instruments, which was purchased with a small grant from the Rumford Fund of the American Academy of Arts and Sciences. Later on, after I had become established at Connecticut College, Fred and I collaborated on the identification of the fluorescent material.

One of my duties in the Botany Department was to care for the university herbarium, which numbered thousands of mounted specimens. Some were the property of the university and many were on deposit from the Rochester Academy of Science. In addition there were huge piles of unmounted material. During my six years at Rochester I managed to sort through the entire herbarium, getting the collections in order, supervising the mounting of specimens and discarding inadequately labelled material. In the process I became very familiar with the local flora, which was tremendously useful to me in teaching systematic botany. Also, the public expects a botanist to be able to identify any fragment of a plant placed before him, and my herbarium experience enabled me to pull this off a few times.

After a year or so I contrived to get the spring semester course in local flora scheduled for Saturdays — all day! As soon as the weather permitted, we went into the field, leaving early in the morning and occasionally getting back fairly late in the afternoon. Most of the students lapped it up, but I remember one time getting the party trapped in a rhododendron thicket. I paid penance by treating the class to drinks and ice cream, when we finally got ourselves extricated. Another time we took a final mid-afternoon sally through a sphagnum swamp. After returning to the car we heard a faint halloo issuing from the depths of the wetland. Before we could return to offer assistance, who should emerge from the woods but our barefooted physiologist graduate student, who had fallen in over his knees. He was carrying his dripping shoes by the laces and was lucky to have them!

As curator of the herbarium I came to meet Royal E. Shanks, an ecologist working on the flora of Monroe County, where Rochester is located. He and I became good friends and collaborated on the publication of new records for plants in the area.[7] At the same time I put together a flora of Mendon Ponds Park — a botanically rich bit of glacial moraine dotted with lakes, eskers, and kettles — that lies a few miles south of the city.[8]

One day as I sorted unmounted specimens, an old letter in brown ink on paper yellowed with age fell out of a genus folder. The letter turned out to be written by the botanist John Torrey to his friend Chester Dewey at Williams College. It was so interesting that I copied it before taking the original over to the archivist at the university library. I wondered when, if ever, this letter would again see the light of day. About nine months later I was reading a life of Torrey written by Denny Rodgers when I came upon a very familiar passage.[9] I suddenly realized that it was a quotation from the letter I had salvaged from the herbarium. The biographer must have retrieved it within days of the time I turned it over to the Library.

Anyone working in the Biology Division at Rochester in those days just before World War II enjoyed a privileged experience. The faculty consisted of exceptionally able scientists in the early stages of their careers. Dave Goddard, the only other botanist, was a brilliant scholar as well as a thoughtful administrator. His lively concern for building up the botanical resources of the university library rubbed off on me and had an impact on the library at Connecticut College after I had relocated there. Dave became head of the Biology Division at the University of Pennsylvania and, later, its provost. The chairman of the Biology Division at Rochester was Benjamin Willier, an authority on feather embryology. He later became chairman of biology at Johns Hopkins and took with him his research associate Mary Rawles, who also became noted for her research. Curt Stern went on to the University of California at Berkeley as one of the foremost human geneticists. I have already mentioned Don Charles' extraordinary contribution to the research productivity of the Division. The person who brought more life to our group than anyone else was Sherman Bishop, its senior member and an expert on salamanders and spiders. A master raconteur, Sherm would regale us at lunch with stories of his youth that would have us all in stitches.

A huge central room on the top floor of the Dewey Building, which housed biology, was referred to as "Himmel." It was surrounded by cubicles for the graduate students. Many of these young Ph.D. candidates went on to distinguished careers. A departmental party was held each year at Christmastime. Everyone picked a name out of a hat and gave a present to that person. The gifts were anonymous and were usually some sort of joke. Sometimes there were a few extra gifts when it appeared appropriate. During the first couple of years of my stay in Rochester Sherm and I drew each others names from the hat, and the custom seemed to become institutionalized. Sherm's chef d'oeuvre for me was a contraption poking fun at my growth chambers that became installed in the middle of Himmel. The contrivance consisted of a toy pistol with a wooden slug to be shot at a wound-up toy alligator that then chased a black boy up a coconut palm, where he knocked down a nut that scared a woodpecker, which flew up and pecked a hole in a tank labelled "plant hormones." Liquid dripped onto the soil below, where out popped a full-grown plant.

I never equaled this production, but did even things up somewhat the next year by producing a little illustrated booklet of verses, each dealing with one of Sherm's better stories. The last one was a sketch of a kitchen stove accompanied by a verse ending with the line "Home on the Range, or why I was breathless in church." I referred to a risqué escapade with which all the assembled males were thoroughly conversant. Everyone was having a great laugh over each item, but when Sherm came to this last verse, Mrs. Bishop, who was looking over his shoulder, said, "Why Sherm, I don't seem to know about that one!" He became unusually pink for a zoologist.

The university library was excellent. One of its assets was a fine collection of journals from learned societies obtained in exchange for the *Proceedings of the Rochester Academy of Science.* This journal, which was published from time to time, had reached about eight volumes and contained many scientific articles, notably in the field of geology. When I came to Rochester, however, the academy as an institution was falling apart. Membership had dwindled to a handful, meetings were not being held, and publication of the proceedings had almost terminated. Goddard, Bishop, and I became concerned that the university would lose the benefits of its exchanges with other learned societies and decided to see what we could do about rehabilitating the academy and its publication program. This effort involved soliciting the support of our scientific colleagues at the university, key people at Eastman Kodak Company and Wards Natural Science Establishment, and others in the city with an interest in the natural sciences, arranging programs that would attract good audiences, and lining up interesting manuscripts for publication in the proceedings. Being the junior member of the three, it fell to me to do most of the leg work. One of the most effective moves was establishing sections centered around special fields of interest — botany, ornithology, astronomy, mineralogy, and anthropology. Groups of people in the community, mostly amateurs, were already meeting more or less independently, and we managed to bring these groups back into the academy. Within three years the academy was nursed back to vigorous health. Nearly six decades later, in 1998, its president, Matt Sinacola, was able to state, "Our organization has an impressively long history. It is no small achievement that this collection of interest groups has been able to sustain itself for over 110 years."

During my stay in Rochester, William Stepka came from Bernard Nebel's laboratory at the Agricultural Experiment Station in Geneva, New York, to work his way through college by taking care of our greenhouse. This young man was a most unusual student, who spared no pains to get to the root of every problem. When he encountered the earthworm lab in the introductory biology course, he actually counted segments on the worms and discovered that the numbers he found between the sperm ducts and the sperm receptacles were not as given in the lab outline. So he proceeded to go out at night armed with a flashlight, two razor blades, and a bottle of fixative, to collect a few copulating worms to document his observations. This stirred the zoologists in the department to check up on the source of the information in the outline. It had been taken from an American text that had been translated from a German source, which, in turn, had been based on a research paper dealing with a species of European worm not found in the New World.

When it was my turn to lecture on the growth of roots, I described the process as set forth in the standard texts. Stepka came up afterward to question me about details. It became clear that there were no quantitative data in the literature on exactly when and where cell division and cell enlargement occurred. At about this time Sinnott and Bloch were reporting studies of fine grass roots on which the growth of epi-dermal cells could be observed under the microscope. It occurred to us that we could grow these roots on glass slides and measure the pro-cesses of cell division and cell enlargement as they were taking place. So Bill and I undertook this project together. We rigged a small mirror on the mechanical stage of a horizontal microscope. The mirror reflected the image of a crosshair onto a wall, thus greatly magnifying a small movement of the stage. Then, using a pure strain of timothy grass, we followed the movement of marker cells at various points along the growing root. Making the assumption that the pattern of cell size remained constant, we could then estimate not only the rate of growth of the root as a whole, but also the rate of elongation of the cells at various distances from the root tip and the rate of cell division required to keep the cell pattern constant. This study developed into a paper we published jointly.[10]

Bill was inducted into the Air Force just before he could complete his graduation requirements. He was trained as an electronics expert and then flew to the Orient in command of a ferret bomber — an unarmed plane especially designed to locate enemy radar installations. I kept in close touch with him during his tour of duty. The mail serv-ice was extraordinary, an exchange of letters to the back country of China taking only three or four days. One of his remarkable experi-ences was being evacuated from Okinawa on a Landing Ship Tank or LST in a typhoon. This type of vessel was not noted for its seagoing qualities, and his ship was listed as missing for three weeks. It was Bill's first voyage on a ship!

Returning to Rochester after the war, Bill completed his under-graduate degree and commenced his graduate studies. By this time both Goddard and I had left the university and F. C. Steward was the new chairman of the botany department. Inspired by a seminar given by Charles E. Dent at the Medical School on filter-paper chromatog-raphy, Bill got permission to explore the possibilities of this new tech-nique for separating and identifying organic compounds. Shortly thereafter he had a falling-out with Steward, but not before the professor had become aware of the potential of the technique. From Rochester Bill went to the University of California at Berkeley, where he studied first under D. R. Hoagland and later with Melvin Calvin. His doctoral research involved biochemical investigations of photosynthesis using filter paper chromatography. Thus it was that Stepka brought this powerful new technique to two laboratories, each of which exploited the method to great advantage. Calvin later received the 1961 Nobel Prize in Chemistry for his contributions to the field of photosynthesis. I remained in close contact with Bill, and he was extremely helpful to me in my research as well.

In the spring of 1944 I was interviewed for an opening at Connecticut College: George Avery was leaving to become director of the Brooklyn Botanic Garden. During his thirteen years at the college, George had built up the Botany Department and developed the Connecticut Arboretum. The position was attractive. However, I returned from my visit to the college somewhat doubtful that I would accept the position if it were offered. I thought it would be an associate professorship. I was already an assistant professor at Rochester, and I figured that Goddard would be very likely leave fairly soon for a more challenging post and I would be in line for the chairmanship of the department. Esther and I liked Rochester and were well established in the community. When the offer came through, however, there was no question about my accepting it. It was a full professorship at double my Rochester salary. It included the directorship of the arboretum and an understanding that I would divide my time about equally between teaching, administration, and research. The college would also provide a research assistant.

The first year after I arrived at Connecticut College my research efforts were directed toward obtaining purified extracts of chlorophyll a and b by separating them on powdered-sugar columns. I was interested in developing a quantitative fluorimetric method for measuring these pigments and also in determining how they were produced in dark-grown plants upon exposure to light. We did not have a spectrophotometer in the department at that time, but I managed to get absorption spectra run off at MIT. These showed that the first type of chlorophyll produced by dark-grown plants in response to light was chlorophyll a.[11]

Olga Owens became my research assistant the following year and worked on an improved action spectrum for the light inhibition of the first internode of oat seedlings. At the same time we began an investigation of fluorescent compounds in roots. A survey of many species revealed the presence of fluorescent compounds in every case. We attempted to extract and fractionate the brilliantly blue fluorescent material that I had observed in oat roots while at Rochester. It soon became clear that not one, but several different fluorescent compounds were present.

In 1947, Helen A. Stafford replaced Olga as my research assistant. During her first year at Connecticut College she worked on various aspects of our program. The following year she enrolled as a graduate student and for her master's thesis undertook a study of the effects of light on timothy grass seedlings. The story was very similar to that for oats.[12] Helen went on for her Ph.D. at the University of Pennsylvania, did post-doctoral research at the University of Chicago, and subsequently had a distinguished career at Reed College in the field of plant biochemistry. Helen was my first graduate student. What would be the probability of my second having the same name? Helen J. Stafford came from the University of Texas to work in our lab during the summer of 1952. Her original name was Russian, but she had changed it to Stafford long before contacting us.

Fred Kavanagh, who was then working with William J. Robbins, director of the New York Botanical Garden, came up to New London on weekends to collaborate on the identification of the fluorescent oat root substances. He suggested that we measure their fluorescence over a wide range of acidity and then see if we could match the resulting pH-fluorescence curves with those obtained from known blue-fluorescent compounds. We tried a large number of known compounds, and the results were negative until we tried one that a

Canadian investigator had isolated from diseased potato tubers. I had read about his work, and he had been good enough to send me a small sample of his compound. Its pH-fluorescence curve was identical to that of one of our unknown fractions. The substance was scopoletin, a coumarin derivative, differing from it in the possession of two small substitutions.[13] Coumarin is a sweet-smelling compound responsible for the characteristic odor of sweet clover and sweet vernal grass. It and some of its derivatives were known to be growth inhibitors. For instance, the presence of coumarin in the flowering dogwood fruit assures the dormancy of the embryo until the pulp rots off. This suggested that scopoletin might also be a growth inhibitor; and so it proved to be.

By corresponding with biochemists all over the world I was able to assemble what was probably the world's largest series of coumarin derivatives, which the scientists were good enough to send me in minute quantities. Fred and I, and later my research associate Bruce M. Pollock, determined the pH-fluorescence curves and absorption spectra of these compounds and published them in a series of papers. that were of interest to chemists in the perfume and tobacco industries, to taxonomists studying the chemical differences between species of plants, to people in the Forest Service concerned with plants having toxic properties, and many others.[14] It was a slight frustration to me to find that reprints of this work were far more in demand than any papers reporting the botanical implication of my research.

One of my undergraduates, Carolyn Taves, as part of an honors project, tested the growth-inhibiting properties of coumarin and a number of its derivatives by applying them to growing oat roots. The technique consisted of incorporating the compounds into thin sheets of agar gel, which were then laid on top of the roots. Growth rates were then compared with those of controls that were treated with pure agar. She found that coumarin and some of its derivatives, including scopoletin, did indeed inhibit growth, unless they were combined with a sugar molecule to form a glycoside. Thus the path of my research brought me back to the inhibitor thicket encountered in Copenhagen.

Carolyn stayed over at the college the summer after she graduated, and we wrote up the results of her study as a joint paper.[15]

In the spring semester of 1950 I had academic leave, which was spent at the Berkeley campus of the University of California. The January night before we left New London it rained hard on top of a foot of fresh snow, so everything was covered with a thick blanket of standing ice water. Florence Baxter, our neighbor across the street, kindly invited us for breakfast. On the way over our eight-year-old son fell flat in the slush and had to change from the bottom up. We finally got off in a heavily laden Jeep station wagon. We learned later that at nine o'clock a big snow slide off the roof of New London Hall crashed through the sloping glass roof of my office, which we referred to as the goldfish bowl, filling the chair where I was usually sitting at that hour with splintered glass.

Our trip west was leisurely. We had taken our two children out of school and figured we would make the trip as educational as possible. We visited our former Rochester colleagues John and Elizabeth Buck, in Washington, D.C., stopped off to see Monticello, and spent a night with Royal and Betty Shanks in Knoxville, Tennessee. We hoped to cross the Mississippi by ferry above Memphis, but at a bluff about ten miles from the river the road disappeared, and all we could see were tree tops standing in a flood. People were camping out in tents on the high ground. We crossed the river on the bridge at Memphis, but found part of the main highway through Arkansas only a foot above the flood. We observed an oil rig drilling a well in Oklahoma, skied with friends on the slopes of the Sangre de Cristo Mountains east of Santa Fe, and visited San Ildefonso Pueblo, where we bought a beautiful black pottery plate from the famous Indian potter Maria. We climbed the mesa to the Acoma Pueblo and drove in foot-deep mud to Zuni just in time, as the only tourists, to witness their buffalo dance. A second ski on San Francisco Peak in Arizona and visits to the Grand Canyon, Hoover Dam, Death Valley, and a snowy Tioga Pass finally brought us to a lush California spring. We moved into a rented house on Marin Avenue near

Minda and Dick at Yosemite National Park.

the crest of the Berkeley Hills with a splendid view of San Francisco Bay and the Golden Gate. The kids went to school several blocks down an incredibly steep sidewalk.

At the university I started to examine a wide variety of plant materials for fluorescent compounds. One of the most interesting finds was in the leaves of a certain species of vetch. Proteinaceous bodies in the epidermal cells adjacent to the stomata exhibited a brilliant orange fluorescence. Stacy French, who was then director of the Carnegie Laboratory on the Stanford campus, had built a device for recording fluorescence spectra, and he was good enough to let me use it. I commuted to Stanford to analyze the spectrum of these orange bodies in collaboration with Violet Koski, one of the research associates there. We were able to establish that the pigment was an octocarboxy porphyrin, a compound closely related to chlorophyll, which has a red fluorescence.[16] Research is sometimes fraught with disconcerting setbacks. Desirous of getting color photographs of these fluorescent bodies, I drove up to the University of California at Davis where Katherine Esau allowed me to use her photomicrographic equipment. The exposures had to be made expeditiously, as the fluorescent pigment bleached rapidly in bright light. Having taken the pictures, I returned to Berkeley and sent the films off for processing. What came back were beautiful shots of skiing in the mountains. It is easy to imagine the reaction of the folks who received mine. Had I been successful they would have displayed orange blobs surrounded by wavy bluish lines. To the best of my knowledge the functions of these bodies and of their pigment have yet to be determined.

Olga Owens came to visit us in Berkeley, and we completed the write-up of her work at Connecticut College on the action spectrum of the light inhibition of dark-grown oat seedlings.[17] While she was with us we had a few glorious days of camping in Yosemite National Park.

Bill Stepka and his wife Bonnie were still in Berkeley. They were most helpful in getting us settled in. Bill, using his technique of paper chromatography, was able to identify the sugars that were part of the scopoletin glycoside.

By this time I had the separate pieces of a puzzle that needed to be put together: first, a method of analyzing the growth pattern of a root, developed initially in collaboration with Bill Stepka; second, methods of extracting and quantitatively assaying fluorescent compounds and sugars, worked out with Fred Kavanagh and Bill Stepka; third, identified two compounds naturally present in the same root — scopoletin and its glycoside, the former shown to be a growth inhibitor; and fourth, a small supply of scopoletin that could be used for experimental purposes. Here was an opportunity to explore the role of an inhibitor in regulating the growth of a root. Upon returning to Connecticut I prepared and submitted to the National Institutes of Health an application for a three-year research grant of $19,000. It was awarded in 1951 and later extended for an additional three years, for a somewhat larger amount.

Bruce Pollock, who had been trained in Steward's department at Rochester, came to work with me as a research associate. Steward apparently felt that my lab was not the place for Bruce. It was with some amusement that I received from Steward a misdirected carbon copy of a letter intended for an investigator at another institution, who had also offered Bruce a position. At the bottom of the letter in longhand Steward had written, "Goodwin will scarcely relish the fact that Pollock is going to work for you." I forwarded this communication to its intended recipient in a Connecticut College envelope.

During the next three years Bruce and I described the inhibitory effects of scopoletin and coumarin on the development of timothy grass roots. Participating in this research was one of my botany majors, Susan Greene. We established that the non-inhibitory scopoletin glycoside was the substance in the growing portion of the root, whereas the aglycone, scopoletin, was the substance in the older portions that were no longer growing. The concentration of free scopoletin in the non-growing portions would, if applied to the growing tip, inhibit its growth. An enzyme was obviously present within the root that could convert the inhibitor to the inactive form. Here were all the requirements for a natural growth-regulating system.

We isolated another blue-fluorescent fraction from oat roots that also proved to be a combination of a glycoside and its aglycone. To the best of my knowledge this substance has still to be identified. Bruce left in 1953 for an academic position at the University of Delaware but returned the following summer to complete part of our study.[18]

Our daughter, Minda, was in high school at Putney School in Vermont. Putney had a midwinter break of about a month, during which each student was to undertake a special project. In 1956 during her junior year Minda asked if she might do some research in my lab, so I suggested that she try to extract the blue-fluorescent compounds from timothy grass roots and then see if she could determine what they were by paper chromatography. It was a tough assignment. I described the procedures, gave her the equipment and reagents, and left her to her devices. She went right at it, made no spills, broke no glassware, and within three weeks came out with some nice clean results. The next semester one of my upperclass majors, during an independent study, was unable to repeat the experiment. It has been no surprise to us that our daughter has turned out to be highly successful in sophisticated biochemical research, first at the National Institutes of Health and later at the University of Kansas Medical School.

In 1953 Charlotte J. Avers replaced Bruce as my postdoctoral research associate and worked on the project for the next three years. By this time we had developed a set-up to grow our timothy grass roots in little culture cells that could be flooded periodically with a standard nutrient solution, to which various test compounds might be added. Every fifteen minutes during the immersed part of the cycle the surface of the root was photographed, to record the outlines of complete files of epidermal cells from the tip of the root to the older portions that had stopped growing in length. This procedure recorded exactly where cell division and cell enlargement were taking place. The resulting data on root growth may still be the best that have been obtained, at least for cells on the root surface.[19] Some of our data have been subjected to mathematical analysis by other investigators.

After establishing the normal growth pattern in the standard nutrient solution, it was possible to determine exactly how the inhibitors scopoletin and coumarin modified that pattern. In addition the effects of the growth hormone indole-acetic acid were also tested. The method was amazingly sensitive, growth responses to these compounds being recorded within fifteen minutes of their application. The results of these experiments were published in a series of papers, the last one in an issue of the *Botanical Gazette* celebrating the eightieth birthday of my old mentor, Ralph Wetmore.[20]

Looking back at the threads of my research, they have been woven into bits of two fabrics — the tapestry of evolution and the cloth of plant development. In each case an army of scientists from many disciplines have been contributing threads. Their interactions are one of the factors that make research such a fascinating enterprise. I was significantly influenced by my father's philosophy, which was reinforced by my mentors at Harvard. The inspiration of my teachers, the ideas and collaboration of my colleagues and the stimulation of my students have all been vital ingredients in whatever I may have achieved.

A detailed study of what was happening in populations of goldenrod revealed a glimpse into the complexity of the process of evolution. Likewise, a detailed analysis of root growth made it possible to document the role of growth-regulating compounds in normal development. Incidental observations turned out to be a very important ingredient. For example, the accidental discovery that high temperatures were required to germinate goldenrods permitted me to grow genetic material from scarce hybrid seeds; the failure of a bioassay for growth-promoting hormones led to the discovery of growth inhibitors; and curiosity about the blue fluorescence of oat roots led eventually to the identification of scopoletin and its role as a growth inhibitor.

* * *

In 1956 I became president of The Nature Conservancy. This demanding commitment on top of my other academic duties precluded laboratory research, at least for the next couple of years. As it turned out, my on-going involvement in the natural-area movement limited my subsequent research contributions to the field of ecology.

It was not until I read the twenty-fifth reunion write-ups of my Harvard classmates that I began to realize how extraordinarily fortunate I had been. We graduated in 1933 in the depths of the Depression. Most had struggled to get established in some sort of gainful employment. By 1941, when many were just getting on their feet financially, Pearl Harbor jerked them into military service. Finally, twelve years out of college, the survivors were in a position to commence their careers. By contrast, I had been financed through graduate school by my parents, my father enjoying the stability of an academic post. I had acquired a lovely wife, had studied abroad for a year on a post-doctoral fellowship, and then fallen into a good teaching position in an excellent department. Our two children had been born before the U.S. entered the war, and I had been disqualified for military service because of perforated eardrums. By 1945 I was already established at Connecticut College as a full professor.

# 6

# WAR AND
# THE UNEASY ATOM

In 1937 international tensions were building. Fascism was on the rise in Italy under Mussolini, in Germany under Hitler, and in Spain under Franco. Leaving Africa we flew over British warships off the Nile delta and later, between the heel and toe of Italy, we saw the Italian fleet on maneuvers. In what I thought was a facetious vein, I mailed a postcard to Dad saying "the Mediterranean was black with torpedoes." He took this very seriously!

During our year in Denmark, while immersed in our own activities, we had several brushes with this tension, especially in Germany. On a mid-winter excursion to Austria we spent a lovely week skiing in Seefeld. On our way back to Copenhagen we stopped off at Heidelberg, where we visited the botanist Professor Lehmann at his home. While we were struggling to communicate with him in German, his son dropped in. It was an unpleasant experience — the young man was rather aggressively nasty to us Americans. Then on the train to Berlin, we shared a compartment with a Dutch woman and a German man. A dapper gent entered, sat down, and engaged me in conversation in fluent English. He revealed that he travelled frequently between Berlin and Munich and had an apartment in each city. In the course of our talk he ascertained exactly what I was doing in Europe and especially in Germany. Afterward Esther and I remarked that our fellow travellers had clammed up as soon as this man entered the compartment. It dawned on us that we had just been checked out by the Gestapo.

That spring a young American couple who were doing research at the Carlsberg Laboratory in Copenhagen went to Graz, Austria, to continue their research. While there they took a weekend off to hike in the mountains. Upon their return to town they encountered a parade. It was Hitler celebrating the Anschluss. Austria had just been annexed to the Third Reich.

While sightseeing along the Hardanger Fiord in Norway a few weeks later, we observed a large German cruise ship anchored offshore. Our taxi driver, who it turned out had for many years driven a cab in New York City, informed us that the people on board were in no way tourists. They were reconnoitering in preparation for war which actually broke out in September of the following year. Several years later the German battleship *Tirpitz* was bombed out of commission by the British in Tromsö Fiord in northern Norway.

The Japanese attacked Pearl Harbor on December 7, 1942, and we were in the war. Everyone in the United States immediately felt the impact. Sugar, gasoline, and other necessities were rationed. I began commuting to work by bicycle. Shoes became a bit of a problem for the Goodwins; our two small children were rapidly outgrowing their footwear. My wallet was stolen with my ration books in it. I was able to get replacements for food and gas coupons, but not for shoes. Before long Esther and I discovered what it was like to be "down at the heels."

Then there was the draft. At first I enjoyed deferred status as a family man, then as an instructor of premedical students under the Navy V-12 program. At length I was called up for a medical exam. During this process, as I moved stark naked along the assembly line, I came up for my ear exam. The doctor at that station took one look in my ears and whistled loudly. "Hey! Come over here Dr. Jones. I want you to see this magnificent case of perforated drums!" This sent me back to the V-12 program, supplemented on weekends with volunteer stints working in canning factories, harvesting truck crops in outlying farms, cultivating a victory garden in my back yard and, in the summer, trying to grow potatoes in the country.

In August 1944 I had the idea of circulating a round-robin letter among the charter members of Troop 4, Brookline. Each correspondent was to add his story to what he had received and send everything on to the next person on the list. The letter took a year to get back to me after reaching eight of the charter members and two other scouts. It then continued for another four months and finally included two additional charter members and four repeats. Two correspondents, Eddie Robinson and Andy Marshall, were serving in the Army, Ed Andrews was in the Navy, and Rich Prouty and Dick Pentecost were in the Coast Guard. The two Vose brothers were in the Massachusetts National Guard. The rest of us were variously engaged in the war effort on the home front. Dick Bent was in the lumber business, Charlie Denny was working for the U.S. Geological Service constructing the Alcan highway through the wilderness to Alaska, Jack Morse was an architect, and Tim Rhodes was teaching school. For the flavor of the times I have included some of these letters in an appendix.

Meanwhile my colleague Don Charles and Dave Goddard's wife, Doris, became involved in a very hush-hush activity in a university building that housed a very high powered X-ray machine. This activity was part of the Manhattan Project. The only other fact we knew about it was that it produced eight barrels of mouse dung a day.

July 16, 1944 was the fateful day of the detonation of the atomic bomb at Alamogordo, New Mexico. I paced the floor after hearing the news. I realized instantly that however important the bomb might be to us for the war effort, the genie was out of the jar — harnessing atomic power had the potential to destroy mankind.

Information soon began to seep out that the portion of the Manhattan Project taking place next door was designed to determine the hazards of radiation to mammals. Mice were being irradiated and then bred to determine what happened to their genetic structure. My two friends Don and Doris had been working in a room adjacent to the X-ray machine. It wasn't many months before both of them succumbed to cancer.

Shortly after the war my student Bill Stepka, who had been serving in the Air Force in the Pacific theater, returned to the States. He paid us a visit. On August 7, 1945, the day after the atomic bomb had been dropped on Hiroshima, his plane was detailed to make a reconnaissance of the site. He showed us a photograph of the central part of the city. Nothing remained standing except a portion of one reinforced concrete building that had been reduced to a shell.

About seventeen years later, in the cold war paranoia of the early 1960s our government began promoting the construction of bomb shelters in every family's backyard. The Department of Civil Defense was in charge of this effort. My colleague Gordon Christiansen, chair of the Chemistry Department at Connecticut College, set out to expose the folly of this effort. He was well versed in physical science and handy with a slide rule. He meticulously calculated what the detonation of an atomic bomb would do, and then published a little paper entitled *Survival in Nuclear War a Vanishing Probability.*[1] It spelled out what would happen if a nuclear bomb were dropped on New London, Connecticut, from the fireball, through the blast, the ensuing firestorm, and the radiation from fallout. On the cover was a map of the area with a series of concentric rings marking five-mile distances from the target. The devastation from such an attack would be totally lethal for a distance of up to eight miles from the center of the blast, and survival from radiation exposure would be problematic over a much larger area. He concluded that the one effective thing we can do is strive to ensure that such an event never takes place.

His was a difficult task because much of the information on nuclear weapons was classified. The publication created quite a stir. The

Establishment was quick to say that the author was unqualified to address the subject, not being privy to the classified information, and to nitpick at details in an attempt to discredit the paper. It was widely circulated, however, and was reprinted with appropriate revisions to make it apply to other locations.

Chris had the courage to publicly debate the merits of the bomb shelter initiative with civil defense officials. On the morning before one such engagement, scheduled in New London, it happened that my wife had jury duty at the Federal Court in New Haven. My son Dick accompanied her. They stopped off at the post office, where Dick picked up a little pamphlet hot off the press put out by the Department of Civil Defense, describing how to construct a shelter. Dick took it right over to Chris. During the debate that evening, when the civil defense spokesman started to tell about how to build a bomb shelter, Chris pulled this pamphlet out of his pocket — to the astonishment of his adversary, who had not yet seen it himself — and proceeded to demolish its credibility.

The whole bomb shelter program rather rapidly melted away. Later Chris told me his own recommended preparation for a nuclear attack: develop a pill coated with a substance that would elevate the spirits, but with a core that would have a quick lethal whammy. He suggested its trade name could be Dismilin.

The atomic bomb ushered in the atomic age, with its enthusiasm for peaceful applications. Soon nuclear reactors were beginning to provide power to generate electricity. I foresaw serious problems posed by these plants. My concern centered around exposure to ionizing radiation, which increase the chance that exposed people will develop cancer or have genetically defective children. Problems included radiation exposure of workers in the plants, radioactive releases to the environment during operation, the possibility of catastrophic accidents, and safe disposal of the spent fuel. My education in these matters came from many sources, but especially from activists who were dedicating their lives to alerting the public to these dangers. One was Dr. John Gofman,

who was researching and publicizing the impacts of radiation on people. His organization, the Committee for Nuclear Responsibility, was
publishing information indicating that there was no truly safe level of
exposure to radiation — a view contrary to that taken by promoters of
nuclear power. A disturbing related issue was the danger posed by exposure to medical X-rays.

As a person concerned about the destruction of coastal marshes I
was alerted to the proposed nuclear power station at Seabrook, New
Hampshire. The site was at the inner edge of an extensive and highly
productive estuary behind Hampton Beach. The proposal was to exca-
vate a 100-foot-deep trench through the marsh and barrier beach; the
trench would hold pipes to circulate sea water through the plant's cooling system. At a hearing in spring 1973 I testified about the extremely
damaging impact this plan would have on the estuary. During the hearing I had the opportunity to hear Dr. Henry Kendall's superb testimony
regarding the dangers posed by the nuclear plant. I was amazed to learn
later that his input was ignored. But the estuary did receive protection. A
tunnel to contain the cooling system was constructed underneath the
whole estuarine complex, leaving the marsh and barrier beach untouched.

At a public hearing in March 1975, I presented a written statement
supporting an act by the Connecticut legislature to create a Nuclear
Power Evaluation Council. In December Governor Ella Grasso
appointed me a member of the newly authorized council. In her letter
she stated that the council should report its findings and recommendations to the General Assembly within the next eight weeks. It was
four weeks before the first meeting was called by the chairman, so one
of the first items on the agenda was negotiating a time frame in which
the council could study the issues involved. From the outset it was clear
that the assignment was highly sensitive politically. The council was
repeatedly subjected to delays in funding and hiring personnel. Two
years of hearings and deliberations went into a draft of the final report.
During that time we lost our original staff member. He was replaced
with a nuclear engineer who refused to include significant testimony
highly critical of the performance of the nuclear industry.

The council was composed of eight members. Four of them were scientists — Gifford B. Pinchot, an M.D. with research experience in biological warfare and biochemistry, whose father had served as director of the U.S. Forest Service; Tom D'Muhala, a nuclear physicist and head of a small nuclear industry; Paul Haake, a member of the chemistry department at Wesleyan University; and myself. The other four comprised two lawyers, an economist, and a college student headed for medical school. The whole council did finally approve and submit a summary report with recommendations. But the final full report, written by the staff, did not represent the judgment of the scientific half of the Council. This led to an impasse, and the final report was never submitted. However, the scientists felt strongly that the facts, as they saw them, should be made available to the governor, the legislature, and the public. So at our expense we prepared our own report, entitled "Nuclear Power in Connecticut: A Scientific Evaluation."[2] I served as editor. It was not signed by the four non-scientists on the council. It is interesting that the press referred to this production, written by half the council members, as "the minority report." Shortly after the report was distributed, it came up in a public debate on nuclear power between me and a spokesman for the industry. Late in the discussion I referred to the report as a source of information. My opponent immediately jumped on the report, branding it as dishonest. When queried as to the basis for this statement, he said we had quoted one expert, without ending the quotation with a series of dots to indicate that the person's statement was incomplete — certainly a failure on my part as editor. In retrospect this was a high compliment. People in the industry must have poured over the report in the minutest detail in order to have picked this up!

Our report noted a number of disconcerting things about the nuclear industry, including failure to notify personnel of the health hazards of the workplace, failure to comply with safety requirements, sloppy workmanship in reactor construction, inadequate design, dishonest presentation of the societal costs of the technology, nasty treatment of whistle blowers, inadequate policing of plant operations by the Nuclear Regulatory Commission, and "events" that could or actually did lead to serious accidents. On a tour of the Millstone plant in Waterford, Connecticut, the members of the council were shown two enormous diesel generators that were there in case of a power failure — to assure that there would be energy to run the cooling system required to prevent a meltdown of the radioactive core. There were two generators to assure a backup in case one failed to operate. We learned that there had actually been an emergency when one of the generators failed to start up, and the second one didn't either, at least for a few minutes. It had the makings of a disaster.

On the national scene, at the Browns Ferry plant in Alabama an improper concentration of electrical cables permitted a fire, started by a candle, to put the whole plant out of commission in 1975. A complete meltdown was narrowly avoided. And then in 1979 in eastern Pennsylvania there actually was a meltdown at the Three Mile Island plant.

In 1986 there was a total meltdown at the Chernobyl nuclear reactor in Russia. This disaster had far-reaching consequences. The radioactive plume reached the Arctic, where the fallout was absorbed by lichens. Reindeer, which feed on the lichens, became too radioactive to serve as food. As the plume passed eastward across the United States, there was a drastic, unprecedented decrease in reproductive success among land birds. The decrease was most pronounced on the West Coast and affected foliage gleaners — those birds eating insects feeding on the foliage.

Three earlier disasters, at least comparable and perhaps even worse that the Chernobyl meltdown, took place at Mayak, the Russian nuclear industrial complex located north of Chelyabinsk. The first occurred in 1946, the second in 1957, and the third in 1967. Little information about these events ever reached the public because they were shrouded in secrecy — a cover-up not only by the Russians, but also by our own CIA, which had intelligence about them. Mark Hertsgaard, who visited Mayak in 1991, describes in detail what happened there in his recent book, *Earth Odyssey*.[3]

Up until 1989, members of the medical profession who were treating the local people suffering from radiation exposure, were not allowed to inform their patients about the cause of their ailments. When Hertsgaard suggested to one of the doctors involved that they had been engaged in unconscionable medical deception, she replied "Yes," and after a pause, "Just like Hanford!" When I read this it reminded me of a man we knew in New London who died at the Hanford facility of a massive radiation exposure. Hertsgaard proceeds in the next few pages to recount some of the horror stories which have taken place at Hanford.

The disposal of radioactive waste is still an unsolved problem. People are used to thinking of twenty-five years as the long view. I was depressed that this was the perspective taken at the Mid-Century Conference on Resources for the Future held at the White House in 1952. It was attended by many of the country's outstanding environmental scientists. I was present at the session with the longest range perspective, the one on education, which was addressing what we should be doing to prepare the next generation to deal with resource problems in the latter part of the twentieth century. But when it comes to many types of radioactive atoms, one must deal with many thousands of years. Plutonium has a half-life of about 24,400 years, and it remains very dangerous for at least ten times that long. We have not yet come up with a safe way to dispose of radioactive wastes that acknowledges such a span of time. Now, as we come to the problem of dismantling our nuclear plants, we have the problem of disposing of metals that have become radioactive. The December 1999 newsletter of the New England Coalition on Nuclear Pollution shows an attractive young girl with a broad smile. Her teeth are covered with metal orthodontia. The heading is "Brace yourself for radioactive belt buckles, auto parts, and orthodontia." The newsletter describes a massive U.S. governmental and international effort now under way to declare that "low-level" ionizing radiation is harmless. The purpose apparently is to reduce costs for electrical utilities and the Department of Energy by fostering transboundary commerce in radioactively contaminated wastes, allowing reuse of volumetrically contaminated "slightly radioactive" materials in consumer products. This suggests we should not count on Uncle Sam to be looking after our health!

The shadow of nuclear war still hangs over us. In 1983 a conference was held in Washington, D.C., on the long-term worldwide biological consequences of nuclear war. At the end of the conference an extensive exchange took place on closed-circuit television between scientists in the United States and the Soviet Union. A consensus was reached by the two groups that there must be no nuclear war, that this would mean disaster and death for mankind. The proceedings of the conference were published the following year in a book entitled *The Cold and the Dark: The World After Nuclear War.*[4] It describes in detail the nuclear winter that scientific studies predict would envelop the globe in the event of a significant exchange of nuclear weapons. Smoke and dust would obscure the sun. For several months temperatures would fall below freezing over most of the northern hemisphere, turning water supplies to ice. Vegetation, deprived of water and sunlight, would die. The ozone layer in the stratosphere, which protects the surface of the Earth from lethal ultraviolet radiation, would be destroyed, and radioactive fallout would be everywhere.

One of the participants of the conference, Dr. John Harte, stated it nicely. He said:

> All of us are as dependent on the ecosystem that surrounds us as an intensive-care patient is on intravenous bottles and life-supporting medical equipment. Waging nuclear war would be akin to throwing a lighted stick of dynamite into an intensive-care ward.

In the foreword of the book Lewis Thomas states:

> I take these reports not only as a warning, but also, if widely enough known and acknowledged in time, as items of extraordinary good news. I believe that humanity as a whole, having learned the facts of the matter, will know what must be done about nuclear weapons.

As the new millennium begins we must refresh the memory of this landmark publication. It seems incredible, for example, that our politicians should have failed in 1999 to approve the nuclear test ban treaty!

I would like to close this chapter with a little poem by Ondra Lysohorsky as translated by David Gill.

## BRIDGES

On bridges are stated the limits in tons
of the loads they can bear.

But I've never yet found one that can bear more than we do,
although we are not made of roman freestone,
nor of steel, nor of concrete.

It's the twentieth century we bear
across the chasms of the universe,
each one of us
a small, narrow bridge
on which the heaviest weight is yet to fall:
the future evolving from this era
in which the greatest evil flourishes:
the lie of power and the power of the lie
in the quagmire of meanness,
in the high alps of arrogance,
in the ocean of blind folly.

And the computer calculates perfectly
in the shadow of the nuclear reactor.

# 7

# WILDERNESS

The late Vannevar Bush, who served for seventeen years as president of the Carnegie Institution of Washington and then for thirteen as a member of its Board of Trustees, made a bequest to the institution to be used toward the renewal of the staff. He had one stipulation: that its use have no direct relation to their regular work. After the institution had created two retreats for the staff in his honor he wrote in a letter of thanks,

> Scientists need recreation. So do their families. So does everyone else for that matter. . . . I write here of recreation, not exercise for physical benefit. And I write of the pause that renders the work that follows more pleasant and fruitful. . . . We need at times the quiet wood, the family happy together, and the song of a humble bird.

Vacations are times when one usually tries to do what one most enjoys doing. Esther and I particularly cherished savoring wild places. So the summer after our little daughter Minda arrived in September 1939 we managed to park her with my parents in Brookline and escape to Maine for a few days in the north woods. On Katahdin, a mountain with which I had obtained some familiarity during my college days, we packed in to Chimney Pond, where we spent our first night. Then, after climbing to the summit, we bushwhacked down into the heart of the mountain — a trailless basin — for two glorious, solitary days on Klondike Pond. It was an extremely steep scramble getting back out. We even had to hoist our packs up over some of the ledges by rope. Then in a dense fog we managed to hit the trail on the tableland without having to struggle too far through the thick scrub.

Our next escapes from civilization were brief ones during the war years. For the summers we rented a cottage on the shore of Lake Canandaigua, one of New York's Finger Lakes, with my parents, and twice Esther and I squeezed in trips to the Adirondacks without the kids. On one of these we canoed from Blue Mountain Lake down through Eagle Lake, Utowana Lake and the Marion River to Rackett Lake. One sulky afternoon while paddling down the Marion River, we came upon a beautiful stand of mature white pines. We pulled up to camp for the night. No sooner had we erected our canvas fly than it started to pour. To our dismay it turned into an electrical storm — and I had located our camp under the tallest tree! We managed to get a fire started under the edge of the tarp, cooked up a hot pot of soup, removed our wet clothes, and crawled into dry sleeping bags for what turned out to be a comfortable night. We learned later that a bolt of lightning had hit the steeple of the church in Rackett Village about four miles to the west. We reported our experience to folks in the botany department at Rochester, and the next year one of the graduate students, Allen Brown, and his bride visited the same area on their honeymoon. They didn't fare as well as we had. They tipped over and spent a miserable night in wet sleeping bags. I am glad to report that the bride was tough, and they remained happily married.

For the next few years, while the children were small, we spent our summer vacations in New Hampshire at Rockywold — a family camp on Squam Lake — where we rented a cottage. Early in 1950 I had a sabbatical semester, which I spent at the University of California in Berkeley. The whole family drove west in a leisurely fashion, sightseeing on the way, and returned in the summer, camping en route in a number of national parks and enjoying a two week stay at a dude ranch in Montana. In subsequent summers we made family camping trips by car to Maine, to the Connecticut Lakes in northern New Hampshire, to the Mojave Desert in California , and to Cape Breton Island in Nova Scotia.

It was not until summer 1956, when Minda was sixteen and Dick Junior fifteen, that we had our real family wilderness experience. It was in the boundary waters on the Minnesota-Canada border, an uninhabited country liberally laced with streams and glacial lakes. Here the international boundary follows waterways used by the intrepid French voyageurs of the seventeenth and eighteenth centuries to gain access by canoe to trap and trade for furs in the country lying west of the Great Lakes. To the south lies the large, roadless Superior National Forest; to the north, Quetico Provincial Park, a wilderness of interconnecting lakes so nearly surrounded by water as to be referred to as Hunter's Island.

With our aluminum canoe on the top of our Chevy station wagon, we travelled west camping in two mountain pup tents. Arriving at Ely, Minnesota, on the fourth day, we stocked up with dehydrated foods, rented a second canoe, and packed for a sixteen-day paddle. We obtained an excellent waterproof map showing the lakes, streams, and portages, and planned a route that would take us in a 150-mile loop: first north from Basswood Lake into the Quetico, then west and south through a series of lakes to Crooked Lake on the international boundary, and thence up the Basswood River back to Basswood Lake. The Basswood River was a major stream, and, not being a white-water canoeist, I wanted to make sure we didn't run into any unpleasant surprises running down unknown rapids or over falls.

After lunch at Basswood Lodge on July 10 we finally pushed off for our adventure. Our gear consisted of four backpacks, two bags of bedding and tents, a bag of tent poles, a carton of perishables, pots, an axe, and fishing gear. From the very outset the kids manned their own canoe. Our first stop was an island where we cleared Canadian customs; the second was a ranger station on an adjacent island, where we obtained a permit to travel in the Quetico and purchased a fishing license. Then onward to another island for a swim and to yet another for our first camp. We had a wonderful steak supper before a violent thunder shower pelted us with half-inch hailstones. Minda developed the technique of staying dry under a canoe.

The next day we made a late start, spending time to dry tents and gear. Paddling north, we had a sunny swim from an island and arrived at the end of North Bay in time for lunch. We then pushed, before a gathering storm, up a deep inlet with long waving eel grass. We had to charge narrow gaps in beaver dams and finally portaged into Lily Lake. From there the route took us through beautiful beaver meadows where we had to get out in knee-deep water to pull the canoes over numerous dams until we reached the ledgy portage into Isabella Lake. I felt rather insecure alone under an eighty-pound canoe, so with the two kids at each end we "caterpillared" the canoes over the rough spots. Another hailstorm caught us with the loads and one canoe over the portage. Three of us took shelter under the canoe, while Esther brooded over the gear under a poncho. Isabella is a narrow lake with cliffs along each side. Part way down it we managed to climb a steep beaver trail to a flat spot just barely large enough for the tents. At sunset the sun came out and bathed the eastern shore with a golden glow. Dick and I went fly-fishing and caught a couple of small pike, while the girls prepared supper.

The above account gives you a taste of what was yet to come — fourteen days on as many large or medium-size lakes and many more small ones — eleven additional campsites. And as for portages, thirty more. That meant the old man had sixty more carries to get the two boats across. It is wonderful what a little exercise will do. It wasn't long before we could forget the caterpillar technique. I was soon carrying alone, along with a pack. Esther referred to herself as "miscellaneous" — she was carrying, among other things, the paddles and the most recently caught fish. There was a period of nine days when we didn't meet a single soul. In the middle of this period Minda pointed out to Esther a footprint in the mud and commented, "It's nice to know someone has been here before!" At about the same time we also found bear prints, large and small, and a day later saw a mother and her two cubs swimming across a lake.

We spent two days at our camp on Lake McIntyre, on a beautiful point of glacier-polished rocks which we called "Waxwing Point." The pink granite was covered with loose tufts of reindeer moss, giving the surface pastel shades of gray and green. It was an ideal place for views and warm sunshine, but we found it advisable to retire to our tents at sundown and stay there until sunup to avoid the clouds of mosquitoes. At that camp, while I was away exploring with the kids, Esther was startled by repeated loud booms. It was courting behavior of a nighthawk. Forbush in his *Birds of Massachusetts* describes the performance as follows: "The male often rises to a considerable height and then falls swiftly, head first, with wings partly closed, until near the earth, when, spreading his wings, he turns upward, producing with his vibrating primaries a resounding boom which may be heard at a considerable distance." A courting loon created another extraordinary disturbance by splashing in a straight line across the lake on its tail, flailing the water with his wings while uttering a special cry. The female meanwhile was coyly ducking her head. After several repetitions, the male took off in a broad, low-angled sweep to sail over the trees to an adjoining lake, calling as he went. Returning a bit later, he made another broad sweep with his usual laughing cry. Answered by his mate with a different note, he dropped steeply to the lake.

We had been counting on fish for a significant portion of our diet. For the first several days we did not have much luck — only a few small pike. Then on the eighth day out, while trolling in Lake McIntyre, Dick caught a beautiful eighteen-inch female trout on Daddy Baxter's bobble. I should explain that our neighbor in New London Mr. Baxter — an ardent fisherman — was the kind source of this attractive lure. After two portages, several miles of paddling, and blueberry picking at our next camp, we had a marvelous meal of trout and roe with instant mashed potatoes. Dick and Minda admitted they felt full for the first time in days. From that time on we had all the fish we could eat, mostly walleyes. Minda caught the largest one on the trip.

At a ledge on Crooked Lake where there were some Indian pictographs, we finally caught up with a family we had met nine days before who were also camping through the Quetico. They asked if we had missed any of the portages on our trip and expressed amazement when we reported that we hadn't missed a single one.

From a distance the old-growth forests of the Quetico have a somewhat ragged appearance — white pines towering above the smaller spruces and firs, which looked as if they were young growth. Upon closer examination, however, the spruces and firs turned out to be very large trees. At one point we entered a desolate area where all the trees were standing dead, except for a few patches here and there. There was no evidence of fire, and it seemed unlikely that a disease or insect pest was responsible, because all species were affected. On our next-to-last day, when we had reached Basswood Lake, we stopped at the Quetico-Superior Wilderness Research Center to visit its director, Cliff Ahlgren. There we learned the cause of the desolation — a very severe hailstorm that had literally stripped the growing points off the trees. Natural disturbances such as this one are what keep old-growth forests in a state of flux.

Our return home included a stop to hike into the Porcupine Wilderness in Wisconsin and visits with friends. The expedition had been one of Vannevar Bush's refreshing "pauses," and one that inspired me for what lay immediately ahead: Becoming president of The Nature Conservancy.

My next wilderness experience came three years later with Dick in Algonquin Provincial Park, which lies about 120 miles north of Lake

Ontario. We paddled for sixteen days through lovely wild country liberally sprinkled with lakes. This trip was more relaxed for me, as we had only one canoe, and we took turns carrying it over the portages. There were about thirty of them, so I didn't have to carry more that fifteen times. The fishing was great, and we were living with the wildlife — deer, beaver, and mink, signs of moose and bear, and wolves howling at night. But we did frequently see people. Early one morning, when we thought we were camping on a particularly remote lake, the wilderness was shattered by the sound of a power saw. Alas, lumbering does take place in Canadian provincial parks.

One night we slept in the open, close to the shore of Big Trout Lake, which, incidentally, lived up to its name. At dawn a thick mist was rising from the lake, and there, not more than thirty feet off shore, were three loons performing an aquacade. Swimming toward one another until they almost met, they simultaneously dove and emerged a few feet away. They repeated the process again and again in perfect symmetry with stately precision. It reminded me of the *Moore's Pavane*, the modern dance so beautifully choreographed by Jose Limon.

On the next-to-last day, on McIntosh Lake, we discovered a forest fire on one of the islands. We paddled over and extinguished the blaze, returning later to work on the smouldering peat. Some thoughtless campers had set their campfire on the forest floor on top of deep organic duff. It had probably smoldered under the surface for a long time before emerging as a blaze.

In 1961 my friend Belton Copp proposed a wilderness trip to Tweedsmuir Provincial Park in British Columbia. He had been in the park before and had advice from an acquaintance Allen Gough, who ran a camp in the area, on a particularly remote section that would be interesting to explore. On August 6 he, Wally Bowman, and I met at Prince George, a town about 450 miles north of Vancouver, British Columbia, for our adventure. We stocked up with provisions, chartered a small hydroplane, called a Beaver, and located and rented two light canoes to lash onto the pontoons. The canoes had been designed for racing down the Fraser River. One was white with large black letters along the sides saying TOMMY RICHARDSON'S MEN'S WEAR, the other black with white letters saying INTERIOR POWER SAWS. The seats were slung low and there were foot braces with a foot-operated bailing pump for use while racing through white water. Their outside surface was so smooth that when drawn up on a beach they would gently slide off into the water if they were not tied fast.

The next afternoon we took off. From the plane we could see a forest fire that had recently started not far from Prince George. We flew west 150 miles across forests broken only by lakes draining east into the Fraser River. When we reached Tweedsmuir Park we were over Eutsuk Lake, which fingers about sixty miles into the snow-capped peaks of the coast range. We swung south up the Chezko River to our destination on Tesla Lake. The plane was to pick us up eleven days later on Pondosy Lake, on the other side of a mountain ridge to the northwest, which we hoped to reach by canoe. This would mean running about twelve miles down the Chezko River to Eutsuk Lake and then paddling about thirty miles on Eutsuk to Pondosy.

We set up camp on an island and spent the first three days exploring the Tesla environment. We climbed Rivers Peak which provided magnificent views of the region. One of the first things we encountered on the lake shore was a large white object, which on closer inspection resolved itself into the skinned carcass of a large decapitated bear. We later met the two prospectors who were responsible. They told us they had not been able to scare the animal away from their camp. These were the only people with whom we had any contact during our stay.

On the fourth day we broke camp. To reach the Chezco we started down the outlet of the lake — a beautiful swift stream and crystal clear. We were quite a crew. I was alone in one canoe, Belton and Wally in the other. Belton had lost an arm in the Pacific during World War II but could do many things with one arm as well as, or better than, I could with two. He was paddling stern and Wally, who was somewhat hard of hearing, was in the bow. While running rapids Wally almost got knocked out of the boat by a snag, and I ran into another one and punched a small hole in my canoe just below the gunwale. After about a mile we reached the Chezko, which proved to be quite a torrent, milky with glacial flour and not much above freezing. We beached the canoes and paused to reconnoiter. Just around a sharp bend, the river dropped off over a handsome waterfall. Scouting the river downstream, we found it went over three more falls, which might be by-passed with a portage. But below that the stream was beset with snags and sweepers, the latter being big floating tree trunks anchored to the bank and vibrating back and forth in the strong current.

An acquaintance of mine defined adventure as an example of poor planning. We spent the next day on a long reconnaissance on foot through trackless country to explore options for getting to the rendezvous with our plane. In one trying passage blown down trees were stacked like jackstraws and we were scrambling over them as much as fifteen feet above ground. The next day we poled and towed the canoes back up to Tesla Lake. It was a windy day, and going back up the lake I discovered that by paddling very close to the windward shore one could enjoy the shelter of a backdraft off the forest trees. I encountered a mother otter and her two pups swimming along with me. Signs of big game were all about us — moose droppings and fresh bear scat. High on Rivers Peak we had glimpses of mountain goats.

Our last two days were spent crossing the ridge between Tesla and Pondosy Lakes. At one time there had been a blazed trail, but it was almost impossible to follow. We had a map showing contour intervals of 500 feet, but a great deal can happen within that interval. After caching our two canoes and extra gear, we started off with packs on a compass course into the dense forest. We began to climb steeply, and after gaining about a thousand feet broke out onto an alpine meadow, having missed Pondosy Pass. We scrambled down to a little lake that showed on our map and slogged through wetlands and waded along the shore to the northern end, where we camped for the night. The next day we beat our way through wet meadows and windfalls to the outlet of Pondosy Lake. At one point Belton and Wally, who were ahead of me, had climbed up on the trunk of a huge wind-thrown spruce tree which served as a pathway through the thick salmonberry brush. What should be coming up the log from the opposite end but a huge black bear. I was alerted by "Bear! Get the gun!" I was carrying it at that point. I jumped toward the upturned roots of the tree, fell flat, picked myself up and turned to see the bear, which had jumped off the log, going through the chest-high bushes as if they were grass. About fifteen feet away it stopped and looked at me sidewise. Meanwhile I had it covered with the rifle. It turned and circled back toward the far end of the log. I passed the gun up to Belton, who noticed there was dirt in the end of the barrel. This he quickly removed with a twig, and since the bear was still lurking at the far end of the log, he fired a shot. The bear took off into the forest. When we reached the shore of Pondosy Bay on Eutsuk Lake, Wally and I had tea while Belton fished. We then walked along the shore of the Pondosy Lake outlet to the lake itself. In the lakeshore gravel there were two sets of huge grizzly bear footprints going the way we wanted to go. Water was still oozing into them. The alder thickets along the shore were thick, and it was a rather tense walk to where we made camp for the night.

Smoke from the forest fire, which had been raging ever since we observed it as we flew in, was now lying over the country like a pall, greatly reducing visibility. The plane was scheduled to pick us up at ten o'clock the next morning. We spread a white tarp at the edge of the water to help the pilot find us. At about noon we heard the plane and saw it briefly emerge through the murk and then disappear. About an hour later it returned. The pilot had already picked up one of our canoes and had come back to find us. The extra flying to pick up our canoes had used up enough gas to require a stop at another lake to refuel from a special cache. Visibility near Prince George was so poor that we had to fly very low to find the winding river and follow it down to port.

Before returning home we flew to Ketchikan on the coast at the southern tip of Alaska, where we chartered a boat to cruise up Behm Canal, one of the deep valleys being drowned by the subduction of the continent under the Pacific. We saw whales sounding and stopped off to camp and fish in a lake emptying into Yes Bay.

About ten years later I had a very vivid dream. It inspired the following poem.

## A DREAM

At break of day I dreamt a dream.
I lounge beside a limpid stream.
    The pool is deep, the current strong
    Gurgling as it sweeps along
Its surface stirred by boils.

The sun is warm upon my face
And lends the spot a luminous grace.
    The shallow sand is clearly seen,
    But shades into a deep blue-green,
A lurking place for trout.

A flick of line, a single cast,
A silver beauty now is fast.
    The tug is strong, the rod is bent,
    But long before the fish is spent
I found myself awake.

Oh that I might resume my sojourn on that sunny shore!
    I must have been there long ago.
Do you suppose it is the same as in the days of yore?

How lucky he who's felt the force
    Of waters fresh derived from snows
That flow impeded in their course
    By only rocks, the roots of trees, and sand!
The urban dweller never knows
    The glories of an unspoiled land;
And can he ever even dream
Of things that he has never seen?

\* \* \*

In 1973 my son, Dick, and I returned to Tweedsmuir to pick up where my friends and I had left off twelve years earlier. This time we drove to Campbell River, a town halfway up Vancouver Island. There we chartered a Beaver, which took us on a spectacular flight up the coast and through the mountains to Pondosy Bay on Eutsuk Lake. We had the next thirteen days to quietly explore the country. It was not, however, quite as devoid of people as the section I had travelled on the earlier trip. There were occasional powerboats on Eutsuk and we saw two float planes besides our own. The only development we ran into was a small heliport and the beginning of a road. It led, as we learned later, to a titanium mine that the government had fortunately shut down. We talked with three different parties and visited several campsites. One was strewn with beer bottles and unburned trash, which we took pains to pick up. We made a real effort to obliterate as much as possible the evidence of our own campsites. When we flew out we took with us all our twenty-eight person-day's worth of unincinerated trash. I still have it as an exhibit — one small jar filled with glass and metal scraps, which weighed in at one pound. I estimated this amount to be about 0.7 percent of what the average person would be producing back in civilization.

One plane we particularly resented dropped down onto Musclow Lake, a small body of water at the very end of Eutsuk, which we had portaged into with considerable effort through alder thickets. Our camp was on a small rocky islet. Before supper I was preparing my fishing gear for action at the waters' edge and was flicking the leader out through the guides on the rod when I hooked a nice little trout before the fly even hit the water! The next morning as we were luxuriating in the peace of the wilderness, it was shattered by the plane, bringing in a customer for an easy day of fishing. Where today can one escape the internal combustion engine? It made us think of the Quetico — that rare park where planes and power boats have been declared off limits. Of course, who were we to complain? We had dropped down on Pondosy Bay!

The paddle along the south shore of Eutsuk was both scenic and potentially hazardous. For considerable distances the near-vertical cliffs plunged into the lake. In the event of a sudden storm there would have been no place to put ashore. As Dick was trolling deep in this section, he had a vigorous strike. A moment later the fish surfaced with a big leap that carried away the lure. We had a glimpse of the tail as it plunged back into the lake. It was huge! *Sic transit troutus maximus.* Our most photogenic campsite was on a small island off this shore. We called it Gull Island because gulls had been nesting on it; we saw the juveniles nearby in the lake. The trees were all dwarfed, contorted, and covered with lichens, and the views of the glacier-hung peaks were spectacular.

Our real taste of wilderness was forays on foot into the back country. On one of the last days, in rather thick woods, we found a moose skull with a full set of antlers attached. Dick strapped this to his pack and carried it out. Even in the vertical position it was a problem getting it through the trees; it made us wonder how an animal encumbered with such antlers in a horizontal position could make his way through a thick forest. When we got back to Campbell River, we fastened the trophy to the top of Dick's car. He got it as far as Vancouver, where someone stole it while he was having lunch.

In January of 1980 Esther and I made a ten-day visit to Everglades National Park. We stayed in a housekeeping cottage in Flamingo on Florida Bay at the southernmost tip of Florida. The mudflats along the shores were completely covered with thousands of shorebirds. Off shore small mangrove islets were harboring rookeries of roseate spoonbills, brown pelicans, nesting ospreys, and bald eagles. There we also saw roosting representatives of almost every North American species of heron and egret.

Dick joined us and he and I spent two days exploring the adjacent, watery mangrove wilderness by canoe. A trail, marked by sequentially numbered stakes, led us on an incredibly tortuous route through the mangroves. It would be hard to imagine an easier place to get lost. There we encountered numerous old friends — catbirds and yellow-rumped warblers — wintering in their leafy condominiums. The trail led to a series of large shallow lakes interconnected by deep winding channels teeming with fish and inhabited by manatee.

A night was spent in one of these lakes on a chickee — a platform mounted on piles about three feet above the water large enough to support a tent and picnic table. It was provided with a chemical toilet, reached by a short walkway. Underneath was a resident alligator hoping for fish heads and perhaps even better things. It was not a place to go sleep walking!

After making camp we went on a leisurely exploratory paddle through the lakes. In the late afternoon, as we were gliding quietly on a glassy surface, the peaceful lake suddenly erupted at the very bow of the canoe as if a herd of elephants had started to charge through the water at fifty miles an hour. We had evidently interrupted the nap of a pod of dolphins.

In 1981 the Fairbanks Environmental Center in Alaska promoted a wilderness trip to the Brooks Range in northern Alaska. Dick and I signed up to go. It turned out to be a party of twelve including the two leaders, John Adams and Cindy Marquette. John has subsequently become well known in the music world as a composer and conductor; Cindy, who was serving on the staff of the center, is now married to John.

In late June two chartered planes lifted our party off from Fairbanks for a flight over the wide, lake-dotted floodplain of the Yukon River to a landing strip at Arctic Village, the continent's farthest north Indian settlement, situated on the southern flanks of the Brooks Range. From there we shuttled in a smaller plane, three at a time, to a gravel bank near the confluence of Red Sheep Creek and the east fork of the Chandalar River, right at the edge of the timberline. Here base camp was established. We slept in mountain pup tents, but for meals enjoyed the luxury of a wall tent replete with cast-iron stove, which was fully appreciated when a front moved in from Siberia with wind, snow flurries and 20° F temperature.

The view was arctic. In the foreground the tundra, dotted with alpine flowers, sloped down to a fifteen-foot laminated ice sheet that filled the quarter-mile-wide bed of Red Sheep Creek. Beyond, in every direction stretched a magnificent panorama of snow-capped peaks gilded by the oblique rays of a midnight sun.

From base camp a four-day backpacking trek took us around a thirty-six square mile block of mountains. On the first day we encountered a small herd of caribou; on the second, some of the younger members of the party ascended one of the mountains to view a salt lick. They found no mountain sheep, but had a close encounter with a grizzly bear, which took off wide open down a forty-five degree slope. Although we saw no other bears on the trip, their fresh footprints and scat told us that our precautions of caching all food in tight plastic containers at some distance from our tents were well advised. On this trek we came upon one especially entrancing spot, a spring from which wound a little stream through a lush blanket of mosses dotted with wild flowers, some standing high with deep red foliage.

The last five days were spent "floating" ninety miles down the Chandalar to Arctic Village. Floating is in quotes. The first day was spent in braided streams, finding it necessary to pull our five rubber rafts over shallow gravel bars and thawing our feet from time to time over willow-twig fires. The second was truly a float in swift, crystal clear water with deep pools filled with tasty grayling. The next two were in deeper, slower-moving meanders that wandered back and forth all the way across the valley. We had to struggle for about a mile against a heavy headwind in one direction, only to get blown back to a point just a short distance toward our destination from the beginning of the meander. The last day we started at two A.M. in order to avoid the wind, which tended to spring up by mid-morning.

Dick's and my third week in Alaska began with a two-day sojourn with Inga Wright in her cozy cabin high up in Rainbow Valley about twenty miles outside of Anchorage. She had shared a raft with us down the Chandalar. From her place we had a spectacular view overlooking an arm of the sea. Hermit thrushes were singing in the lush coastal forest — a dramatic contrast to the Arctic landscape from which we had just come. After seeing Inga off to the East, we returned to Fairbanks by train and then spent three days backpacking into a wild valley on the north slope of the Alaska Range, the huge chain of glacier-hung peaks to which Mt. McKinley belongs.

Hiking on the tundra with a pack is vigorous exercise. The footing is uneven, usually soggy and sometimes treacherous; and living without the amenities of furniture or even convenient rocks or logs to sit on adds significantly to the conditioning. I took at least two inches off my waistline on this vacation and raised a thrifty crop of white whiskers, which still adorn my face.

The following year I signed up for another foray into the Arctic with the same organization, which had changed its name to the Northern Alaska Environmental Center. This time we went to the Arctic National Wildlife Refuge on the North Slope. Two very well-informed and capable women led the trip, Marilyn Sigman, a wildlife biologist with a master's degree from the University of Alaska and Roseanne Densmore with a doctorate in botany from Duke University. The other two participants were also women, one a wildlife biologist working for the Fish and Wildlife Service on remote Adak Island in the Aleutians and the other engaged in remote sensing research at the University of Alaska.

We flew from Fairbanks directly north to the Eskimo village of Kaktuvik on Barter Island in the Arctic Ocean. The route took us right over the valley of the Chandalar, down which we had floated the year before. It was thick weather over Barter Island. We had to circle for about half an hour with many glimpses through the clouds of ice floes, tundra, and open water before we finally spotted an air sock and managed to land in a freezing rain. There was a strong breeze coming off the ocean. It had been about 80°F when we left Fairbanks and we sure dove into our packs for sweaters and parkas on the airstrip.

That afternoon we were ferried by a small plane about a hundred miles eastward to a gravel bar on the Kongecut River at a spot known as Caribou Pass. This is a favored crossing for the Porcupine caribou herd. I was with Marilyn on the first run. As we were landing, the brake on one of the wheels grabbed and the plane jerked to the left and nearly tipped over. It was hours before the other three arrived, and they told us the pilot's comment was that Marilyn and I should "be aware that the plane would need a repair."

There had been a storm in the mountains to the south and the Kongecut was a muddy torrent. It continued to rise until the bar where we had made our camp became an island. The flood crest came within inches of inundating our tents. Fortunately the flood abated during the night, and in two days the river had dropped about five feet and become crystal clear. The fishing was fantastic. Arctic char about twenty inches long were running up the river. They resemble rainbow trout and are delicious. We caught all we could eat in minutes.

Marilyn summed up our experience as follows:

> From the gravel bar of base camp, purple and scented with wild sweet pea, to the ridges with lupine meadows and fell-fields of phlox, saxifrages and forget-me-nots, the foothills area was at the peak of the wildflower season. Much time was spent photographing the flowers and just stopping to be surrounded by the lushness and sunshine.

Golden plovers, longspurs, horned larks, and semipalmated plovers were defending territories, and a white-crowned sparrow was nesting a few yards from my tent. There were fresh bear tracks close by in the newly deposited mud. Caribou either singly or in small groups slipped by our camp, partially concealed by willow thickets; about a dozen were spending time in the middle of a nearby icefield, probably seeking relief from the mosquitoes, which were present in clouds. Fortunately insect repellents were very effective. The weather was warm most of the time and the women were comfortable wearing shorts and sleeveless tops.

On a three-day foray up a mountain ridge we had an opportunity to observe moose in the willow thickets. We deliberately made quite a bit of noise wherever we thought we might encounter bear. As we came over one ridge we saw two grizzlies foraging at the bottom of the next valley. They both took off as soon as they heard us — one over the opposite ridge and the other up the valley. The latter was going through the muskeg at an incredible clip and was soon out of sight around the bend. It was a clear lesson that one doesn't run away from bears.

The reason for the bears' behavior soon became apparent. With binoculars we were able to observe Fish and Wildlife Service personnel engaged in a research project on the bears. They shot the bears with a tranquilizer from a helicopter, weighed and sexed the animals and got other pertinent data, including extracting a tooth, before the animals recovered from the drug. This practice is a very stressful procedure for the bears, and sometimes results in their death. Mortality from this cause is about four percent in Yellowstone Park, one of the last places where these animals can be found in the lower forty-eight. See Chapter 10, page 236 for an approach to reducing this impact.

On the evening of our eighth day in the refuge, three of the party had to fly out to make plane connections. Marilyn and I back-packed up to the crest of a ridge that commanded a splendid view of the Kongakut Valley, Caribou Pass and the broad sweep of the flat coastal plain — a vast treeless, roadless wilderness shining in the midnight sun and bounded to the south by distant mountains. At eight o'clock the following morning a wolf appeared in the valley to the east, and we watched it for over half an hour as it trotted across the tundra and disappeared over a low ridge to the south. And then came the caribou! They streamed in single files out of the high country to the east. For hours they poured from the valleys and across the high rocky slopes to aggregate on the tundra. We estimated there must have been at least 5,000. As they grazed, the advancing edge of the dense herd was always sharply defined. After a time the advance would reverse direction. The ebb and flow of the animals over the countryside was reminiscent of the behavior of a myxomycete plasmodium as it moves over its substrate. The caribou were still there a couple of miles to the south, when we retired at about ten o'clock. The following morning they had all vanished.

This was the Arctic National Wildlife Refuge. How long will we be able to restrain greedy interests from crushing this fragile treasure?

# 8

# LAND SAVING ACTION

While serving as curator of the herbarium at the University of Rochester from 1939 to 1944, I had opportunity to arrange thousands of specimens, most of them collected by very competent amateurs, notably Milton S. Baxter and Warren Matthews, and by young men like Walter Phillips and Ellsworth P. Killip, professional botanists who had grown up in Rochester. I had a chance to meet these men and to learn from them about some of the botanically exciting areas in the vicinity. One of these was the Bergen Swamp, a 2000-acre wetland about twenty miles west of Rochester.

The Bergen Swamp was originally a post-glacial lake occupying a shallow depression underlain by Niagara limestone. It had gradually filled in with white marl deposits and been invaded by a rich diversity of plant and animal species. These included the endangered massasauga rattlesnake and such rare plants as the small white ladies' slipper

(*Cyprepedium candidum*) and Houghton's goldenrod (*Solidago houghtonii*) that grow on the open marl beds. The wetland had an enormous appeal to me as a young botanist, and I soon learned that I shared this interest with a group of local people who, in order to preserve the area, had formed the Bergen Swamp Preservation Society. Although established for several years, the society had not, when I joined it, been able to make any headway in acquiring real estate. The land ownership was very complex. The swamp supported extensive stands of inland white cedar (*Thuja occidentalis*), and every farm for miles around owned a narrow strip as a source of rot-resistant fence posts. As our society member, attorney Walter Swan put it, a survey would cost at least $5,000, and the Society did not have that amount in its treasury.

Not daunted by this, I obtained from the U.S. Soil Conservation Service a free aerial photograph of the area, which showed the wooded boundaries of the swamp surrounded by the geometrical pattern of the adjacent farms. An old county atlas showed the ownership pattern not only of the farms, but also of the woodlots within the swamp. I constructed a passable map by superimposing the two. With this a guide, I began to visit farmers in the neighborhood of the swamp and soon encountered Mr. Alexander who was willing to sell his five-acre lot on the periphery for $125. The trustees of the Society approved this initial purchase, which was soon followed by others, including an especially beautiful twenty-five-acre tract adjacent to the marl beds. It was owned by the Greens and was known as Hemlock Knoll. Esther and I made a number of modest contributions, most of them anonymously, toward these early land acquisitions, while I was the society's treasurer. The Preserve soon became designated a National Natural Landmark by the National Park Service.

Shortly after I left Rochester, Edwin C. Foster, a recently retired railroad attorney, became interested in the swamp and undertook the monumental task of documenting its complex ownership pro bono. His paperwork came to two thick bound volumes. Today, more than half a century later, the society owns most of the two thousand acres in the swamp and employs a full-time warden.

At the dedication of the Goodwin-Niering Center for Conservation Biology and Environmental Studies at Connecticut College in May of 1999 I spoke about Bergen Swamp as my first involvement in the preservation of natural areas. A few days later I received a lovely note from Ruth Parnall, an alumna who had recently received her master's degree in botany at the College. She wrote:

> I always learn something new when you speak. This time it was not only the subject matter, but your background in Rochester. I grew up in Rochester. My tenth grade biology class had a field trip to Bergen Swamp in 1959. It was rainy. The naturalist smoked his pipe upside down to keep it dry. We walked among the trees on hummocks and mossy roots — dark, wet, lush. When I was asked recently to recall my earliest memories of science teaching, the Bergen Swamp trip was among the few. I'm involved now in efforts to bring that evocative environmental experience to children much earlier than high school.

When I became Director of the Connecticut Arboretum in 1944 it consisted of about ninety acres of land adjacent to the Connecticut College campus. The college was situated at that time at the northern edge of New London, bounded to the east by the Thames River and to the north and west by open farmland. My predecessor, George Avery, had, during his thirteen years of administration, initiated a land acquisition program. Two tracts totaling twenty-five acres had been purchased with funds raised through his efforts, and a third tract was being negotiated by his friends and partly funded with gifts contributed in his honor.

With this as a precedent I set about to continue the expansion. In the ensuing years another twenty tracts totaling some 300 acres were acquired for the Arboretum, mostly with funds contributed by friends of the Arboretum, and an additional 120 acres of open space were acquired by the college. The story is recounted in *Connecticut Arboretum Bulletin*, No. 28, published in 1982 in celebration of the fiftieth anniversary of the founding of the Arboretum. In 1984 I was honored to receive the Connecticut College Medal, partly in recognition of this achievement.

One of the important tracts we acquired was a forty-acre rocky peninsula extending into the Thames River and connected to its west bank by a small, unditched salt marsh. This property was part of one of the earliest land grants in New London, and the marsh was one of two meadows that were mowed for salt hay in 1645, the very first year of colonial settlement. It became part of the Mamacock (later Mamacoke) Farm, held for seven generations by members of the James Rogers family. By 1942 it had been acquired by the Merritt-Chapman & Scott Corporation, a marine construction company. At a meeting of the Connecticut Forest & Park Association held at the Arboretum in the fall of 1947 attention was drawn to this area as a possible addition to the State Park system. It was also obviously a very desirable potential addition to the Arboretum, being contiguous to the tract just acquired and named in honor of George Avery. I was anxious to see it protected before it was quarried or otherwise despoiled by development. My initial negotiations with the corporation stimulated Miss Katharine Blunt, president of the college, to write a letter requesting me to refrain from further activity in this matter. She was concerned that fund-raising for Mamacoke Island would interfere with her ongoing efforts to finance the new infirmary. In flagrant insubordination I continued a contact with the corporation, but it was seven years before an option could be negotiated. Within eight months of signing the contract the $15,000 purchase price had been raised from 257 individuals and twenty-nine organizations, all friends of the Arboretum.

Toward the end of this fund-raising effort several poisonous editorials appeared in one of the local papers. They were authored by Captain Jack Rosenthal, who resented the removal of this waterfront property from commercial use. He referred to the project in post-war German as Goodwin's "drang nach Norwich." This publicity so incensed some of our friends that additional contributions poured in, the last two of which put our fund drive over the top.

The transaction was consummated by me as trustee for the donors, and the property was subsequently conveyed to the college. My friend Belton Copp and his junior colleague Sid Miller, drew up the deed, the terms of which were unique. They provided that the land should forever remain in its natural state and that no roads could be constructed on it. If the college did not adhere to these restrictions, title to the land would pass either to the Connecticut Forest and Park Association or to The Nature Conservancy. Also, if the college found stewardship onerous, the property might be sold, but the College would have to offer it first to each of these organizations at a price not to exceed $500. This was a most fortunate foresight. Only two years later the college was offered $50,000 — more than three times the purchase price — for the privilege of covering that precious little piece of salt marsh with sixty feet of hydraulic spoil that would be dredged from the river to deepen the channel for the large atomic submarines. The contractors pointed out that after the mud had settled the college would have a prime industrial site.

I became a member of The Nature Conservancy (TNC) in 1951, the year of its incorporation. At that time its board of governors was composed almost entirely of biologists who were scattered all over the country. Since the organization had no funds to defray travel expenses, it held most of its board meetings in conjunction with the annual meetings of the American Institute of Biological Sciences. Being much interested in the Conservancy's program of preserving natural areas, I made it a point to sit in on these meetings as an observer and came to know the people active in the movement.

In order to promote its program throughout the country the Conservancy initially attempted to find a volunteer in each state to serve as its representative. It was quite natural that I should have been asked, in 1952, to become the representative for Connecticut. In this capacity I convened a meeting of Connecticut members and other knowledgeable people to discuss the types of habitats that should be preserved within the state. Among those immediately identified were the tidal wetlands, sand plains, black spruce bogs, cedar swamps, and old-growth forests. Shortly thereafter Connecticut College hosted a Conference on the Biology of Connecticut, sponsored by the Connecticut Geological and Natural History Survey Commission. At that time the commission consisted of five scientists, one from each of the state's five major educational institutions — Yale, Wesleyan, Trinity, Connecticut College, and the University of Connecticut. I had been serving as the Connecticut College commissioner since 1945. During this conference the participants broke into small subdisciplinary workshops, one of which was on ecology. The ecologists present included Paul B. Sears, in charge of the Conservation Program at Yale; Harold Lutz, Professor of Forestry at the Yale School of Forestry; and Frank E. Egler, proprietor of the Aton Forest in Norfolk, Connecticut. They recommended establishing a natural areas system for the state and initiating long-range studies on permanent quadrats within the system.

Participants at the conference were enthusiastic about the Bolleswood section of the Arboretum as a potential natural area, and so it appeared feasible to start implementing the ecologists' suggestions close to home. At my request, the Connecticut College trustees authorized the establishment of the Bolleswood Natural Area in the spring of 1952, and that summer I initiated long-range vegetation studies by laying out four six-meter-wide transects that traversed the area from east to west. These were mapped in great detail by some of our botany majors, and the plants carefully identified and measured.[1] It was planned that these quadrats would be resurveyed at ten-year intervals for the next hundred years. One garden club lady, when Esther told her about the projected time span of this study, exclaimed, "Oh! How gruesome!"

William A. Niering, who had recently received his doctorate in ecology at Rutgers University under Murray Buell, joined our botany department in the fall of 1952 and assumed a leadership role in this project, which is now in its fifth decade. The data are becoming increasingly valuable. In 1999 Sarah Goslee, one of our Connecticut College botany majors used them as the basis of her doctoral dissertation at Duke University.[2]

The three directors of the Connecticut Arboretum at its fiftieth anniversay celebration, June 6, 1981: (*left to right*) the author, William A. Niering, and George S. Avery, Jr.

Shortly after the 1952 Conference on the Biology of Connecticut, the Connecticut Geological and Natural History Survey proceeded to establish a Committee on Natural Areas with me as its chairman. A little later this committee was transferred to the Connecticut Forest and Park Association. By early 1960, membership in the Conservancy in Connecticut had grown to the point where it became feasible to form a state chapter. This chapter took over the function of the Natural Areas Committee.

Edward C. Childs and H. Lincoln Foster called our attention to the Beckley Bog in Norfolk as an outstanding example of a black spruce bog worthy of preservation. This was one of the high-priority habitats on our list. Bill Niering and I negotiated a purchase option for the property and managed to raise the $21,000 required to close the deal. It was the TNC's first project in Connecticut and was named the Frederic C. Walcott Preserve, in honor of the late senator. It has now grown to over 600 acres as a result of subsequent additions. A colony of beaver moved in during the 1960s, damming the outlet to Beckley Pond and raising the water level in the bog. This regressed the succession by killing trees that were invading the periphery, which not only protected the bog habitat by delaying forest invasion, but also made it less accessible and, hence, less vulnerable to human impacts.[3] The bog vegetation became a floating mat that undulated as one walked across it. At about this time a group of Conservancy members visited the preserve on an overnight field trip. At breakfast the following morning one of the participants reported he had had an extraordinary dream. He dreamed he had been walking on a sea of women's breasts! An evaluation, commissioned by the National Park Service, of the site as a potential National Natural Landmark criticized the Conservancy for failing to remove the beaver. I wrote to the Park Service to inquire as to when the service started to list beaver as vermin in natural areas. Although I never received a direct reply, the Walcott Preserve soon became designated a Natural Landmark.

In 1956 the annual meeting of The Nature Conservancy was held at the University of Connecticut in conjunction with the annual meeting of the American Institute of Biological Sciences. The year also coincided with the twenty-fifth anniversary of the founding of the Connecticut Arboretum, in celebration of which *Connecticut Arboretum Bulletin*, No. 9, entitled "Six Points of Especial Botanical Interest," was prepared for distribution at the meetings. A post-meeting field trip was organized to visit a number of these sites, all of which had been chosen as suitable for preservation as natural areas. Two of these were later acquired by TNC.

Meanwhile all was not well with the Conservancy at the national level. The preservation of endangered habitat was a concept whose time had come, and the Conservancy had been created as a vehicle to implement it. The potential was there, but the organization was financially undernourished and inadequately staffed. The executive director, George Fell, and his wife Barbara, were struggling to coordinate the efforts of a

In 1956, the changing of the guard of the Nature Conservancy. (*Left to right*) Richard H. Pough, the retiring president; the author, the incoming president; with Victor E. Shelford, "father" of the Natural Areas Movement.

growing roster of untrained volunteers, some of whom were much more interested in their local projects than in developing an effective national organization. No land had been acquired during the first four years of the Conservancy's existence, but after Richard H. Pough became president in 1953 the program began to take shape. By 1956 fifteen projects, all but two of them in the Atlantic states, had been undertaken. However, the relationships between TNC and most of the project committees were very strained.

Dick Pough was retiring as the volunteer president. There was little prestige involved in heading up a small, struggling organization already experiencing acute growing pains, and nobody was stepping forward to undertake the assignment. It was clear to me that there was great need for leadership of the natural areas movement. When asked to run for president, I accepted with considerable misgivings, not half realizing the impact this decision would have upon my career as a botanist. Bill Niering took over the chairmanship of Connecticut's Natural Areas Committee.

The first few months after I became president were especially hectic. Several decisions were made immediately. One was to change the title of the newsletter from *Nature Conservation News* to *The Nature Conservancy News* — a small matter, perhaps, but one involving a sharpened focus on the new organization and its developing program, and one that proved satisfactory for the next three decades. The first issue under the new title was devoted to descriptions of the Conservancy's fifteen projects, written, or at least approved by the person or persons in charge of each one. This gave me an opportunity to discover exactly what TNC's public relations problems were, to smooth ruffled feathers, and generally get the ship on an even keel. All this was somehow accomplished while carrying a full-time teaching and administrative load at the college.

Another critical issue was to decide the location of the national office. The Fells proposed to move it from the national capital to where they used to live in Rockford, Illinois. Fortunately the board of governors decided against such a move.

TNC was fortunate in those early days, when it had not yet proved itself, in having two fairy godfathers with the imagination to see the potential of the natural areas movement. These were Theodore Edison, the youngest son of the inventor, and Ernest Brooks, Jr., president of Old Dominion Foundation. Mr. Edison's benefactions began in the 1950s, when the entire annual budget of the Conservancy was around $10,000. They made it possible for TNC to expand its program. Substantial grants from Old Dominion Foundation established a revolving loan fund, which turned out to be an enormous help to local project committees attempting to raise funds for land acquisition. A

Ten Mile Creek, the Northern California Coast Range Preserve.

loan from this fund was used to finance the initial purchase for the Conservancy's first project, the Mianus River Gorge.

In May 1957 George Fell reported he had been out to see a beautiful property in the Coast Range of northern California that was being offered to TNC for $100,000. It seemed to be an opportunity that should be explored. I flew out to San Francisco after my Thursday class, and the following morning drove the 200 miles up to Branscomb in Mendocino County to see the owner, Heath Angelo, at his place on the Wilderness Road. There I was most cordially welcomed. During my two-day visit Mr. Angelo proceeded to bounce me all over the property in his Land Rover. The area consisted of 3,000 acres of glorious mountain country, the slopes of which were clothed with old-growth forest. Small settlers' clearings on the valley floor, surrounded by towering firs and redwoods, were being invaded by perfectly shaped specimens of *Ceonothus* and other native shrubs. It struck me as a bit of paradise. Saturday night we had a six-inch rainfall, and Sunday morning I

Heath Angelo.

took a picture of Elder Creek gushing crystal clear from its undisturbed watershed into the chocolate brown water of the South Fork of the Eel River.

I returned to New London on Tuesday, somewhat exhausted, just in time to deliver an inspirational final lecture to my introductory botany class on the importance of protecting natural areas. In closing, I described the Elder Creek watershed and suggested that the class might like to make the initial contribution toward its acquisition. The ten dollars, collected on the spot, became the nucleus of the fund that eventually secured the Northern California Coast Range Preserve.

This project was by far the largest and most expensive as yet undertaken by the Conservancy. It took a $5,000 grant from the Conservation and Research Foundation, which my mother and I had established in 1952, to persuade the Board of Governors to enter into a purchase contract. Mr. Angelo had ambitions to make his place an outstanding preserve. He drove a hard bargain, pushed the Conservancy into acquiring adjacent properties at additional expense, and expected a stewardship performance that the Conservancy was incapable of delivering for quite a few years. TNC's failure to live up to expectations resulted in a deteriorated relationship with Mr. Angelo, and he refused to accept final payment on the basis of his dissatisfaction with the Conservancy.

Fortunately my relations with Heath were always cordial as they were founded on mutual respect. In 1977 I was asked to deliver the final check to him in person to close the contract and he agreed to do so. The Preserve was soon recognized by the United Nations Environmental Programme as a Global Biosphere Preserve. In 1994 ownership was transferred to the University of California as an addition to its outstanding Natural Reserves System. It is now known as the Heath and Marjorie Angelo Coast Range Reserve.

When I became president in 1956, TNC was a very modest operation. Yearly dues were only two dollars, the staff consisted of one underpaid executive, the office his living room, and the annual budget was a mere $10,000. Most of what was accomplished was done by volunteers. Kenneth Hunt, the director of Glen Helen, adjacent to Antioch College, felt the time was ripe to establish a chapter in Ohio. He arranged for us to barnstorm the state, with stops in Cleveland, Columbus, Yellow Springs, Dayton, and Cincinnati. We were most cordially received everywhere we went, and the environmentally oriented leaders were favorably disposed toward organizing. However, it required a second trip two months later to persuade the group to take action. Established in 1958, the Ohio Chapter flourished and became one of TNC's more effective subsidiaries.

As TNC commenced to have successes with its program, two other organizations that were involved in natural-area preservation began to be concerned about potential competition. These were the National Audubon Society and Wildlife Preserves, Inc. In 1957 they invited the Conservancy to discuss the whole problem of preserving natural areas. The meeting took place in Paul Sears' office at Yale. Professor Sears was at that time chairman of the board of the Audubon Society. He was joined by the society's president, John Baker. Wildlife Preserves was represented by its president, Robert Perkins, Jr. and one of its trustees. The Conservancy delegation, consisting of F. Raymond Fosberg, Conrad Chapman, and I, was presented with a proposal to form a special Natural Areas Committee that would carry out all the land acquisition functions for the entire country. This committee was to consist of six members, two to be appointed by each of the three organizations represented at the meeting. For the National Audubon Society, natural-area acquisition was only a minor part of its program. Wildlife Preserves was not a membership organization, but governed by a small board of trustees. Our delegation made it clear that the proposal was totally unacceptable to a membership organization whose sole purpose was to save land. It would leave the members with nothing to do but elect two representatives to serve on this small committee. As time went on TNC's program became increasingly effective, and its successes had a stimulating impact on the National Audubon Society and other organizations, which began to accelerate their own land acquisition programs.

As soon as I became president in 1956, I realized that the administration of an effective national program had already become far too heavy a load for a part-time volunteer. I had a sabbatical leave beginning in the fall of 1957 that permitted me to devote full time to the Conservancy. Both our children were away at school and college, and Esther and I were able to travel together to various parts of the country. But this was not a permanent solution for the organization.

TNC required more competent staffing, and someone other than the Fells had to be in charge at the national office. Daniel Smiley, a member of the Board of Governors, had already made a rather extraordinary analysis of the problem before I ever became engaged with it. To accomplish this change was a most difficult task and painful to many of us involved. It required eighteen months of persuasion and diplomacy, while at the same time continuing to promote the land-saving program. The Board of Governors consisted of thirty members, all of whom knew the Fells well and respected their dedication to the movement. Some had been especially chosen by the Fells to join the board. During my first year as president I endeavored to make a personal visit to every member of the board and to discuss the problem with them. It became necessary to increase the number of board meetings. Funds were not available for travel, so it was an additional administrative problem to get a large enough turnout to assure a quorum. This required hours of "church work" over the telephone. Meetings often were far too long, as administrative details had to be carried out by the volunteers.

A decision was finally reached in the spring of 1958 to hire an executive director, and George Fell was appointed executive secretary, and the search was on for a new top executive. We were most fortunate in finding Edward Munns, who had just retired from the U.S. Forest Service. He had long been active in promoting Research Natural Areas in the National Forests. He and his wife were partly motivated by their desire to help a close friend in Washington who was suffering from a terminal illness. They came from California in June, and Ed moved into the office under very difficult conditions.

At the first governor's meeting attended by Mr. Munns in early July the slate of officers and board members to be presented for election in September at the annual meeting was announced. My term as president was up, and we had been fortunate to persuade James B. Ross, who was in the publishing business, to accept the nomination as my successor. Immediately thereafter every member of the Conservancy received a letter from Mr. Fell enclosing a complete opposition slate with himself listed as nominee for president. In his proxy solicitation I was accused of having been financially irresponsible. The basis for this allegation was my failure to approach potential donors while the Conservancy's administrative set-up was in turmoil.

The Fell's communication galvanized the board into action. My first meeting was at the Williams Club in New York City, courtesy of board member Robert Hammerschlag. From there I hopped the next air shuttle to Washington to meet with other governors and arrange the board's own proxy mailing. Individual governors solicited new members and additional proxies. I spent much of the summer asking all my friends to join the Conservancy.

The annual meeting was held in September 1958 at Indiana University in Bloomington. It was a very tense one with forty-five members in attendance. Before the election someone moved that only those who were members before the date of the Fell's proxy letter would be eligible to vote. As presiding officer I ruled that there would be no second-class citizens in The Nature Conservancy. No one sought to challenge this ruling. Then a large man arose in the back row and announced that he was Professor Davis of the Indiana Law School and wished to speak to the legality of the proxies. Our secretary, Elting Arnold, also an attorney, was madly recording the proceedings. He interrupted to request a slowdown to permit him to take down the details. It was comforting to know I had the support of a competent lawyer. As I recall it, Professor Davis indicated there might be a cloud on the legality of the proxies. I can remember pacing the floor a couple of times considering the possibility of ruling the proxies invalid. There was no way of knowing the outcome of the proxy vote. The Fells had had an initial advantage in the first mailing and were widely known to the membership. However, TNC was a membership organization, and everyone had been informed and had had an opportunity to participate in the decision. The chair ruled that the proxies would be considered valid, but that separate counts would be taken of the proxies and of the ballots of those attending the meeting. In this way an argument over the validity of the proxies would not invalidate the election. After an election committee had been appointed — consisting of a person representing the Fells, a person representing the board, and a neutral third party — ballots were cast and we adjourned for dinner to the Van Orman Graham Hotel.

James B. Ross (*left*), the incoming president of The Nature Conservancy, and the author (*right*), the retiring president in 1958.

Bill Niering, the board's representative on the election committee, reported that the Fells were pretty relaxed and confident at the beginning of the count. Their stack of proxies, which were on cards, was at least twice as high as the board's. As the count proceeded, however, it turned out that many of the board's proxies were on onionskin paper, and often with many signatures on a single sheet. As the count neared its conclusion, the proceedings became extremely tense. Upon reconvening the meeting after dinner, the count was announced. The board's slate won by ninety votes out of about 1,400 recorded. Of the members attending the meeting forty-two were in favor of the Board and three were for the Fells.

\* \* \*

Jim Ross assumed the presidency. One of Jim's legacies was the creation of the TNC's logo, the white oak leaf depicted at the heading of this chapter. I accepted chairmanship of the fund-raising committee. With the assurance of a strong administration I expended a lot of energy soliciting funds for the growing program. One of the most productive contacts turned out to be a visit Esther and I made to see George R. Cooley at his home in Rensselaerville, New York. George was in the investment business in Albany, and had a lively interest in botany as a hobby. He became a life member of the Conservancy as an immediate result of our visit and proceeded to goad the members of the Eastern New York Chapter into more ambitious fund-raising efforts through the challenge of matching gifts. He soon joined the national Board of Governors and helped the growing TNC in innumerable ways through his generosity, financial contacts, and wise counsel. One of the innovative ways in which he helped the Conservancy broaden its financial capability was to persuade banks to make substantial loans to the organization without requiring the deposit of collateral.

Fund-raising can have its high points as well as its discouragements. I vividly remember picking up my mail one day at the college post office and opening an envelope from an unfamiliar bank—from which fell an anonymous check for $25,000. At that time such a sum represented about 12 percent of TNC's annual budget.

In those early days of the Conservancy's history, establishing preserves was of critical importance in developing the organization's credibility, and efforts were made to find natural areas that could be acquired by gift. Most of the early preserves were small, and many protected rather typical habitats. One of these was the Burnham Brook Preserve, established in 1960 by a gift of 46 acres from Dr. and Mrs. John M. Ide, Esther and myself. It was a piece of woodland bordering a lovely trout stream in the town of East Haddam.

About 1958 I learned about an exciting bit of country in western

George R. Cooley with his wife Myra.

Rhode Island threaded by an old Indian path known as the Narragansett Trail. It included a wild little body of water called Ell Pond, the outlet to which flowed through a spectacular cliffy defile into Long Pond. A bog mat covered the eastern end of Ell Pond and the adjacent wetlands supported a coastal white cedar swamp and lush stands of rhododendron. A key seventeen-acre piece of this area had been acquired by Eva Butler, a remarkable archaeologist and colonial historian. I came to know her as the founder of the New London County Children's Museum, which later became the Thames Science Center with its headquarters located in the Connecticut Arboretum. She was also a member of All Soul's Church in New London and wife of its treasurer, Sylvester B. Butler, the superintendent of schools in Groton.

Eva had developed close relationships with the local Indians, particularly the Narragansetts, and she told me that the cedar trees in the swamp adjacent to Ell Pond had served the Indians as a source of bark for the construction of their wigwams. I suggested that she permanently preserve the property by giving it to the Conservancy. Her response was that she was already protecting it. When she died a dozen of her Indian friends, decked out in full ceremonial regalia, replete with eagle feather headdresses, served as pallbearers.

Ell Pond was inherited by Sylvester, and I suggested that he establish the preserve; but he also died without taking action. Title passed to the Butlers' son, Sewall, and he agreed to sell the land to TNC. We soon raised the very reasonable purchase price of $1,500 from fifty-two donors and closed the transaction in 1972.

The next adjoining property to the east had substantial frontage on Long Pond, and I initiated friendly negotiations with the owner, Mrs. Albro Dana. At that time TNC still had no chapter in Rhode Island, and Al Hawkes, director of the Rhode Island Audubon Society, became interested in the project, which was on his "turf." He took over and, due to his efforts, the Audubon Society acquired the shores of Long Pond. Now, many years later, TNC is undertaking large landscape scale projects. One of these is the relatively undeveloped sweep of country lying along the Connecticut-Rhode Island border. Ell Pond and Long Pond shine as little gems embedded in this landscape.

In southern New Hampshire, the owners of cottages along the shores of Lake Nubanuset wished to preserve what they called "The Island" — their view across the lake. It was a 400-acre tract of wild woodland almost surrounded by water. It was bounded to the south and east by Lake Nubanuset, to the north by Lake Spoonwood and its outlet, which flows into Nubanuset by a short stream. A narrow neck at its northwestern corner connects it to the mainland. The property was owned by Dr. L. Cabot Briggs. Negotiations were initiated in 1959 and by 1963 Dr. Briggs had agreed to sell the property to TNC, requesting that it be known as the Louis Cabot Preserve. The purchase price was met in part through TNC's revolving loan fund and the local committee, headed by Richard Bennink and George Ripley, proceeded to complete the fund-raising effort. That summer one of my botany majors, Patricia Stocking, undertook to make a vegetation inventory of the entire preserve all by herself — quite an undertaking! Among other things she discovered an impressive stand of the round-leaved orchid, *Platanthera orbiculata*, growing on the property. This plant has only two leaves, about the size of butter plates, lying appressed to the ground below its flowering stalk.

The new preserve fell within the towns of Nelson and Hancock. No sooner had the Conservancy acquired the property when these municipalities doubled the real estate taxes. In 1964 TNC applied for tax exemption as an educational enterprise, and as president I appeared in court several times to testify in behalf of the application. To my chagrin TNC lost the case, and our appeal to the state's Supreme Court was rejected. One of my concerns was that this action would set a precedent in other parts of the country. Sure enough, a similar case soon came up in Minnesota. But to the joy of all of us interested in preservation of natural areas, the judge in Minnesota found in favor of tax exemption, commenting that he didn't think much of the New Hampshire decision. TNC negotiated a gift of the Cabot Preserve as an educational facility to the Keene branch of the University of New Hampshire that enjoys tax exempt status. I wrote to a member of the Preserve Committee that it would give me satisfaction to have the officials in the towns reminded that they had "cooked the goose that laid golden eggs and that it was now stuffed and hung on the shores of Lake Nubanuset."

There was much interest in the use of natural areas for teaching and research. The Conservancy formed a committee, chaired by John Brainerd of Springfield College, to promote such resources for schools, and for several years there was some activity along these lines. In 1961 the Council of the American Association for the Advancement of Science appointed a study committee on Natural Areas as Research Facilities. This one was chaired by F. Raymond Fosberg. Ray was a very active member of TNC, as were the other members of this study committee. It published a 376-page report,[4] which included as an appendix the proceedings of the first National Symposium on College Natural Areas sponsored by the Conservancy and held in 1963 in Allerton Park, a property administered by the University of Illinois. I was very much involved in both of these ventures.

In Connecticut habitats of high priority were the tidal wetlands, which were rapidly disappearing as a result of various human encroachments. By 1959 almost half of those present at the beginning of the century had been lost. To publicize this problem we published *Connecticut Arboretum Bulletin*, No. 12 entitled "Connecticut's Coastal Marshes: A Vanishing Resource." In it the artist Louis Darling, describes in detail what had happened at Sherwood Island State Park in Westport. There three and a half million cubic yards of gravel, hydraulically dredged from Long Island Sound, had been stockpiled on the state-owned marsh — the last one of any account on the Connecticut coast west of the Housatonic River. This widely disseminated bulletin was partly responsible for the enactment in 1969 of legislation giving protection to this highly productive resource. Meanwhile, TNC was active in acquiring title to pieces of these wetlands and their barrier beaches and providing wardens to protect their endangered wildlife — a notable example being the piping plover. The Cottrell Marsh Preserve in Mystic was intensively studied and mapped with one inch contours by E. Zell Steever, a graduate student at Connecticut College. This study had to address the difficult question of what precisely is the present level of the ocean. As global warming melts the ice sheets, particularly in the Antarctic, it is predicted that accelerated sea level rise will have a drastic impact on our coasts.

Another serious environmental threat in the 1950s was the increasing use of pesticides, For example, the non-biodegradable DDT, much used on the marshes in mosquito control, was found to be concentrated by the food chain. In birds it interferes with eggshell production. Thus the osprey, as a top predator of the coastal environment, was being eliminated. Thanks to many activists and to the powerful message

Myra Hopson with the author.

in Rachel Carson's *Silent Spring*, published in 1962, use of this compound was banned. Since then the osprey population has recovered.

It was Frank Egler who called our attention to a beautiful 700-acre tract in Kent, Connecticut, situated north of the Kent School and just east of Macedonia Brook State Park, the largest one in the state. The gem shining in the middle of this property was a pristine, spring-fed body of water known as Fuller Pond. The owner, Myra Hopson, had inherited the land from her father and wanted to preserve it in its natural state. I put her in touch with Belton Copp, who in the early 1960s, drafted a testamentary trust that would give the area permanent protection. However, Miss Hopson decided to set up the trust during her lifetime, and thus, in 1966, the Pond Mountain Trust came into being.

Alexander B. Adams with Gloria Anable,
founder of the Mianus River Gorge Preserve.

Originally there were five trustees, including the donor and me. The trust document gave the trustees more discretionary power with respect to the disposition of the land than seemed desirable, so I persuaded the trustees to remedy the situation. They made a gift of the property to TNC and the Conservancy reconveyed it back to the trust with stringent reverter restrictions. Miss Hopson died in 1970, leaving her house to the trust and most of her residual estate as a stewardship endowment.

Since then the preserve has been enlarged by three more tracts, one by gift and two by purchase assisted by loans from TNC. More recently the National Park Service has purchased from the trust a strip along the eastern edge of the preserve for a portion of the Appalachian Trail. The proceeds of this sale has been used to augment the endowment.

A very similar situation developed in Mystic, Connecticut. The donor was Mary L. Jobe Akeley, widow of the African explorer. I had become acquainted with her back in the 1940s, when I had arranged to have her speak about her African experiences before the Rochester Academy of Science. Several years after I had moved to Connecticut I received a letter from her. She wanted to preserve her place on Great Hill. She had been using it as the site for a girl's camp, of which she had been the director. At my suggestion she gave an eight-acre piece of the property to TNC, and Belton Copp prepared a will for her that, unbeknownst to me, named me as her executor. When she died in 1966, the remainder of her real estate was left in trust, along with a stewardship endowment. This preserve, formerly the site of peace meetings organized in the early part of this century by the Quakers, is now known as the Peace Sanctuary. It is a scenic part of the historic district of Mystic, overlooking the Mystic Seaport.

These were two of the early land trusts established in the State. Now there are over a hundred. The Connecticut Chapter of TNC has been encouraging their formation and increasing their effectiveness through the Land Trust Service Bureau, housed and staffed in the chapter's office.

At the national level one of the most important additions to TNC's Board of Governors in the early 1960s was Alexander B. Adams. Alex brought to the organization broad experience in administration, public relations, and finance, having served with the Mellon Bank in Pittsburgh as well as with the F.B.I. One of his innovations was the establishment of the Guarantee and Income Fund — an endowment the principle of which could be used for project loans. A capital gift to this fund had the double attraction of providing operating income from the loans, while at the same time expanding the Conservancy's capacity to undertake larger projects.

Another of Adams' contributions was making a hard-nosed evaluation of the Conservancy, both of its performance and its public image. The study was commissioned by the Board of Governors. It is uncomfortable to face shortcomings, but the exercise can be enormously helpful if the information is used in a constructive way. For example, Adams showed why the promotional activities of TNC were failing to reach the audience it so desperately need for support. He subsequently became president in 1962, succeeding George Collins, and helped the organization implement many of the suggestions set forth in his report.

In 1964 I was reelected president and served for a second two-year term. During the first year a sabbatical leave again permitted me to devote full time to the job, which included frequent visits to the national office in Washington and travel all over the country on Conservancy business. One day, for example, included a breakfast meeting in Boston, a conference in Chicago, a dinner meeting in Salt Lake City, and a late evening with staff in San Francisco. Another was spent shuttling between engagements in Reno and Carson City, Nevada. Everywhere I enjoyed the hospitality of kindred spirits in such places as Santa Monica, California; Portland, Oregon; Tacoma, Washington; Granville, Ohio; Estero, Florida; Little Cumberland Island, Georgia; and the Northeast Kingdom in Vermont. Nights were spent in athletic clubs, motels, ranches, research stations, attics, living rooms, trailers, empty apartments, and under the stars.

Once an extraordinary coincidence occurred in Boise, Idaho. I was on my way to Pullman, Washington, to present a charter to the Inland Empire Chapter, which covered the western portion of that state. It was only the second time I had been in Boise, the first having been the previous year, when I made a similar presentation to the Idaho Chapter. The plane made a brief stop, and I jumped off to make a friendly

Lucy Baines Johnson (*left*), Walter S. Boardman, Executive Director of The Nature
Conservancy (*middle*), and the author (*right*), in 1965 at the
White House presenting Ms. Johnson with a life membership in TNC.

phone call to Franklin Jones, with whom I had spent the night on my
previous visit. Back on the plane I started writing a letter on TNC
letterhead but noticed quite a few additional passengers were getting
on. The fellow who sat down in the vacant seat across the isle leaned
over and said, "It seems to me I have seen that letterhead before." It was

Ernie Day, one of the officers of the Idaho Chapter. After we had exchanged greetings he continued, "Did you know that the entire membership of the Idaho Chapter is on this plane?" They were all headed for a wild life meeting in Coeur d'Alene.

The major accomplishments during this tour of duty as president were reorganizing the Conservancy's corporate structure and negotiating a grant from the Ford Foundation to provide four years funding for an expanded staff. Up to this point the Conservancy had been operating under a volunteer president, elected by the membership, and a staff consisting of an executive director, a Western regional director, and a few supporting personnel. The reorganization involved making the president the top paid executive, elected by the Board of Governors, backed up by a competent financial officer and other personnel. The top volunteer position then became the chairmanship of the Board of Governors. A finance committee, appointed by the board, was responsible for overseeing financial matters.

During initial discussions with Gordon Harrison of the Ford Foundation it became clear that any support of TNC's operating budget from the foundation would be contingent upon effecting this reorganization. The Board of Governors encouraged the submission of a grant proposal. Alex Adams, Cyrus Mark, and I were all involved in discussions with Mr. Harrison concerning the grant proposal, which requested $550,000 to supplement the Conservancy's operating budget over a four-year period, after which it was hoped that the Conservancy would have grown sufficiently to continue to fund the expanded operation on its own. The proposal was finally completed with much "coaching" from Alex.

Word came through in the fall of 1965 that the Ford Foundation had approved the grant conditional upon the acceptance by the Conservancy's board of the proposed changes in corporate structure. The matter came up for a decision at the annual meeting held that year in Buffalo, New York. Before the meeting Walter Boardman, the executive director, let it be known that he would resign if the changes were approved, and several governors decided at that late date to oppose accepting the grant on the basis that the Conservancy's program would be adversely affected by coming under the control of the Ford Foundation. This turned out to be another unpleasantly tense meeting. Fortunately the changes were approved, but I came out of it feeling as though I had been through a debarking machine at a pulp mill.

The next few months were frantic ones. Walter Boardman did resign. With a rapidly accelerating acquisition program and no executive director in the Washington office, I had to hold things together while meeting a teaching schedule and administering the Botany Department at Connecticut College. Fortunately Huey D. Johnson, our Western regional director, was willing to come East to serve as the acting executive director during this critical period while the search was on for a president.

At about this time word came from Alex Adams that he had become disenchanted with TNC and had decided to sever his connections. When I told this sad news to Esther, she said, "We are going down to Westport to see Alex right now!" This we did, and Alex, seeing how much we cared about the future of the organization, decided to stay on.

At the 1966 annual meeting, Charles H. W. "Hank" Foster, formerly Commissioner of Natural Resources for the State of Massachusetts, was selected to become the first paid president of TNC. Alex Adams became chairman of the board. I replaced Alex as chairman of the National Council, which had been set up as a device to attract the advice and financial support of key people around the country.

In 1967 there were only six professional biologists on the board of Governors, and they became deeply concerned that there was no trained ecologist on the national staff. The Board appointed a special Scientific Focus Committee, consisting of Ray Fosberg, Graham Netting, and me. We submitted a report the following year recommending, among other things, that a staff ecologist be employed to help coordinate activities involved in project evaluation, inventory,

Robert E. Jenkins.

research, and scientific publication. All of the recommendations of this committee were implemented, and Robert Jenkins, who had received his doctorate in biology at Harvard, was appointed scientific director in 1970. This turned out to be one of the most significant events in the growth of the Conservancy, for Bob proceeded to do what various scientists had been boasting for years that they would do, but never did, namely to develop and find funding for an open-ended, computerized system for storing a tremendously complex natural-areas database.

Jenkins soon became vice president for science and assembled a scientific staff, which proceeded to enter the available data on all TNC's preserves into the system. He then initiated state "natural heritage" programs. These consisted of databases for rare and endangered species and biotic communities — developed, maintained, and funded independently by the states. Later such programs were also promoted in

Patrick F. Noonan.

Central and South America, through TNC's International Program, which had its inception in 1974. Through these activities Bob enabled TNC to sharpen its scientific focus.

In the 1970s three men were especially responsible for the blossoming of the Conservancy. One was Patrick F. Noonan, who served for seven years as president commencing in 1973. Pat was a great administrator. His dedicated leadership and innovative approaches to land preservation were key to the organization's extraordinary growth during this decade. Five years after he left the Conservancy he established The Conservation Fund, which, in its first fifteen years, has managed to protect from development nearly 2.3 million acres with a market value of over a billion dollars. Wallace C. Dayton became chairman of the board in 1972. Wally was the person who quietly organized the board of governors into working committees, which met the day before the board meetings to prepare recommendations for action. This enormously increased the effectiveness of this able body of volunteers. The third man was Alfred E. Heller. As a member of the board he insisted that the organization make long-range plans.

I retired from the board of governors in 1980, but have continued my involvement with the organization, for a while as a trustee of the Connecticut chapter and continuously as a member of its Science and Stewardship Committee and chair of the Burnham Brook Preserve Stewardship Committee. In 1998 I had the honor of becoming a founding member of the President's Conservation Council, which keeps me informed of TNC's goals and achievements. In 2000 TNC set a capital campaign goal at one billion dollars, in order to launch 500 new landscape-scale projects! And its theatre of operations has expanded to embrace the Pacific and portions of the Orient.

# 9

# DOLBIA HILL AND THE BURNHAM BROOK PRESERVE

This is the story of the establishment and growth of one of The Nature Conservancy's largest preserves in the state of Connecticut. The story begins with Esther and I becoming acquainted with John and Margaret Ide. When we first moved to Connecticut in 1944 the Ides became our neighbors in Quaker Hill. John was then civilian director of research at the Navy Underwater Sound Laboratory in New London. Gas was rationed in those war years, and we carpooled our children to school. Later both families sent them to Putney School in Vermont. For the first ten years it was a rather casual relationship. Then one day in April of 1956, Esther's garden club and Margaret's held a joint meeting featuring a conservation speaker. John and I were the only men in attendance, and after the lecture we gravitated to a corner where, among other things, we exchanged aspirations of owning a small woodlot somewhere, perhaps in southern Vermont. This was on a Monday. Two days later Margaret, all excited, called me at work. She said, "Dick, we've found it!"

"Found what?" I queried.

"Why, just the place you and John were talking about at the meeting. It's in Lyme, and I want you and Esther to go and look at it right away."

It was a busy time, but that very weekend we did manage to get out for an inspection. The property actually turned out to be a bit north of Lyme, in the town of East Haddam. We drove up a narrow dead-end road that terminated on the broad crest of a hill at a small farmyard bounded on three sides by open fields and pasture. The farmhouse was a simple, one-story structure covered with red brick-patterned tarpaper, and the barn and outbuildings were in a dilapidated condition. We walked north across the pasture and down a wooded hillside to Burnham Brook, a lovely little trout stream, and then through a handsome hemlock forest in a rocky ravine. By that time we were "sold."

The Ides and Goodwins promptly contracted to buy the farm jointly. We are indebted to Marguerite Slawson for bringing its availability to Margaret's attention. Marguerite ran a bed-and-breakfast in Lyme called the Green Shadows. The deal was closed in June, and to celebrate the occasion we held a picnic for forty of our special friends out on a beautiful series of rocky ledges in the midst of mountain laurel in full bloom. Not long afterwards we found a whippoorwill's nest on the ground close to this spot, so we refer to this area as the Whippoorwill Ledges.

We purchased the 170-acre property from Andy and Dottie Tarpill, who had inherited it from Dottie's father, a Ukrainian, whose original family name was Hryhorka. In this country he legally changed it to York, so the place was locally known as the York Farm. In casting about for a name for our new estate, I suggested Burnham Wood. This floated like a lead balloon with Margaret who, during World War II, had been left to cope with three little children in a cottage in New Hampshire that was heated by a wood stove referred to as "burn 'um wood." We settled on Dolbia Hill, as that is the way it is designated on the U.S. Geographical Survey's topographic map. Dolbia is evidently a corruption of Dolbeare, the name of a former nineteenth-century owner.

For four years the Ides and the Goodwins enjoyed Dolbia as an escape from administrative pressures and other hassles of urban life, usually on alternate weekends. We kept each other apprised of seasonal events and wildlife observations in a log. The first improvement we made on the farm was reroofing the outhouse. Then the shack in the front yard and a collapsing shed behind the house were removed. Subsequently the farmhouse received a face-lifting in the form of new clapboard siding and new windows, including a picture window in the living room overlooking the west pasture.

The land on the crest of the ledges immediately south of the farm-yard supported a handsome stand of red cedars. This property was part of a large farm belonging to our neighbor, Ed Strong, who lived in a the valley below us known as the North Plain. One day we discovered a lumbering operation in progress, and the lumberman wanted access to the area through our farmyard. This stimulated us to negotiate the purchase from Ed of an additional thirty-two acres, which we called Oklahoma because of its shape, and from the lumberman the rights to 12 acres of its timber.

By 1960 John had undertaken a foreign assignment, and the Ides, having no further use for Dolbia, sold their half-interest in the farm to us. At that time I was of course very actively promoting the program of The Nature Conservancy, and, partly to enhance the orga-nization's credibility as an institution, I persuaded the Ides to join us in establishing the Burnham Brook Preserve by making an initial gift to TNC of the forty-eight acres of wild land lying to the north of the brook. This tract has been dedicated to Dr. Ide, who died in 1988. In his memory a bronze plaque has been mounted on a boulder over-looking the brook.

And then who should turn up on our doorstep but Ed Strong. He said, "Someone has approached me about buying my woods, but I

thought you might be interested." It was another hundred acres to the south. Our daughter Minda was about to be married, and we had just bought a new car, but this was an opportunity too good to be missed. We managed to scrape up the very modest sum required for this expansion of the "estate."

Shortly thereafter Esther and I conveyed an additional fifty acres on the south side of Burnham Brook to the Conservancy.

In those early days we had lots of opportunity to enjoy nature in the preserve. In order to increase its usefulness we began an inventory of the flora and the vertebrates, which was published in 1966.[1] The next year we wrote the following poem which captures the spirit of our experience.

## DOLBIA HILL

Along the ridge behind our walls
    The snow in sculptured drifts lies deep,
While in the woods it gently falls
    And wraps them for their winter's sleep.

It's cozy in our house upon the hill
    Releasing last year's sunshine on the hearth.
The deer knee deep attempt to get their fill
    Of prickly cedar twigs along the pasture path.

Reluctantly the ice yields to the thaw,
    And in the pasture pool the peepers peep,
While once again the melting snows restore
    The well, the springs and every muddy seep.

As April twilight mutes the lingering glow,
    The woodcock struts and with ecstatic flight
Drops from the sky. Six migrant herons flow
    Up through the trees and on into the night.

The quickening pasture now supports the cows,
    Brought to our hilltop from some year-round farm,
Whose constant cropping is just what allows
    The open fields to keep their rural charm.

Maternal duties occupy the drowsy hours,
    Preparing for the calves the evening meal,
And thus mankind derives in part his powers
    From soil, air, sunshine, grass, cow, milk to veal.

In summer's breathless moisture-laden days
    The sun browned out before it went;
And on the land the air lay in a haze
    By twenty million motors spent.

Resting on our wires the twittering swallows
    Are few this year. We wonder where they went.
We'd like to think we kept our hill and hollows
    Clean and healthy for them to frequent.

Not enough, our modest place,
    To save the birds for our delight.
Some creatures need a lot of space,
    And man must help to set the world aright.

> The snow and rain that give us drink,
>     The grass that purifies the air,
> The quiet space that lets us think
>         Are things that all of us must share.

In 1965 we had news that our home in New London would be condemned for an expansion of the Coast Guard Academy. We began to plan for a replacement at Dolbia Hill, atop a ledge behind an old lilac hedge to the south of the farmyard. The first step was to drill a 150-foot well to assure an adequate water supply. Although Dolbia Hill Road, which ran westerly between the old farmhouse and the place selected for the new house, had been closed off at our farm for many years and the right-of-way used for pasture, it was still a legal right-of-way. The second step was to petition for the road's official abandonment. This was required in order to eliminate the zoning set-back regulation, and gave us an excuse to meet all the neighbors living on our block — a circuit of about ten miles by road. The petition was accepted without dissent at the town meeting, but after the matter was closed a latecomer, a local politician, got up to splutter an objection.

We engaged the services of architect Richard Sharpe and worked with him for over a year on plans for the house. Considerable amusement was generated when Ed Strong, the very person from whom we had bought the land to save the cedars, appeared as the builder's assistant, to clear the land. Fortunately we were able to save all but those occupying the immediate house site.

Being out in the country at the end of a dead-end road, we wanted to minimize the problems inherent in being completely dependent upon electrical power. In case of an outage, the oil furnace and the water pump in the well would cease to function, as would an electric stove. In winter an unheated house would invite frozen pipes. So we planned the following features: Core plumbing avoided freezing pipes in outside walls. A supplementary gas space heater in the basement, activated by a bimetallic temperature control and supplied by a large gas tank, would keep the pipes from freezing in case indoor temperatures dropped. A water supply was assured by installing a thousand-gallon cistern in the basement, fed by rainwater from the roof. Fireplaces, a wood stove in the basement, a gas cookstove, candles, and kerosene lamps completed the arrangements.

These precautions really paid off. One December some years after we moved in, a severe ice storm resulted in five days without power. Although the house got pretty cold, we bundled up and managed to live through it with minimal difficulty. During another power and telephone outage I wanted to see our plumber on a matter unrelated to problems in the house, so I drove to his home early in the morning — to catch him before he was off to take care of emergencies — and rang his doorbell. He opened the door, looked me up and down, grinned, and said, "You know, you were right!" It made me wonder what the artisans must have been saying about the kooky prof at the time when the house was being constructed.

We did run into one problem. After a few years the cistern began to leak, and we discovered that the rainwater was so acid that it was dissolving the cement walls. This was corrected by our son, who lined the interior with a heavy coat of epoxy. We now keep it filled with well water that has become neutralized by passing through the soil.

The main portion of the house is all open. The living room rises two stories to a cathedral ceiling and has fourteen-foot tall plate glass windows facing south, mounted between wooden fins. On sunny winter days the house is solar-heated. The one-story kitchen and dining area are under a balcony bedroom and are separated by a slate counter about six inches higher than the sink and work space. The ridge pole is a massive laminated beam supported by three pairs of vertical beams; between these beams at the eastern and western ends of the house are tall slot windows. Some time after the house was finished the roof was fitted with solar panels to provide hot water. These save us about fifteen percent on our electric bill.

We were able to occupy the finished structure in August of 1968. We had originally envisioned using the little farmhouse as a guest cottage, but it soon became inhabited by the first of a succession of tenants who have lived there rent free, in return for help with the stewardship of the property. Through their interest in natural history and creativity they have significantly enriched our lives and contributed to the program at the preserve.

The first of these was Allen Carroll, one of my earliest students majoring in human ecology. He moved in right after graduation in the summer of 1973 and remained for five years, during which time he developed his talents as artist and editor. He left us for Washington, D.C., where he soon joined the staff of the *National Geographic* magazine and in time has become the head of NG Maps, a commercial spin-off of the magazine. Our second tenants were also two of our botany majors, Tim Reynolds and his wife, Karen Pfanner. After graduating Tim got an administrative job working on the Pfizer farm, while Karen did landscape consulting. In 1981, when Karen's father died, they left us to help her mother manage the Point Pleasant Resort on St. Thomas in the Virgin Islands.

Just at that time I had a letter from Bill Stepka telling me about a young friend of his named Julie Zickefoose, who was graduating from Harvard and was interested in becoming involved in conservation. I wrote to TNC's Eastern regional office in Boston asking if they would be willing to give her some advice. About three weeks later I had a phone call from Susan Cooley in TNC's Connecticut office asking whether there might be housing at Dolbia for a new summer employee. It turned out to be Julie! She moved in for the summer, bringing with her extraordinary talents as wildlife artist and naturalist. She was especially knowledgeable about birds, but also well informed about other vertebrates, insects, and plants. She left us that fall.

Our fourth occupants for an extended period were Rick Wahle and Carol Lariviere, who got married while they were with us. Rick was a biologist on the teaching staff of the Thames Science Center in New London and Carol was studying for a degree in education at the University of Connecticut. They left after three years when Rick went to the University of Maine to get a Ph.D. in marine biology.

In 1985 Julie returned with Rob Braunfield, also an artist and

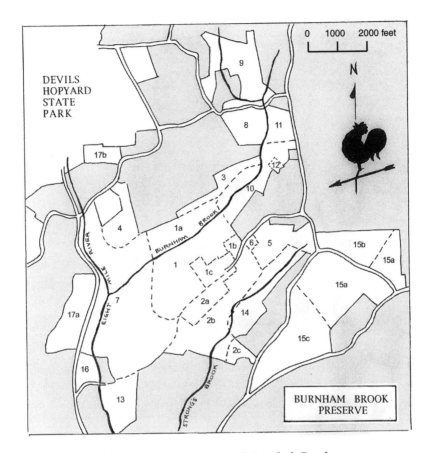

1. The Dolbia Hill Farm
   1a. Ide Tract
   1b. Jordan Lot
   1c. Farmyard and pastures
2. The Strong Farm
   2a. Oklahoma
   2b. Goodwin Woodlands
   2c. Conklin Gift
3. Duer/Pattison Tract
4. Ricky Memorial Tract
5. Goodwin Woodlands,
   Belardo Section
6. Falvey Purchase
7. Chauncey Hand Tract
8. Webber Purchase

9. Spitzschuh Purchase
10. Robertson Purchases
11. Hula Purchase
12. Jewett Purchase
13. Kashanski Easement
14. Hatfield Easement
15. Woodbridge Bingham Farm
    15a. Marian Bingham Easements
    15b. Evelyn Goodman Easement
    15c. Ann Pierson Easement
16. Hammond Mill Preserve,
    East Haddam Land Trust
17. Devil's Hopyard State Park
    17a. Devil's Ridge Addition
    17b. Danikow Addition

wildlife sculptor. After six years Julie left to get married and Rob stayed on. He is still with us in 2002.

* * *

Beginning in 1975 the Burnham Brook Preserve, which was by then just short of a hundred acres, began to grow. The next addition was a twenty-acre tract from our neighbors Gertrude and Edith Lefebvre, who lived in a lovely little colonial house on the north side of the preserve. This property was a gift in memory of Mr. Leland B. Duer and Mrs. Ethel Pattison their friends and benefactors. The Lefebvres were French. Edith came to this country as a governess to join her sister. She has reminisced with us about the time during World War I when, as a little girl, she was evacuated by train to Paris from her home in northern France during the German invasion.

Two years later we gave the western portion of the Dolbia Hill farm to TNC. We called the tract Nodding Fern for a frond that was in constant motion in a notch between the ledges, where a cool breeze was rising up a defile occupied by a little stream that flowed into the Eight Mile River just south of Burnham Brook.

The following year we sold two lots to colleagues, each of which was encumbered by a conservation easement limiting its use to a single dwelling and stipulating various environmental restrictions. The first, a five-acre tract adjacent to the hayfield, was sold to Philip and Sheila Jordan. Phil, the dean at Connecticut College, had just accepted the presidency of Kenyon College in Ohio. He and Sheila were reluctant to sever all their roots in Connecticut. A portion of this lot supported a small bit of prairie grassland being invaded by huckleberry. The second lot was a ten-acre parcel on the southern edge of the woodland purchased from Ed Strong. It was sold to Marilyn Conklin who was retiring from the physical education department. On it she built a modest house with attached kennel for her pedigreed basset hounds. Both of these properties later became part of the preserve. In 1995, Marilyn gave her house and lot to TNC, retaining life-time use, and the Jordan lot was purchased by TNC through a bargain sale in 1997.

We used the proceeds of the sale of these lots to finance the next

William D. Blair, Jr., (*left*), president of the Nature Conservancy, and W. Kent
Olson (*right*), executive director of the Connecticut chapter, present a
congratulatory resolution from the national Board of Governors
to Richard and Esther Goodwin, September 14, 1985.

addition to the preserve, a thirty-two-acre tract to the northwest. It was
purchased in 1978 by bargain sale from Patricia Pindar who requested
that this be known as the Ricky Memorial Tract in memory of her
favorite dog.

On the western end of the now abandoned Dolbia Hill Road lived
our neighbor Mrs. "Bill" Clark. Bill was a widow with whom we had
friendly relations. In July 1969, at the time of the moon walk, we had
no television set, so she invited us to view that exciting event with her.
In our Christmas letter that year I wrote:

> This year man has been privileged to get a new look at
> the blue planet, a small illuminated ball spinning through
> the vast unfriendly blackness of galactic space. It is our
> space ship; it is all we have. Do you suppose we can come to
> love it a little more? As Thoreau wrote, "What is the use of
> a house if you haven't got a tolerable planet to put it on?"

Eight Mile River below the Jones Hill Bridge ca. 1993.

The sooner we abandon the cornucopian philosophy the more likely will be the survival of our species.

When Bill decided to move to West Virginia, we brought the availability of her place to the attention of our friends John and Barbara Kashanski, who purchased it. Immediately adjacent was a lovely twelve-acre property on the Eight Mile River given by the Hammond family to the Pequot Council of the Boy Scouts of America to use as a camping area. It was an old mill site with the remains of the dam and sluice-ways still in evidence. It was known as the Hammond Mill. We were dismayed one day to discover that the council had placed this property on the market. In order to save it from development, the Kashanskis and the Goodwins provided funds that enabled the newly formed East Haddam Land Trust to acquire it as its first preserve in 1980.

The next year the Kashanskis gave TNC a conservation easement on thirty-eight acres of their land along the Eight Mile River. This included a precious little piece of flood-plain meadow supporting a number of uncommon species of plants including Indian grass (*Sorghastrum nutans*) and Nuttall's milkwort (*Polygala nuttallii*). Barbara, who had been one of my botany majors, was especially interested in the growth and stewardship of the Burnham Brook Preserve. The maintenance of this meadow became one of her concerns.

In 1985 Esther and I gave the Conservancy the lands we then owned lying to the south of the original farm. These included the property we had acquired from Ed Strong and a forty-two-acre tract to the east, which we had purchased from the daughter of our recently deceased neighbor, Joseph Belardo. These holdings protected much of the upper watershed of the north branch of Strong's Brook and nearly doubled the size of the preserve. In September of that year the Connecticut chapter held its annual meeting on Dolbia Hill, at which this gift was celebrated. Most fortunately the date had been advanced two weeks in order to accommodate the schedule of William Blair, the national president. On the day originally chosen New England was hit by hurricane Gloria and our road was totally blocked by fallen trees. But the fourteenth was a gorgeous day with the goldenrods and asters in full bloom. The horses had been removed from the pasture where a large tent was erected. To be tidy we carefully tossed all the horse droppings away from the site, and later to our amusement found that many of the 350 attendees chose to eat their lunches in the sunshine on top of the somewhat more concentrated dung. After the formal meeting, tours of the preserve were led by twelve experienced leaders. Some of our family and special friends came from out of town — Esther's nephew Roger Burke and his daughter, and three of my old Troop 4 pals, Tim Rhodes and Mort and Bob Vose.

Burnham Brook being one of TNC's earliest preserves, has experienced changes that have taken place in the organization's conservation philosophy. At first the Conservancy was interested in preserving natural areas as undisturbed places where one could study nature, and the preserve very nicely filled this need. However, as TNC successfully expanded its portfolio of sites, responsibilities of stewardship began to emerge and the organization became more selective with respect to the properties it would accept. In the early 1970s great emphasis began to be placed on preserving rare and endangered species and communities. Thus Burnham Brook, which had not originally been selected on this basis, became classified as one of the Conservancy's least important holdings. Then, twenty years later, it was realized that to truly preserve biodiversity one needed to adopt a broader perspective — to preserve whole ecosystems and even complexes of them on a landscape scale. In the 1990s the Conservancy instituted its Last Great Places initiative. A modest number of specially chosen portions of the Western Hemisphere were selected for conservation action. One of these was the watershed of the lower Connecticut River. For a number of reasons, the mouth and lower reaches of this largest New England river have escaped the impacts of urban development that have destroyed most of the others. The Connecticut chapter established its tidelands initiative, directed toward the preservation of the wetlands along the river, but it was soon recognized that the quality of the whole system was dependent upon the preservation of the tributary streams and their associated uplands. An important tributary to this system is the Eight Mile River. Its whole watershed is still in a relatively undeveloped state and has been recognized by the Connecticut Department of Environmental Protection as one that should be preserved. Thus the Burnham Brook Preserve now took on new significance as an integral part of this larger system.

Since 1985 recent additions to the Preserve have again more than doubled its size. They fall into several categories — upper portions of the Burnham Brook watershed; lower reaches of the brook and banks of the Eight Mile River; portions of the Strong's Brook watershed; and woodlands to the east. Of these the most important has been a 215-acre tract extending the preserve to the west and connecting it to the Kashanski easement, the Hammond Mill, and the Ricky Memorial. This land protects nearly a mile of the Eight Mile River. It had been acquired by Chauncey Hand as a fishing preserve in the 1930s. For

Aerial photo of Dolbia Hill Farm.

many years I had cultivated relations with Chauncey, who was a trustee of Connecticut College, and members of his family. Eventually it became possible to negotiate a bargain sale with his daughter's heirs. The tract is named in his honor.

To the north five additional tracts, totalling 184 acres, are now helping to preserve the headwaters of Burnham Brook. To the south and east of the preserve four friends have given easements that are protecting about 300 additional acres of forest and the watershed of Strong's Brook.

In 1998 Esther and I made a final gift of the remainder of our property in the heart of the preserve, retaining life-time use. This included the hayfield, pastures, farmyard, two houses, and a barn. After we are gone this should help the Conservancy maintain a presence in the area, where stewardship responsibilities will be increasing.

The Conservancy has also been instrumental in acquiring two adjacent forested tracts which have been added to the Devils Hopyard State Park. Between the preserve and the park over 2,000 acres are now being protected from development. In addition, substantial headway has already been made through the activities of the Conservancy, the local land trusts, and the state in creating a protected corridor along both branches of the Eight Mile River all the way to the Connecticut River.

\* \* \*

Back in 1960, when we established the preserve, there were very few natural areas under permanent protection. On this one the guiding management philosophy has been to minimize human impacts, so that the dynamics of the undisturbed ecosystem might be available for study. In order to maximize the usefulness of the preserve as a research area an effort has been made to restrict its use to those who are seriously interested in some aspect of its natural history. The entry sign and register are located about 500 feet from the road. The trails are narrow, somewhat obscure and unmarked, with the exception of one-mile loop, which has been described in Susan Cooley's *Country Walks in Connecticut: A Guide to The Nature Conservancy Preserves.*[2]

At the time of the preserve's establishment it had been my thought that appropriate uses would be made of the area and others like it if they became available for study, and at no expense to the Conservancy. This has surely proved to be the case at Burnham Brook. Here is an account of some of the projects — most of them unsolicited — that have been undertaken.

A gypsy moth infestation in the 1960s resulted in a severe defoliation of the forest for two successive years. The public response was to attempt to control the outbreak by blanket spraying the forests from the air with Sevin, a carbamate pesticide, toxic to insects generally, to aquatic life, and possibly to people. A major portion of the town of East Haddam was so treated, with the exception of our 2,000-acre block. This was because we made the effort to circulate a petition among our neighbors requesting that we be left unsprayed. Everyone signed it with the exception of the one who should have been the most interested, namely the "honey man," who maintained hives of bees on the Hopyard Road. Since the preserve was uncontaminated, Dr. Benjamin Cosenza at the University of Connecticut selected it as the place to make a study of gypsy moth epidemiology. At the same time entomologists from the federal research station in New Haven came to the preserve to collect healthy moths for genetic studies, and another entomologist came to study the population of Calosoma beetles, a predaceous species that had been imported from Europe to help control the moth. I was familiar with this beetle, which has spectacular blue-green elytra, but was not aware that we had any of them on the Preserve until I discovered masses of their wing cases in skunk scats in the farmyard. Here was a little piece of the web of life.

In 1979 a team of scientists from the Department of Epidemiology and Public Health at the Yale Medical School sought permission to use the preserve as a place to study the role of ticks in transmitting Lyme disease. This was shortly before the discovery of the bacterial agent causing the disease and they thought they might be dealing with a virus. They were live-trapping small mammals and needed a place where their traps would not be subject to vandalism. One interesting spin-off from this study was the information we obtained concerning populations of the nocturnal mammals present on the preserve, to say nothing of their parasites. Over 10,000 ticks, representing seven different species were collected in the course of their study, as well as fifteen species of mosquitoes.[3]

It is worth noting that up to the mid-seventies we were constantly walking in the woods and never picked up ticks. Also, at that time Lyme disease was a newly reported ailment. After 1980 it became a different story. We were frequently picking off ticks, and in 1987 I became afflicted with the disease. It was not promptly diagnosed, and I became quite ill. Among other symptoms, my blood platelets were being destroyed. As soon as I started taking the appropriate antibiotic, I made a quick recovery. Two years later Esther became infected, and then two years after that we both had a recurrence. In 1992 Esther again became ill. She started taking the antibiotic for Lyme disease, but fortunately, her problem was immediately diagnosed as babesiosis, another, rather rare, tick-borne disease, that attacks red blood cells and requires an entirely different treatment. She was in the hospital for a week receiving intravenous medication. Needless to say, the build up of

Fly agaric (*Amanita muscaria*) —
poisonous.

the tick population and the presence of their microorganisms has been a rather unwelcomed change in the ecology of our area.

Two University of Connecticut doctoral dissertations have been partly based on research carried out on the preserve. One was by Joyce Hemingson on the pollination biology of sweet pepperbush (*Clethra alnifolia*), which involved the identification of the insect visitors and a chemical analysis of the plant's chemical attractants.[4] The other, by Deborah Lee, grew out of a survey of the insect fauna of the streams. It involved the role of chironomid midge larvae in the decomposition of submerged wood.[5] In the course of the survey Deborah identified sixty genera of midges!

Dr. Robert A. Askins of the zoology department at Connecticut College, in researching the relationship between breeding bird populations and the size of the forest tracts that support them, used the preserve as one of his study sites because it was embedded within one of the largest undisturbed forests in the state. He found that a number of species, such as the hermit thrush, brown creeper, blue-gray gnatcatcher, yellow-throated vireo, cerulean warbler, and worm-eating warbler, all of which are rather scarce in Connecticut, only breed in larger tracts. All of these were found breeding on the Preserve.[6]

Another Connecticut College zoologist, Dr. Benjamin A. Pierce, and his student John Harvey, were investigating the tolerance of wood frogs to acidic conditions, a matter of great interest in view of the prevalence of acid rain and the acidity of some of the small bodies of water in which amphibia breed. They recorded the survival of tadpoles hatching from eggs collected from various places, including the vernal pools on the preserve, when subjected to a range of acidities. They found that there is considerable genetic variability within this species with respect to acid tolerance.[7]

In 1986 we had a visit from Dr. Robert Wintsch, a member of the Geology Department at Indiana University. He and two of his graduate students were visiting the preserve to study the ancient bedrocks of the area in an effort to unravel their complex history. A few hundred feet south of our house the Honey Hill fault crosses the preserve from east to west. It marks the margin of the ancient African plate that collided with the American plate to form the super-continent of Pangaea over 300 million years ago.

In 1985 a new oriental pest arrived in Connecticut, the hemlock woolly adelgid. This small aphid-like insect has a devastating impact on the eastern hemlock. The Burnham Brook Preserve has been supporting a portion of one of the largest hemlock stands in the state. It is not clear exactly when the adelgid hit the preserve, but air photographs show the canopy intact in 1990. However, by 1995 there had been a ninety-seven percent mortality in portions of the stand. The staff at the Harvard Forest in Petersham, Massachusetts, interested in studying the forest response to this pest, chose the preserve as one of their eight study sites in southern New England.[8]

In 1991 a cooperative agreement between the Conservancy and Connecticut College was consummated. It formalized an arrangement that had been in effect for years. In return for research and teaching access to the reserve, the College agreed to establish a Burnham Brook Science Advisory Committee to provide volunteer advisers for research and scientific matters pertaining to the property and would also continue to maintain the preserve's herbarium of voucher specimens. The preserve had already been used as a site for a number of student projects and continues to do so.[9]

In order to increase the usefulness of the preserve, an effort has been made through the years to document what is there. The first inventory of its flora and vertebrates was published in 1966. This was at least ten years before the program of the Conservancy had matured to the point where baseline inventories were a required part of a preserve's master plan. The presence of the vascular plants, bryophytes and lichens has been documented by voucher specimens, and several revisions of the inventory have been produced.[10] We have been fortunate in being able to enlist the aid of experts in this work. Dr. Antoni Damman has helped with the identification of bryophytes, sedges, and grasses; Kenneth Metzler and Carol Lemmon, the lichens; our neighbor, Gerry Miller, the fleshy fungi; and Dr. Noble Proctor and Margaret Ardwin, the slime molds. Dr. Michael Klemens of the American Museum of Natural History worked up the reptiles and amphibians, while Stephen Gephard, fisheries biologist with the Department of Environmental Protection, has identified the fish. Our lists of birds and mammals are largely based on sight records, supplemented for nocturnal mammals by the live-trapping program of the Lyme disease study.[11] For many years we have been keeping monthly records of the birds seen, and breeding bird censuses have been conducted for sixteen different years. We are indebted to Robert Braunfield for most of these and to Julie Zickefoose for participating in three of them.[12]

Our updated records list the following numbers of species as having been seen or collected: 24 fish, 14 amphibia, 17 reptiles, 190 birds, 33 mammals, 727 vascular plants, 47 mosses and liverworts, 39 lichens, and 422 fungi. The invertebrates present quite a challenge. A start has been made with a few groups. For instance, fifty species of butterflies have been identified, thanks to the work of Kerry Pado.[13] Deborah Lee has produced a long list of aquatic insects, and ticks and mosquitoes have been recorded.

"Grandma's Pool" on Burnham Brook in 1960.

Until a careful inventory is made, it is impossible to tell whether or not a natural area is protecting something quite unusual. In the case of Burnham Brook it has turned out that two grasses, false melic grass (*Schizachne purpurascens*) and a Panicum, are in this category. One butter-fly, the inornate ringlet (*Coenonympha inornata*) was only the second one recorded for the state.

One of the pleasures of living within the preserve has been our privilege of guiding visitors through it. Some of these, such as Bo-Quan Chen of the Chinese Academy of Medicine and the British mycologist Roger Phillips, have been distinguished scientists from overseas.

At the time of the preserve's establishment in 1960 the brook was recognized as being a very special feature. So it was with considerable dismay that we learned two years later that the Soil Conservation Service had recommended to our up-stream neighbors, the Robertsons, that they dam it to construct a six-acre pond. There were a number of potential impacts that this might have on the system: blocking movement of the fish in the stream, raising the temperature of the water beyond the tolerance of trout, and possibly eliminating flow during dry spells. Two years later, in 1964, a fishery biologist from the Board of Fisheries and Game made an electrofishing survey of the brook and found it a valuable nursery stream for brook trout. At about the same time we installed a V-notch weir on the stream and measured flow during the summer months. It was a dry summer, and the rate of flow dropped to as low as one gallon a minute. Experts informed us that the loss of water from a six-acre pond on a summer day would be about forty gallons a minute. This led to protracted negotiations with the Robertsons. Fortunately plans for the pond were abandoned.

The brook was resurveyed in 1985 by Stephen Gephard. Above a little cataract on its lower reaches the stream supports only three species of fish: brook trout, black-nose dace, and American eels. These are all natives uncontaminated by introductions. The eel is a catadromous species that breeds in the Sargasso Sea of the Atlantic Ocean. Steve stated that this fish community has "great museum significance."[14] In 1995 we had a severe drought. Burnham Brook and many other small streams dried up. I thought this would be the end of our special museum community. However, Steve resurveyed the brook again the following year and found all three species present, the brook trout being as abundant as ever. He suggests that they have evolved mechanisms to adapt to such occurrences, and that these probably include a quasi-estivation state in the stream substrate followed by post-drought dispersal.

With the exception of the hayfield, pastures, and a few adjacent thickets and openings, the preserve now in TNC ownership has been left to recover from the human impacts of the last three centuries. Much of it had been cleared for agriculture and pasture; some of the steeper and rougher land, used as woodlots. In 1956 much of the land was in post-agricultural forest, but in places there were still grassy openings supporting interesting wildflowers, such as the fringed gentian (*Gentiana crinita*) and Indian paintbrush (*Castilleja coccinea*). These have now been lost from the inventory due to closure of the canopy. One summer day I discovered the floor of a young forest looking as if we had had a snow storm. It was covered with the trunks of the short-lived gray birches that had invaded a pasture and had all fallen simultaneously. The plant communities have been studied and mapped as tracts have been added to the Preserve.[15]

The maturing of the forest has brought about a change in the wildlife. This is particularly noticeable with the bird populations. Those that nest in thickets, like the chestnut-sided warbler, yellow-breasted chat, Nashville warbler and brown thrasher, are gone. The rufous-sided towhee is getting scarce. The hooded warbler, which likes open woods, has also disappeared.

The forest has suffered very little from natural disasters, such as hurricanes and ice storms, during our stewardship of the preserve, but the introduction of foreign diseases and pests has caused some major disturbances. Two of these occurred in the early part of this century. Dutch elm disease killed off the American elm. In 1956 one last tree was standing dead at the edge of Burnham Brook. The chestnut blight removed the American chestnut from the forest as a component of the canopy long before we arrived, but numerous root-sprouts still persist. We have already mentioned the gypsy moth. The forest has experienced outbreaks of this insect in the 1960s, again in the 1970s, and then the most serious one in 1981. An analysis of the impact of this last outbreak on the hemlock population showed that wherever hemlocks were invading oak stands there was almost one hundred percent mortality. In mixed stands of maple and beech the loss was much less severe, while in nearly pure hemlock stands there was none. The young caterpillars, which prefer oaks, are unable to chew the tough, evergreen hemlock needles, but after they get big they move over onto the hemlocks. A fungus disease has now turned up that attacks the gypsy moth larvae, and we have experienced no new outbreaks since the one in 1981.

Since 1982 we have been measuring the amount of rainfall in the farmyard and recording its acidity. Much of it has been in the pH 4 to

pH 5 range and some of it well below pH 4.[16] The data have been useful to Dr. Peter Siver and his associates in studies of the acidity of lakes
in the neighborhood. On the preserve this acid precipitation may be
having deleterious effects upon the nutrients and microorganisms in
the soils and also on the flora and fauna. Observations at the preserve
indicate that the system is under stress. Individuals of quite a few tree
species are in poor health for one reason or an other. These include the
dogwoods, ashes, and oaks, and we have observed the disappearance of
the butternuts and basswoods in the past forty-five years.

The changes in the animal populations are worth mentioning. In
colonial times the wolf and mountain lion were eliminated as the top
predators in New England. In recent years they have been replaced by
the coyote, which has moved east and has become well established. We
now see them occasionally and hear their choruses. They may be
displacing the foxes and bobcats, which are becoming much less in
evidence, and may also be responsible for the growing scarcity of the
ruffed grouse. Beaver, which had been trapped out in colonial times, are
also returning. Their activity has recently been observed along our
portion of the Eight Mile River. The wild turkey, recently reintroduced
into the state from New York, was first recorded on the preserve in
1982. Its population has exploded. Everywhere scratchings are in
evidence on the forest floor and we occasionally see flocks of thirty or
more in the pastures.

White-tailed deer have become our most troublesome vertebrate.
When we first acquired the farm, we rarely saw these animals. Their
population may have been kept somewhat under control through
hunting pressure, including quite a bit of poaching. Through the years,
however, the population has grown, despite the fact that we have
allowed hunting on the land we still own. An air survey in 2000 by the
Department of Environmental Protection estimated the density in our
vicinity as eighty per square mile. The impact of the herd is very evi-
dent — the browse line in the forest and the erosion of biodiversity. In
some cases we have observed rare wildflowers and shrubs actually bit-
ten off. These include several species of orchids, wood lily, giant

solomon's seal, pipsissewa, prairie willow, and various cultivated species right around our houses. In 1993 two exclosures were fenced off in the forest, and within two years one of these was a green emerald surrounded by a barren forest floor. It was filled with tree seedlings of several species, and numerous species of wildflowers. In 2000 a study by Dr. James Hill has documented the present status of the woody vegetation. It is hoped that the deer herd can be thinned to the point where the forest can recover.

One of the stewardship tasks at the preserve has been to control the invasion of aggressive exotic shrubs and vines. One of the worst of these, Japanese barberry, is quite shade tolerant and spreads through the forest. If not checked it can soon become a dominant prickly understory. Others species include autumn olive, winged euonymus, and oriental bittersweet. We have been mechanically removing these whenever we encounter them, and have been assisted from time to time by work parties of volunteers.

In order to preserve the rural setting of the farm, the seventeen-acre portion of Dolbia Hill adjacent to the buildings has been maintained as open land ever since we acquired the farm in 1956. The farmyard has been mowed and a small vegetable garden fenced with a seven-foot fence to protect it from rabbits and deer. The barn has been extensively repaired and the summer kitchen replaced by a woodshed. With the decline of agricultural activity in this section of the state, the maintenance of hayfield and pastures is becoming an increasingly complex problem. Without acquiring heavy equipment and becoming involved in year-round animal husbandry, we have been dependent upon neighbors for help. The four-acre hayfield has been mowed almost every year. During the first two decades it was harvested for hay and at one point plowed and planted to alfalfa by a nearby dairy operation owned by our friend Dr. Joseph Lubart. More recently it has been mowed with a brushhog or grazed at the end of the season.

The twelve acres of pasture have been regularly grazed. Between 1958 and 1979 we had an average of seven head of cattle during the summer months. They were mostly dry heifers or pregnant cows that dropped their calves while on the farm. They came from various sources. The first were from Leon Tiffany's farm in Lyme. One bit of excitement occurred with his animals when one of the heifers caught her hoof in an old discarded aluminum coffee pot. This spooked the whole herd which sailed over our four-bar gate and thundered off down the road. For several years we bought pregnant cows in the spring and sold off mothers and calves in the fall.

Then one year we had a disaster. We bought four young Hereford heifers. The very first day they jumped the pasture fence, ending up in the woods at the northeastern corner of the farm, which was fenced. For days we tried unsuccessfully to entice them back to the pasture with grain. Finally they broke out and ran away. Two turned up about three miles away in the Wlodarczyk's bull pasture on Witch Meadow Road. They had been had by the wrong type of bull, so we had to sell them at a loss for beef. One we were able to catch and sell back to the person from whom she was purchased. The fourth remained at large for forty days, presumably feeding on skunk cabbages. Finally her white face turned up looking forlorn at Louis Darling's fence, about a half mile south of the farm. Louis enticed her in, and I told him he could have her! And thus began a new chapter. The Darlings christened her Aster in honor of Esther, bred her and in due course she had a calf they called Daisy. A later production born in a heavy rainstorm they named Waterlily. Our eventual pay-off was receiving a very fine steak.

We came to know our livestock and gave them names. Flicker was an athletic Holstein which hopped out of and back into our pasture at will. Mudder and Nudder were heavy Black Angus that were a bit pushy. I always made sure I didn't get crushed between them and the barn. Our neighbor's lad Jimmie was handicapped by very poor eyesight. We helped him raise calves for veal. Finally Joe Lubart's heifers grazed the pasture until he closed out his operation. Our cattle raising days were over. We wondered what to do next.

At this point a young couple who lived just north of the farm knocked on our door and asked if they could put their horse in our pasture for a couple of weeks. This developed into a permanent summer arrangement supplemented by horses from a friend of theirs in Chester. So from 1980 on we have had horses, which have come from various sources. They are much easier on the fences.

Looking to the future it is our hope that, through the efforts of the Conservancy, its partners and neighboring landowners, it will be possible to maintain at least some of the rich biodiversity of southern Connecticut, and that the preserve will play a significant role in this enterprise. The problem is enormously complex, requiring sophisticated management practices and subject to influences far beyond the immediate area. These include climate changes due to global warming, destruction of the ozone screen, air pollution, further introductions of exotic species, and far-off disturbances in the habitats of migratory birds.

## FOR ESTHER

Would'st come with me down through the fields and sun-lit glades
    into the forest dim?
The breath of evening cools the brow, though high the noon.
The turgid stream glinting fills each trout pool to the brim
And rushes on, just as the precious hours that pass too soon.

This wonderful world of ours made mad by man,
Whose thundering jets draw lines across the cloudless skies,
Where rivers hide in foam and atoms split by plan,
And pesticides pose threats to every living bug and bird that flies.

This world of ours has need of those who deeply care.
There's work for us to do this very day.
And joy attends this enterprise we share
Together. The apple has been plucked. We may not stay.

# 10

# THE CONSERVATION AND RESEARCH FOUNDATION

After my father's death in 1949, it became my task as executor to settle his estate and to help take care of mother's financial affairs. By this time I had become impressed by what could be accomplished with very modest sums imaginatively expended in neglected areas. After a bit of figuring, taking into consideration income tax deductions and savings in estate taxes and legal fees, it appeared that mother could make a charitable contribution of $100,000, spread over several years, at an annual cost to the family of not more than $1,000. The concept began to emerge of a foundation designed to support undernourished causes in the fields of conservation and biological research.

Various facets of this idea were discussed with my friend Jim Marvin, chairman of the Botany Department at the University of Vermont, with whom I went skiing each winter; Fred Kavanagh, the biochemist with whom I was collaborating in my research; Belton

Founding members of the Conservation and Research Foundation.

James W. Marvin.

Federick W. Kavanagh.

Grosvenor Bemis.

Copp, the attorney who had been helping me with legal matters relating to land preservation; my brother-in-law, Grosvenor Bemis, a trust officer in a bank in Springfield, Massachusetts; John Fuller, our minister at the Unitarian-Universalist Church in New London; and, of course, with mother. The upshot was a decision to establish a foundation, to be funded with income from a trust set up for this specific purpose. Financial matters would be handled by the trust, but all decisions with respect to the disposition of the income would be controlled by the trustees of the foundation, a majority of whom, as provided in the by-laws, were to be scientists. Thus the Conservation and Research Foundation and the Mary B. Goodwin Trust were established in 1952.

To give the trustees maximum flexibility with respect to the disposition of the funds, the purposes of the foundation were set forth in the most general terms: to "promote the conservation of our natural resources, encourage study and research in the biological sciences and deepen understanding of the intricate relationship between man and the environment that supports him."

Initially there were five trustees — Grove Bemis, Belton Copp, Fred Kavanagh, Jim Marvin, and me. At our early meetings we spent time discussing how we might best order our priorities. We decided that the foundation would not fund research that would be eligible for funding from conventional sources. Rather we would favor projects that had potential for improving environmental quality, were politically or sociologically unpopular, or were carried out by persons who lacked institutional support. We were also interested in seminal grants to help environmental organizations get on their feet and, when we saw the opportunity, to initiate our own enterprises.

## 1953–1962

During the first decade resources permitted an expenditure of only about $30,000 in grants. The operation was entirely a volunteer effort with administrative overhead being held to about four percent. Grants were principally directed toward the preservation of natural areas. This was during the formative years of the natural areas movement, and a grant of $5,000 to The Nature Conservancy, for example, was of critical importance in keeping its operation in the black. Grants also initiated a number of Conservancy projects, among them the Northern California Coast Range Preserve, the Frederic C. Walcott Preserve in Connecticut, and the Tannersville Cranberry Bog in eastern Pennsylvania. All three of these preserves became designated by the National Park Service as National Natural Landmarks. Other projects receiving assistance were the Bergen Swamp in upstate New York and Mamacoke Island, an addition to the Connecticut Arboretum.

The Tannersville Cranberry Bog was an exceptional bargain. It was identified as an important natural area by Bill Niering, who had been raised in the Poconos and whose uncle owned a piece of the wetland. The foundation provided the initial $200, which secured the option on the first purchase. Bill and I led a field trip to the Poconos for Connecticut College botany majors shortly after the disastrous flood of 1955 and observed a dramatic demonstration of the value of this wetland in flood control. About the only highway bridges in the entire county that were not washed out were the two just downstream from the bog.

In 1957 an opportunity presented itself to preserve a critical tract of land in New London. It was adjacent to the Bolleswood Natural Area of the Connecticut Arboretum and was needed to protect the natural area from encroachment. It had been acquired by the Federal Government for Navy housing during World War II, and the undeveloped portion was being disposed of by the General Services Administration. An initial attempt to get the government to convey it to Connecticut College as an educational grant failed, because no buildings were to be constructed thereon. At this point Edward Henkle, the city manager of New London, called me down to his office, where he informed me that the city was going to acquire the property to put it into private hands as a revenue-bearing asset. In order to save it from development I arranged a grant from the foundation to the State of

Connecticut which enabled the state to acquire the tract as a state wildlife refuge. When news of this transaction reached the ears of the city manager, he hit the ceiling, and the *New London Day* carried a headline on page one that read, "Dr. Goodwin State's Catspaw Says Henkle." Some time thereafter Henkle got a local representative to introduce a bill in the state legislature that would require the state to sell the land to the city. When the state's attorney general reviewed the bill, he ruled it improper in view of the city's stated intentions, because he discovered that the deed — thanks to Belton Copp's careful drafting — provided that "the land shall forever remain in the hands of the public."

One of the lively conservation issues of the 1950s — before the publication of Rachel Carson's *Silent Spring*—was the devastating impact of DDT upon the environment. The foundation made two small grants at that time, one in support of research documenting the effects of DDT on aquatic life in Massachusetts streams and one to publish the proceedings of a symposium on the issue sponsored by the Farmington River Watershed Association.

Another grant was made to help underwrite the expense of a survey of the Mau Mara Plateau in Kenya. This grant, solicited by the late Sir Frank Darling, was made provisional to its being matched from other sources. It was instrumental in getting additional funding from the Rockefeller and Conservation Foundations.

## 1963–1972

During the foundation's second decade the treasurer, Grosvenor Bemis, retired. He was replaced by Melville Chapin, our family attorney at Warner & Stackpole in Boston, and the board was expanded to eight. The additions were Wallace D. Bowman, Dr. Winslow R. Briggs, and my daughter, Minda. Wally brought an extraordinarily broad background to the board. This included graduate training in experimental biology, wildlife, forestry, ecology, and public administration, and research on the effects of noise for the Office of Naval Research and on plant disease control for the United Fruit Company in Honduras.

Melville Chapin

He also had administrative experience as executive officer of the Conservation Foundation, as a member of the staff that organized Alaska's Division of State Planning, as the person responsible for establishing and operating the Reports Division of the United Nations Development Programme, and as assistant chief of the Environmental Policy Division of the Legislative Reference Service in the Library of Congress. Winslow, one of the world's leading experts in the field of photobiology and plant development, served for twelve years on the faculty of Stanford University and six as professor of biology at Harvard before becoming director of the Division of Plant Biology of the Carnegie Institution of Washington on the Stanford University campus. My daughter received her doctorate in zoology at the University of Maryland and research experience in electron microscopy and biochemistry at the National Institutes of Health, where she held a position as research fellow.

The foundation's grant expenditures in this ten year period grew fourfold to $124,000. Only a fifth of the money went toward the preservation of natural areas. The most significant single item was the publication by the foundation of Russell L. Brenneman's very useful legal handbook, *Private Approaches to the Preservation of Open Land,* in 1967. The book was written under contract, and the foundation eventually recovered its entire investment through sales of the book. The research required to produce the publication made Russell the leading expert in this aspect of environmental law and led to his distinguished career in the field. The book soon became out of date and a revision was needed. However, by then the field of land preservation had burgeoned to such an extent that the task had become too much for one person, and the project had become too expensive for the foundation; so the foundation funded the preparation of a grant proposal that led the Richard King Mellon Foundation to finance the book's production at a cost exceeding $50,000. The new book, *Land Saving Action,* was published commercially by the Island Press in 1984.

One of the foundation's most productive investments was funding a conference, held in Airlie House in Virginia in 1969, on Law and the Environment. Cosponsored and staffed by the Conservation Foundation, this meeting brought together, for the first time, leaders of the environmental movement and members of the legal profession to discuss problems of mutual concern. Environmental law was at an embryonic stage when the conference was convened. Law schools across the country were just beginning to develop environmental curricula, and few conservation groups had investigated the utility of court intervention. Partly as an outgrowth of the conference, extensive environmental materials became incorporated into law school curricula, environmental law associations became established on college campuses, a rash of environmental law publications sprang up, and environmental organizations became involved in litigation. The proceedings of the conference were edited by Malcolm Baldwin and James K. Page, Jr., and published under the title *Law and the Environment.*

A number of environmental organizations were given pump-priming support during this period. Two of these, the Rachel Carson Trust for the Living Environment (later to become the Rachel Carson

Council) and the Institute of Ecology (TIE), received seed money for their operating budgets at the time of their formation. Another grant to the Thames Science Center in New London, Connecticut, was the initial $5,000 toward a $150,000 fund being raised to construct an interpretive headquarters building on the Connecticut College campus.

Lynton K. Caldwell, professor of political science at Indiana University, was a most effective proponent of international cooperation in environmental matters. The foundation supported his research in the preparation of *In Defense of Earth: International Protection of the Biosphere.* This important sourcebook on political solutions to global ecological problems was distributed to official delegates to the United Nations Conference on the Human Environment held in Stockholm in 1972. Ten years later Professor Caldwell brought the subject up to date under the title, *International Environmental Policy: Emergence and Dimensions.* The foundation again supported his efforts and the circulation of this new book, for which he received the Harold and Margaret Sprout Award from the International Studies Association for the best book on an ecological approach to international relations.

When William J. Robbins retired as director of the New York Botanical Garden, he was still productively engaged in research on the growth of plant tissues in culture. He was ineligible to receive grants from conventional sources, but support from the foundation, made possible through the generosity of Fred Kavanagh, enabled him for several years to continue his investigations in collaboration with Dr. Annette Hervey. The foundation later made a $15,000 grant to the New York Botanical Garden to help finance Dr. Hervey's plant tissue culture program at the Harding Laboratories. This was unhappily cut short by her untimely death.

Another noteworthy project funded by the foundation was conceived by Dr. Hubert W. Vogelmann, Professor of Botany at the University of Vermont. He had been measuring the extent to which vegetation in the Green Mountains had the capacity to capture moisture from air masses passing over the range. On a trip to Mexico he observed that some of the forested mountain ranges were adequately supplied with moisture in contrast to comparable deforested slopes that were barren deserts. A grant from the foundation in 1968 enabled Dr. Vogelmann to establish weather stations in these Mexican mountains. The data gathered demonstrated clearly that sufficient amounts of water were condensed from fogs passing across the vegetated slopes during the dry season to support the flora, whereas no such capture occurred on denuded terrain. The widespread deforestation of such areas in Mexico and other Latin American countries is creating long-term changes that are an ecological disaster. It is hoped that Vogelmann's reports may have some influence on land-use policies in regions where these climatic conditions prevail.

A gift from Fred Kavanagh endowed an award to honor the memory of Jeanette Siron Pelton, an inspiring teacher whose special field of interest had been plant morphogenesis. The Pelton Award, which carries a stipend of $1,000, is made from time to time to recognize sustained and imaginative contributions in the field of experimental plant morphology. Candidates are selected by a special committee appointed by the Botanical Society of America. The first recipient in 1969 was my mentor at Harvard, Ralph H. Wetmore; the second, in 1970, his friend, Claude W. Wardlaw of the University of Manchester, England. Both were near the end of very distinguished careers. In 1971 the Foundation, wishing to encourage younger investigators, requested the Pelton Award committee to nominate candidates in the earlier stages of their careers. Subsequently, the following outstanding researchers have received the Pelton Award:

1972  Paul B. Green, Stanford University
1975  Peter K. Hepler, Stanford University
1978  Brian E. S. Gunning, Australia National University
1980  Lewis J. Feldman, University of California, Berkeley
1983  Todd J. Cooke, University of Maryland
1985  Tsvi Sachs, Hebrew University, Jerusalem
1988  Scott D. Russell, University of Oklahoma
1989  Elizabeth M. Lord, University of California, Riverside

1993   Richard Scott Poethig, University of Pennsylvania
1994   Elliot M. Meyerowitz, California Institute of
       Technology
1996   Sarah Hake, Plant Gene Expression Center, U.S.D.A.,
       Albany
1998   Donald R. Kaplan, University of California, Berkeley
2000   Ben J. G. Scheres, University of Utrecht
2002   Karl J. Niklas, Cornell University

## *1973–1982*

During the third decade we lost Jim Marvin, the second of our original incorporators, who died in 1977. He was replaced by his colleague Dr. Vogelmann. Mel Chapin retired, and two additional members were elected, Sarah M. Bates — who became Sarah Bates Henry when she

Trustees at the 1980 annual meeting at Cloudy Ridge Ranch, Alberta.
(*Left to right*): Wallace Bowman, Hubert Vogelmann, Winslow Briggs, Mary Wetzel, the author, and Belton Copp.

Alexander Wilson, Wallace Bowman, and Sarah Bates Henry at the 1987 annual meeting of the Foundation, Dolbia Hill, East Haddam, Connecticut.

married Dickinson Henry during her term on the board — and Alexander T. Wilson, thus increasing the board to nine. Sarah held a Master's degree from the Yale School of Forestry and Environmental Studies and a law degree from the University of Connecticut. She had also served as council to the Conservation Law Foundation of New England. Alex Wilson was active in the promotion of energy conservation and the use of renewable energy sources. He had served as the executive director of the New England Solar Energy Association and was an independent consultant.

In this third decade the foundation awarded grants totaling $238,000, approximately double what it did in the previous ten years, an increase made possible through the generosity of 233 friends.

A national shortage of funds for research, coupled with growth in the reputation of the foundation, resulted in the receipt of over 1,200 unsolicited grant applications, of which less than five percent could be funded. In a brief review it is possible to highlight only a few special projects and trends.

The Insitute of Ecology (TIE) had been established in 1971 to answer the need for a scientific organization that could undertake basic ecological research and environmental programs of regional, hemispheric, and global scope too large and complex to be handled by a single educational institution or mission-oriented agency. The founders had visions of generous unrestricted financial support to underwrite this ambitious undertaking. The services of a public relations firm were engaged to direct the fundraising drive for core funding, which at once saddled the institute with a substantial obligation. Only two small grants for uncommitted funds came in from other institutions, one of which was from our foundation.

Research grants from foundations and governmental agencies enabled the new institute to undertake a number of significant projects, but the TIE trustees found themselves limited by constraints imposed by the interests of the granting sources. Funds were not available for the types of programs originally envisioned, and TIE became a job shop for governmental agencies.

I became a member of the board of TIE in 1973. It was not until 1975 that the trustees began to realize the magnitude of the financial crisis facing the institute, which had been too effectively obscured by a key member of the staff. At this juncture I was appointed treasurer. Drastic remedial action included a tightening of financial controls, reductions of staff, and the initiation of a $100,000 fund drive. It was quite an experience for a Scotch Yankee to go to bed with a huge pile of the institute's bills under his pillow and to write letters to creditors asking them to consider forgiving the institute's indebtedness. In order to help TIE weather the crisis, the foundation made two $10,000 loans, each of which could be converted into a grant if matched by other gifts on a four-to-one basis. By the end of 1977 these loans had been matched and the most critical of TIE's debts paid off.

The institute then underwent a basic corporate reorganization and found a new home on the Butler University campus in Indianapolis, Indiana. Had it not been for the generous and timely action of the Holcomb Research Institute, mediated by its president, Thomas

Malone, TIE would not have survived. After several more years of operating in the black, it became apparent that TIE would not grow to fulfill its original mission, and a decision was made to terminate the operation. In retrospect, the institution did complete quite a number of significant projects and reports. The foundation's support during the financial crisis averted a bankruptcy that would have given a black eye to the environmental movement.

It was increasingly apparent that the destruction of tropical rainforests and other natural areas in Latin America was becoming a conservation issue of global proportions. In the 1960s Dr. Maria Buchinger de Alitiz, a very dynamic woman who had been trained as a forester in Germany and was interested in the preservation of natutral areas in Central and South America, obtained permission to operate out of the national office of TNC. She was given a little corner, which was referred to as the Latin American Desk. This somewhat free-wheeling arrangement was terminated during Hank Foster's presiden-cy, and Maria moved to Buenos Aires, Argentina. A number of the early members of TNC's board and staff, among them Elting Arnold, Chuck Mason, Ray Fosberg, Conrad Chapman, Eleanor Smith, Dick Miller, Charlie Grace, Walter Boardman, and me, feeling that Maria's activities were effective and deserved financial support, formed what became known as the Latin American Natural Areas Program (LANAP). Contributions from members of this advisory committee, some of them through the foundation, enabled Maria to continue her activities under the auspices of the Foresta Institute for Ocean and Mountain Studies. LANAP served for twenty years as a resource center and clearinghouse for information relating to the establishment and stewardship of natural areas throughout Latin America. Maria arranged and attended international meetings, prepared and distributed publications, and provided advice to individuals and organizations involved in the land preservation movement. Hers was a dedicated commitment. The foundation supported LANAP with small grants over a period of eighteen years. The program was terminated in 1988 after the untimely death of Elting Arnold, who had been serving as its coordinator.

In 1981 TNC renewed its concern for the preservation of biodiversity in Latin America through the establishement of its International Program. At first the most encouraging progress was made in Costa Rica, where, under the leadership of Alvaro F. Ugalde and Mario A. Bosa, about ten percent of the entire country's land had been set aside as national parks. Alvaro, with encouragement and guidance from TNC staff, established the Fundacion de Parques Nacionales to help enlist private support for the National Park System. In 1982 the Conservation and Research Foundation made a grant of $5,000 to help the Fundacion's fund-raising efforts.

Two other enterprises were also in progress in Costa Rica. One was the Monteverde Cloud Forest Reserve, established by a community of Quakers who came from Alabama to settle just west of the continental divide. They needed funds to construct a modest research facility at the entrance to the preserve. The foundation made a small grant that permitted the completion of the project. It later provided funding for the acquisition of an additional tract near the crest of the range

Another exciting bit of rainforest, Finca la Selva at the foot of the mountains on the Caribbean side, was being preserved by the Organization for Tropical Studies (OTS). This station had been selected by a committee of the National Academy of Science as one of the four primary sites in the world for detailed studies of tropical ecosystems. An opportunity arose to acquire an adjacent 1,000-acre property, much of it in pristine condition. The foundation made a $5,000 grant to help OTS raise the $330,000 required to purchase it and the transaction was successfully completed. But a critical strip of untouched forest connecting La Selva with a large national park along the crest of the mountain range remained in private hands. This forest was critical for the survival of the birds that migrate vertically through this transect. The president of Costa Rica gave the land temporary protection by declaring it a *zona protectora*, but in order to preserve it on a permanent basis the land had to be purchased from the owners. This meant raising two million dollars. The foundation made initial grants toward this project of $12,000, which enabled TNC to persuade the MacArthur Foundation to offer a million dollar matching grant for the acquisition of the *zona protectora*. The matching million was raised. The land was purchased and added to Braulio Carillo National Park in 1986, and just in time. When I visited La Selva for a second time with my family for a Christmas holiday in 1991, the adjacent forested mountainsides had been denuded since my previous visit in 1983.

In May 1975 the foundation held a two day colloquium at Dolbia Hill to discuss innovative approaches to coping with intrusions of large-scale development on land use. Charles E. Little, an authority on land policy, presented a paper entitled "Land and Community," based on a nationwide field trip that he had made under the auspices of the foundation. The colloquium participants included Richard Bolan, professor at Boston College and editor of a journal for the American Institute of Planners; Leon Eplan, commissioner of the Department of Budget and Planning of the City of Atlanta; Andrew Scheffey, professor of landscape at the University of Massachusetts; Thomas Jorling, director of the Environment Institute at Williams College; Huey D. Johnson, president of the Trust for Public Land; and Donella Meadows, coauthor of *Limits for Growth*.

The Dolbia Hill colloquium served to sharpen the focus on community land issues for all the participants. But the most important outgrowth was the establishment of the American Land Forum (ALF). The foundation made a grant in 1978 to defray the costs of organizing the forum. Although it amounted to only $2,000, it was truly a seminal investment, enabling Mr. Little, who became ALF's first president, to meet initial organizational expenses and fundraising. ALF held its first forum in Washington, D.C., in December 1978 on Issues of Farmland Retention. Subsequent forums were held dealing with a spectrum of issues relating to the protection of farmland. The results were published in the *American Land Forum Magazine*, which became the *American Land Forum*. ALF, later called the American Resource Association, gained the support of several major foundations and federal agencies and developed a substantial membership constituency. For a brief period it served a unique function in providing leadership on crucial land-use issues.

In May 1981, the foundation hosted another colloquium at Belmont Manor House in Elkridge, Maryland to review the influence of ecological thought on attitudes and behavior toward the environment over the previous thirty years and to discuss the implications of this perspective for the management of natural resources. The twenty-four participants were chosen as being persons vitally concerned with ecology, conservation, and environmental protection and as having an understanding of the history of man's effects upon the planet. A concencus emerged on three objectives for environmental management: 1) maintenance of essential ecological processes and support systems; 2) preservation of biological diversity; and 3) sustainable utilization of species and ecosystems.

The foundation supported a number of projects relating to the environmental hazards to humanity posed by nuclear technology. The first was a film on the dedicated efforts of Dr. Helen Caldicott to stem the drift toward nuclear war. The foundation contributed toward the production of this outstanding film, *Eight Minutes to Midnight*, which was nominated for an Academy Award. The foundation later made an additional grant to promote the film's distribution. A grant to the Council for Economic Priorities to study the hazards of tranporting high-level radioactive wastes, permitted it to produce a report that was instrumental in stopping shipments of this lethal material through New York City. Another grant to the Powder River Basin Research Council underwrote a study of the potential impact on water quality of a technique for extracting uranium that involved injection of chemicals into a Wyoming aquifer.

Among the additional grants made by the foundation in this decade, a number centered around energy issues. These included costs of the use of coal, increasing the efficiency of energy use, and the potentials for tapping renewable sources — wind and solar energy. A $3,000 grant to Connecticut College in 1974 really paid off. It funded an engineering study that showed how changes in the college's physical plant could effect substantial savings. An initial investment of $40,000 in a single college building, ironically the one most recently constructed, enabled the college, after amortizing the investment, to make an annual saving of $10,000, to say nothing of the environmental benefit of saving fossil fuel and reducing air pollution.

## THE CHOICE

When men have walked the moon a second time
    and come back grateful
For another chance on earth to breathe the air,
    to swim, to love, to pick a flower,
Is it our fateful
Wish to lose those things that Midas lost?

In days gone by we built the steeple spire
To symbolize our upward striving. It was higher
Than other structures in our town. But now
    it is surpassed by far by monstrous poles
That carry power.
Is this the last quintessence of our goals?

Soon, soon must people with a common voice
Shout out the values of their choice,
And choosing, cultivate the way and bear the cost.

## 1983–1992

The fourth decade saw the retirement of two trustees, Fred Kavanagh, one of the foundation's incorporators, who was elected an honorary trustee in 1986, and Sarah Bates Henry, who, after ten years of service, decided to devote herself to a medical career. During this period the Foundation made grants to ninety-five different grantees totalling about

The trustees of the Conservation and Research Foundation at the 1988 annual meeting, Cloudy Ridge Ranch, Alberta, Canada. (*Left to right*): The author, Mrs. Copp, Belton Copp, Mrs. Vogelmann, Winslow Briggs, Mary Wetzel, Hubert Vogelmann, Richard Goodwin, Jr., Esther Goodwin, and Alexander Wilson.

$404,000. This was an increase of seventy percent over the previous decade, again made possible through the generosity of many supporters.

Here is a brief review of some of the accomplishments. Twenty-seven of the grants were in support of environmental research. One of the most productive was to Sandra Lanham, an entrepreneurial aviatrix. Portions of Mexico, including the islands and shores of the Sea of Cortez, are accessible only by small "work horse" planes, and research in the region had been hampered by the unavailability of an affordable charter service. To fill this void Sandra established her Environmental Flying Service, based in Tucson, Arizona. She flies her own plane. The enterprise may well be one of the most dangerous in the field of conservation. Here are some examples of her recent missions: 1) to assess the status of the endangered green sea and leatherback turtles on

Mexican beaches; 2) to collect live shrimp from the Sea of Cortez for a study of a viral infection that was threatening the shrimp industry; 3) to help the Mexican government control poaching of ironwood, a tree with dense wood that is being illegally harvested for the production of charcoal with devastating ecological consequences; 4) to make an inventory of whales in the Sea of Cortez, which showed for the first time the year-round occupation of the area by a number of species, including the endangered blue whale with calves, the sperm whale, and the rare pygmy and Cuvier beaked whales; and 5) to survey the population of the peninsula pronghorn antelope of the Baja, Mexico's most endangered land mammal. Perhaps her most hazardous assignment was conducting a shorebird and wetland inventory along the entire coast of the Gulf of Mexico from the Texas Border to Belize. It required very low-level flights under turbulent conditions. The Foundation offered Ms. Lanham a challenge grant of $5,000 to help her get her flying service established. This was successfully matched two-to-one. Later it financed a major overhaul of her plane and helped defray the cost of insurance. In 2001 Ms. Lanham was awarded a $500,000 MacArthur Foundation fellowship. Informing us of her award she writes: "Because of your matching grant in 1992, my work got off the ground, quite literally. It was the first money my fledgling project ever received. I had sent fifty letters similar to the one I sent you. All were rejected."

In the tropics the upper forest canopy has been inadequately studied due to difficulties in gaining access to the treetops. There one can examine the interaction between the forest and the atmosphere, crucial to understanding the global climate, can study the complex interactions of the biota, and can analyze canopy diversity, which is basic to reaching wise conservation decisions. In 1987 the Foundation made a grant to Melvin T. Tyree to help fund a feasibility study for developing a structure that would provide random access to the canopy of tropical forests. The grant was matched four-to-one by the Lintilhac Foundation. The study was carried out in cooperation with the Smithsonian

Tropical Research Institute, which rated the forest canopy research program a top priority. The mechanical solution turned out to be in the form of a canopy crane. As a first step, one was rented for use in a tropical forest on the outskirts of Panama City.

It is amazing how much can be accomplished with a very small amount of money. For instance, in 1986 an award of $510 to Professor Allan J. Hruska provided supplies and equipment for a project to develop alternative methods in the control the fall army worm, the most important pest of maize in Central America. The prevailing approach was heavy applications of pesticides. A promising alternative appeared to be the use of a pathogenic fungus, *Metarrhizium anisoplias.* This had been shown to be effective in the control of several other pest species and would be safe for humans, the environment, and other beneficial insects. In a report received eight years later, Professor Hruska stated that the grant "was seed money that reaped large returns." It underwrote some of the operating expenses of a group of researchers, both faculty and students, at the Instituto Superior de Ciencias Agropeucarius for the initial year of the investigation. After that the Norwegian government funded a full two and a half year proposal for integrated pest management (IPM). Over twenty students completed theses, and four faculty members completed research within the project. The work has been documented by six research papers, ten reports, and three popular articles. Based on the promising results obtained, CARE Nicaragua initiated a project under the direction of Dr. Hruska to implement an IMP project in the northwestern part of Nicaragua. This was very successful. Pesticide use was reduced by 80 percent among farmers who received IPM training. This resulted in significantly increased net returns to the farmers and dramatically reduced pesticide poisonings and exposures. Many of the students went on to pursue careers in plant protection in Nicaragua and Costa Rica. One of the staff members became dean of the Department of Agronomy at the Universidad Nacional Agraria of Nicaragua at Managua, another became the vice rector, and a third, now married to

Dr. Hruska, is advisor to the IPM Program at the National University in Leon, Nicaragua.

The Mekong Delta in southern Vietnam is one of the largest in the world, covering vast areas of that country and adjacent Kampuchu. It provides critical habitat for many wetland species. Several national reserve areas have been established to protect the largest and most diverse of the wading bird colonies, one of the best being Dom Doi. In 1990 the foundation made a grant of $350 to underwrite the expenses of a study of this colony. This covered the cost of travel, food, lodging, and supplies for a student from Hanoi University for six months! The objectives of the project included obtaining data on the stability of the colony, strengthening the conservation program in the area, emphasizing the importance of the colony to the local officials, and encouraging the reserve wardens and increasing their effectiveness. As a by-product it served to train a Vietnamese student in science and conservation.

In Chapter 6, mention was made of the book entitled *The Cold and the Dark: The World After Nuclear War*. In order to enhance the political impact of its vital message, the foundation funded the free distribution of this book to people of influence both in the United States and abroad. One example of the catalytic effect of this investment came from Ambassador V. J. Gauci, Malta's permanent representative at the United Nations. In a letter thanking us for the book, he wrote, "You may be gratified to note that I put it to immediate use, and I have the pleasure in enclosing a copy of the statement I delivered yesterday in the First Committee of the United Nations dealing with disarmament. I believe the statement attracted considerable attention." Included in the Ambassador's speech were some very pertinent quotes from Dr. Thomas' foreword.

The far-reaching effects of radioactive pollution derived from accidental releases have been documented. The life histories of birds, monitored over time, can provide a measure of the capacity of organisms to respond to environmental stress. Quantitative population data on breeding birds through a systematic mist-netting program have been accumulated at the Palomarin Field Station of the Point Reyes Bird Observatory located on the California coast. In 1986 David F. DeSante discovered a drastic and unprecedented decrease (over 62 percent) in the reproductive success of land birds in the period between May 10 and August 17. The species affected were foliage gleaners that were breeding during this period and were directly dependent upon the primary production-based food chain. The bark feeders were not affected. This failure coincided with the passage across the United States of the radioactive cloud released by the meltdown of the Chernobyl nuclear reactor in the U.S.S.R. Subsequent analysis of breeding bird census data taken throughout the country showed that this drop was country-wide, but became less pronounced as one passed from west to east. It was very closely correlated with the amount of the radioactive iodine isotope reported in milk in various regions across the country. Fortunately radioactive iodine has a very short half-life. The foundation made a grant to DeSante to encourage the dissemination of this information.

Seven grants were made to help acquire special habitats, three in Costa Rica, and four in the United States. One of these was a 247-acre tract of undisturbed tropical forest lying at mid-elevations near the Panamanian border on Costa Rica's Pacific slope. It was adjacent to a 300-acre piece of forest owned by the Organization for Tropical Studies as part of the Las Cruces Biological Field Station. Together these two tracts represented the last remnant of the original forest in the valley. The Foundation made a $5,000 grant to help OTS fund raise for this addition. An immediate result was the receipt of new pledges totaling $30,000, a success crucial in persuading the board of OTS to approve the purchase, which was consummated in 1993. Eight years later OTS acquired an adjacent 75-acres of degraded pasture, and the foundation contributed $2,500 toward its reforestation.

\* \* \*

Other initiatives designed to help protect biodiversity supported by the foundation have been well scattered over the globe. They start with documentation of the importance of the Arctic National Wildlife Refuge, threatened by oil extraction, and the Guanica Commonwealth Dry Forest at Bahia de la Ballena on the south shore of Puerto Rico, under pressure from development. They also include better planning for El Triumpho Biosphere Reserve in Mexico and the Sierra de las Minas Reserve in Guatemala, and membership promotion for S.O.S. Mata Atlantica, an organization attempting to preserve the remaining fragments of the Atlantic forest of Brazil, not to be confused with the vast forest of the Amazon basin. Other projects were publishing maps for the National Park System of Venezuela, helping the inhabitants of Madagascar save the rare gallery and spiny forest of the Beza Mahafaly Special Reserve, eliminating introduced rabbits that were devastating the endemic flora and fauna of Round Island off the northern coast of Mauritius in the Indian Ocean, conducting a survey of the Uvs Nuur Basin of western Mongolia, and, on Borneo, helping the Indonesians of Sarawak save the magnificent tropical forests adjacent to the Gunung Palung National Park.

Deforestation is taking place in many parts of the world to satisfy the local need for cooking fuel. One of these areas is on the erosion-sensitive southern slopes of the Himalayas. I had an opportunity to observe this taking place in 1986, when trekking in Nepal with Tim Rhodes. There we saw piles of freshly cut rhododendron trees stacked for firewood. Mary Lou Krause of Seattle, Washington, developed a very simple, but effective, solar cooker, that can be made out of corrugated cardboard and a sheet of glass. In 1990 the Foundation covered the cost of a three month trip she took to promote solar cooker technology on the mountainous slopes of Pakistan and Nepal — an investment of $3,000! In the Hunza and Baltistan regions of Pakistan, with the help of the Aga Kahn, she was able to set up workshops and demonstrations in the girls' schools and villages, which were enthusiastically received. In back country it is difficult to find corrugated cardboard, so in the mountains of Nepal she ingeniously designed a cooker using the native packbasket as the outer layer of the cooker. It takes a lot to change a way of life, but she made a good start.

Malawi, a long thin country lying between Mozambique and Tanzania, has experienced dramatic loss of forests in recent years — a loss accelerated by an annual population growth of 3.7 percent and a large influx of refugees from Mozambique. It is reported that it takes 914,000 acres of forest each year to supply Malawi households with cooking fuel. These losses are reflected in the cost of wood, which increased 600 percent in the first half of 1992. Mary Lou, who had served as a member of the Peace Corps in Malawi thirty years earlier, returned there in 1993 on another solar cooker mission, again supported by the foundation. Although her workshop participants were enthusiastic, she commented that an obstacle to the new technology was the relatively modest cost of the materials required for cooker construction.

The grizzly bear is a formidable animal, but an important element of our wilderness heritage. Its present endangered status has been due in part to aggressive confrontations with people invading its habitat. The foundation supported a project by Martin Smith to develop an effective non-toxic repellant spray which could serve as a protection to people carrying it and which could condition the bears to avoid human contact. The product developed is now widely used by national park rangers and others traveling in bear country. It has saved the lives of people and bears, and its latest use is by people living in much more dangerous habitat, the inner city, for protection against assault. Another foundation-funded project, undertaken by Jay Kirkpatrick, was to obtain data on the sex and age of brears through a chemical analysis of their scats, thereby avoiding the sometimes lethal trauma of capture.

One of the distressing trends taking place in the United States is the rapid depletion of the nation's agricultural resource base. The

American Farmland Trust (AFT) was organized in 1980 to deal with problems posed by this attrition. One of AFT's early projects was an effort to preserve the beautiful farmlands in Pleasant Valley, Vermont, located just west of Mount Mansfield. The Rockefeller Brothers Fund, a major supporter of AFT, had this to say in its 1983 annual report about the project.

> The confidence that the AFT's "middleground" philosophy has earned it resulted in an extraordinary contribution to the organization, a 390-acre Vermont dairy farm located in the very heart of a fertile picture postcard valley that has supported agriculture since the birth of the Republic, but a region now under development pressure generated by a nearby city and by several ski resort communities. Inspired by the generosity of the donors, . . . the AFT accepted the challenge of preserving the entire Pleasant Valley for agriculture, a project that will require all the ingenuity and resources the organization can muster. With support from a New England Foundation, the AFT recently completed the first step, a comprehensive inventory of the agricultural resources of the valley, including surveys and ownership patterns. Its staff has now begun to work with individual land owners to devise private conservation strategies to assure that each working farm can remain economically viable and that the land on which agriculture depends will be protected in perpetuity. Proceeds from the eventual sale of Sugar Bush Farm, to a family that continues to operate it will be plowed back into the valley to help finance private farmland conservation transactions. Meanwhile, with AFT encouragement and technical assistance, Vermont officials are examining a range of potential governmental programs that could be applied to save Pleasant Valley farms, and would become a model for a statewide agricultural land conservation program. The AFT annual report perhaps sums up best the organization's optimistic expectations: "From a single seed, a bumper crop is in prospect."

The Foundation referred to in the quotation is the Conservation and Research Foundation, which supported this project with two grants totaling $7,500.

## 1993–2002

In the fifth decade Wally Bowman retired from the board, having served as trustee for twenty-eight years. Four new people joined, David R. Foster, Crea S. Lintilhac, Jeffrey F. Griffin, and Louise M. Tritton. David was one of my last students at Connecticut College, who went on for a doctorate at the University of Minnesota and has become Director of the Harvard Forest in Petersham, Massachusetts, and professor in the

David R. Foster

Department of Organismic and Evolutionary Biology at Harvard University. Crea holds a masters degree in geology from the University of Vermont and has been involved in educational and conservation activities in Vermont. Jeff holds a masters degree in environmental studies from the Yale School of Forestry and Environmental Studies and had been involved with conservation issues for ten years before joining the board. Since 1992 he had been working with the Global Environmental Facility of the United Nations Development Programme, developing biodiversity conservation projects throughout the World. Louise holds a doctorate in Forest Ecology from Yale University and has conducted research in the Hubbard Brook Ecosystem Study in New Hampshire and at the Northeastern Forest Experiment Station of the U.S. Forest Service both in Connecticut and Vermont.

During this decade the foundation has already expended nearly $440,000 in support of the activities of 105 grantees. Approximately one quarter of this amount went toward promoting activities directed at retarding growth of the human population; one quarter went toward the establishment and management of natural areas; one quarter was in support of biological research, most of it with environmental implications; and the balance supported environmental education and efforts to control pollution.

One of the great tragedies of the twentieth century has been the failure of the human race to confront the problem of overpopulation. The number of human beings has been doubling in progressively shorter periods of time and has already surpassed six billion. This failure has not been due to a dearth of prophets, nor to a lack of signs. The latter have erupted at Daschau, in Bosnia, Somalia, Cambodia, and Ruanda. They manifest themselves in choking smogs in Indonesia and Mexico, in vanishing rainforests, in desertification and in the accelerated extinction of species. In the United States politicians and religious communities are blind to the problem, and even some of our environmental organizations duck the issue.

At the foundation's very first meeting in 1953 the trustees

identified overpopulation as one of the major threats to the integrity of the earth's biosphere, but at that time they saw no way in which small sums of money could be effectively spent in attacking the problem. Two years later my old cytology professor at Harvard, Karl Sax, published a book entitled *Standing Room Only: The World's Exploding Population.* It projected a frightening future and gave me propaganda to present to my students in introductory biology. However, it was not until 1992 that organizations came to the foundation's attention that had approaches that seemed worthy of support. One was Population Communications International (PCI), which was developing television programs designed to influence people to desire smaller families.

The power of TV as a tool to alter human behavior was demonstrated in Mexico in the 1970s by Miguel Sabido, who developed a series of *telenovellas* — soap operas — to attack the problem of illiteracy. As a result of his programs 840,000 people signed up for literacy courses. This astonishing success and encouragement from PCI led him to tackle contraception. At the end of this second series there was a thirty-three percent increase in family planning appointments at clinics in Mexico. PCI has been exploiting this technique in countries around the world, especially those with the largest and fastest growing populations. These include India, Pakistan, China, the Philippines, Kenya, Tanzania, Nigeria, and Brazil.

An effort has been made to measure the success of these programs. The most exacting research along these lines was carried out in Tanzania, where, in 1993, a radio serial was broadcast in all regions of the country but one (the control area). Nation-wide random sample surveys measured changes in attitudes and behavior both in areas receiving the broadcast and in the area not covered. This research demonstrated very significant changes in family planning use, spousal communication about family planning, ideal age for marriage, and other key variables in the region receiving the broadcast, while those changes were not found, or found to a much lesser degree in the control area. As soon as the control area also received the message similar changes were recorded there.

In the United States PCI has been attempting to overcome the reticence of the broadcast media to recognize population growth as a factor in shaping the news. It established its Population Broadcast Service, which distributes broadcast-ready population news stories to about 9,000 radio and television newsrooms across the country. Interviews with a sampling of the recipients indicated about half used at least one story from each issue to develop a news release on the air.

The RARE Center for Tropical Conservation, which had developed an outstanding program of conservation education on a number of islands in the West Indies under the imaginative leadership of Paul Butler, came to realize the critical importance of controlling population growth in order to preserve the environment of these islands. In 1994 the center initiated a pilot family planning project on the British island of St. Lucia, modeled after the media approach developed by PCI. This has more recently been expanded by PCI to the islands of Antigua, Dominica, Granada, and St. Vincent.

The programs of four additional organizations dealing with population have also received support. One of these is the Population Media Center headed up by William N. Ryerson, who previously had served as executive vice president of PCI. Since its establishment in 1998, the center has been using the PCI broadcasting approach and has initiated its own activities in Mexico, China, India, the Philippines, Nigeria, Kenya, and Ethiopia. To help the center get underway the foundation made a grant to it of $5,000 in its first year of operation and has continued its support.

Another organization, the Amazonian Peoples Resources Initiative (APRI), is attempting to improve the quality of life for indigenous communities in the Peruvian Amazon. It is taking holistic approaches to improving sustainable community-based enterprises, the reproductive health of the women, and family planning. Since the initiation of the program in 1997 there has been a noticeable mobilization of the people around population issues and an increase in the number of younger couples seeking family planning services. These include voluntary submission to tubal ligation procedures and the acceptance of contraceptive devices from APRI-trained health workers. Radio broadcasts are greatly enhancing APRI's ability to bring its family planning message to a wide regional audience, as attested by the many letters being received from young girls in the audience indicating their desire to avoid a lifetime of repeated pregnancies. Since a large portion of the population is too poor to purchase a radio and batteries, many listeners care enough about the program to congregate and listen to a single functioning radio. APRI is now attempting to assure that every one of its *promotoras* has one. This initiative has received support.

One of the most serious human impacts on the environment is the pollution of the atmosphere. No longer can one see any but the brightest stars on cloudless nights in many parts of the world; but far more worrisome are the invisible pollutants that are changing the global climate. Carbon dioxide derived from the combustion of fossil fuels is largely responsible for global warming. Temperatures are rising throughout the world, glaciers are retreating, and melting of the antarctic ice cap is causing a rise in the level of the sea. In addition, long-lived chlorinated compounds, which are being released to the atmosphere, are destroying the protective ozone screen when they reach the stratosphere. The resulting increase in ultra-violet light reaching the earth's surface is placing the health of the more sensitive organisms, especially the amphibians, in jeopardy. Although international action has already been taken to reduce releases of chlorinated compounds, it may take a long time to repair the damage already done. On the other hand, the enormous vested interests in our energy-consuming economy and our extravagant way of life make the carbon dioxide production problem extremely intractable. One of the disturbing consequences of the carbon dioxide build-up is the cooling of the stratosphere, which, strangely, accelerates the destruction of the ozone shield by the chlorinated compounds.

The foundation has supported the Atmospheric Alliance, a grassroots project of the Earth Island Institute working in the Pacific Northwest, which is dedicated to promoting citizen activism on behalf of the atmosphere. It has been systematically tracking and debunking the misinformation being spread by fossil fuel corporations to confuse the public about global warming and the depletion of the ozone screen, and has been publicizing the impacts of the deterioration of the atmosphere through workshops and publications.

The atmosphere is also suffering from another human impact — the discharge of combustion products resulting in what is referred to as "acid rain." The Appalachian uplands of the United States are clothed by the richest temperate forest in the world. It was studied during the first half of this century by the botanist and forest ecologist, E. Lucy Braun, who called it the mixed mesophytic forest. Charles E. Little, in his book *The Dying of the Trees*, relates what has been happening to "Lucy's Woods" — a prime example of this rich forest of the central Appalachians. He quotes a local resident as follows, "The whole forest, at least in Rock Creek hollow, situated in the mountains of West Virginia west of Beckley, is simply rotting on the stump and falling. This is a hard story to tell, especially to the establishment press, because the public perception is so far behind the reality. We're losing 100 million years of evolution in less than 100. This is a tragedy." The U.S. Forest Service and state agency foresters, under the leadership of a public-relations executive of the Westvaco Corporation, were whitewashing the situation, maintaining that the mixed mesophytic forest was in "robust" health. Little comments that when the government fails to meet the needs of the people, the people must take matters into their own hands.

The Lucy Braun Association for the Mixed Mesophytic Forest was formed in 1992 to sponsor field research, hold conferences, publish information, and do whatever else was necessary to call attention to the plight of the ecosystem. The foundation helped the association with a start-up grant and with further support. The association in cooperation with other conservation organizations, initiated the Appalachian Forest Action Project. Its first report, published in 1997, revealed that trees were dying at two to four times expected rates in forests that extended from Alabama to Pennsylvania on the west-facing slopes of the Appalachians. Mortality rates were up to five times historic norms in areas exposed to higher levels of acid rain and ozone pollution, particularly in West Virginia. Furthermore, tree species were being differentially affected, some being eliminated more rapidly than others. Hickories were especially susceptible. The report concluded that the mortality rates, if continued over decades, would have catastrophic consequences for the value of timber lands and for biodiversity. Orie Loucks, the principal scientific advisor to the Project, stated that, "The only plausible causal agents extending over such large areas are pollutants from the burning of fossil fuels, particularly ground-level ozone and acid-forming oxides of sulfur and nitrogen. Nitrogen emissions from cars and power plants must be reduced, as well as sulfur emissions."

Another research study of a very different nature suggests further impacts of acid rain. Dr. Frances C. James published a fascinating analysis of data derived from Breeding Bird Surveys administered by the U.S. Fish & Wildlife Service and the Canadian Wildlife Service, which was funded by the foundation. She and her colleagues wrote:

> Our work on the large data set for the Breeding Bird Survey has always indicated that many species of birds that have healthy populations generally are experiencing declines in the eastern uplands: the Adirondacks, the Blue Ridge, and the Cumberland Plateau, with lesser effects in the Ozarks of Missouri and Arkansas. We have been very cautious about assigning causes to this phenomenon. But now research in Europe is showing that atmospheric deposition may cause disruptions in the nutrient content of insects, which are the diet of most songbirds in summer. This kind of report keeps reminding us that ecosystem level effects associated with acid rain could be having indirect effects on bird populations.[1]

The devastating impact of acid rain on fish in the Adirondack lakes has been well documented, as has its effects on the evergreen forests on the Green Mountains of Vermont. In 1995 the foundation funded a resurvey of forest plots on Camels Hump by Timothy Perkins, which indicates that the previously recorded dramatic decline may have ended, but it is too early to draw conclusions as to long term trends.

Pollution of the environment by the improper disposal of radioactive wastes has become a serious problem. Five grants were made dealing with it.

Here are two examples:

West Valley, New York, is the site of a former reprocessing plant for spent nuclear fuel and two burial grounds for radioactive waste. It is reported that there are at least eight kilograms of plutonium, among other dangerous radioactive isotopes, in these dumps. This is one of the nation's environmental disaster areas. Its clean up is now costing the federal government millions of dollars. In 1991 the local politicians in the town of Ashford were enticed by an offer of $4.2 million to ask the state to lift the existing ban on the siting of a new radioactive waste facility at this location. The action was taken despite a negative vote by the local residents in a referendum. Don't Waste New York, a statewide activist coalition formed to ensure the responsible handling of radioactive waste, mounted a campaign to prevent West Valley from becoming the site of another radioactive dump. The foundation made a grant of $2,000 in support of this effort. A group of Ashford residents took legal action to annul and set aside the town board's resolution consenting to the siting. The New York Supreme Court ruled in favor of the petitioners. The Court cited the board's failure to comply with the requirements of the State Environmental Quality Review Act.

Another potential disaster area is Ward Valley located in the desert eighteen miles west of Needles, California and the Colorado River. This had been proposed as the site for the disposal of radioactive waste generated, for the most part, by the nuclear power industry. The plan was to bury the waste in unlined trenches, which are above an aquifer connected via potential pathways to the Colorado River. This is the source of drinking water for 22 million people and of irrigation water for crops that are shipped worldwide. The corporation licensed to build this dump was U.S. Ecology, formerly known as the Nuclear Engineering Company, an organization with a record of past failures to contain the radioactive materials at other sites. Examples are Maxey Flats in Kentucky, Sheffield in Illinois, and Beatty in Nevada — all closed due to serious environmental contamination. The terrain and climate in Ward Valley are similar to those at the Beatty site.

Save Ward Valley is an entirely volunteer activist group that has been opposing this dump for the past three years. Its membership includes a large contingent of Mojave Indians, for whom the Valley and its resources are sacred and whose livelihood depends on the uncontaminated waters of the Colorado River. The foundation has supported this effort with grants totalling $2,000. On February 13, 1998, the Bureau of Land Management tried to close the valley to the public as the next step in the process of establishing the dump. Over two hundred protesters, including many Native American elders, occupied the site. The bureau did not attempt to remove the protesters, and on February 25 withdrew its law enforcement officers. Subsequently the Department of the Interior initiated negotiations with the Indian tribes, during which it threatened to cut off federal funding to the tribes if they failed to permit the project to go through. Despite this, the Indians reaffirmed their resolve to oppose the dump, deeming the sacrifice small compared to that of future generations who would have to live with the legacy of radioactive contamination.

The Conservation Fund (TCF), which was established in 1985, is one of the country's most active organizations in saving land from development. In its first fifteen years it has already protected 2.25 million acres. In 1999 it negotiated one of its most exciting deals — the purchase from the Champion International Corporation of about 300,000 acres of forest lands in the Adirondacks and in northern Vermont and New Hampshire. Sensitive portions — about a quarter of the total — were transferred into public ownership, the remainder was sold into private ownership, to be managed as sustainable working forests under conservation easements. Importantly, the arrangements assure traditional local employment and economic opportunities, as well as permanent habitat protection and public access for outdoor recreation. The foundation, which had been supporting TCF with token contributions helped finance this negotiation with a grant of $10,000 in 1999.

Several more modest projects directed at preserving biodiversity received help from the foundation. Three were for land purchases, one to protect the Los Cedros Biological Reserve in Ecuador, another to acquire land for the new La Cangreja Preserve in Costa Rica. The other projects were to help develop management strategies. For example, on the Osa Peninsula, in forests serving as buffer zones to Costa Rica's Corcovado National Park, Fundacion TUVA has been carefully salvaging valuable fallen hardwoods with teams of oxen, which minimizes damage to the ecosystem.

## Summary

The Conservation and Research Foundation has been a highly productive investment. The following things have been achieved: 1) An organization has been established that has gained an international reputation as a source of financial support for environmental projects; 2) Over $1.2 million has been expended over the past forty-nine years in grants, contracts and awards; and 3) A roster of at least 237 friends have contributed over $550,000 toward its program.

Among the most productive grants have been those to organizations in their critical formative years. Foremost among these is The Nature Conservancy, which has now become the world's largest and most effective land-saving organization. Others include the American Rivers Conservation Council, devoted to protect the quality of our best free-flowing rivers; the Rachel Carson Council, which deals with pesticide pollution problems; and two organizations addressing the problem of human overpopulation, Population Communications

International and the Population Media Center.

Seminal grants have been instrumental in preserving a number of outstanding natural areas, among them the Northern California Coast Range Preserve and critical portions of La Selva, Costa Rica, owned by the Organization for Tropical Studies.

The field of environmental law was effectively promoted by the Conference on Law and the Environment and by the preparation and publication of Russell L. Brenneman's handbook *Private Approaches to the Preservation of Open Land*, which was subsequently revised as *Land Saving Action*.

Over seventy somewhat unusual environmental research programs have been given assistance, and numerous grants have funded activities and educational projects dealing with such urgent issues as global warming, more efficient use of energy, solar options, pollution by radioactive and other toxic wastes, and strip mining impacts. These are significant investments in the future of the planet.

# 11

# SUNSET RAMBLES

By 1965 I was becoming increasingly concerned that educational institutions were failing to take leadership in encouraging students to cope with the many environmental problems besetting the planet. There was need for a new generation of activists, well trained in science, who also had some sophistication in the social sciences. This led me to promote the development of an interdepartmental major. It was approved by the faculty in 1969 as the major in Human Ecology — one of the very first of its kind in the country.

Botany had always been a small department with few majors. My botanical colleagues were concerned that this new program might still further shrink its enrollment. What actually happened, however, was that the number of student electing botany immediately doubled, despite the fairly large number signing up for human ecology. I found it amusing later to discover that home economics was called human ecology at Cornell University.

Our interdepartmental program flourished at Connecticut College. After I retired in 1976, Bill Niering took over as director. The program's name was changed and by 1993 it had become the Center for Conservation Biology and Environmental Studes. Six years later Helen Mathieson, an alumna of the class of 1952, and her husand Andrew endowed the enterprise, which was dedicated as the Goodwin-Niering Center.

Eleven years before retirement I made a deal with the administration at the College to go on half time. This turned out to be about three quarter time on half salary, but had the great advantage of allowing me to spend more time on conservation activities with a clear conscience. And then my official retirement enabled me to travel to far-off places during the academic year.

## The Caribbean

Our first Caribbean sojourn was in 1970 — an idyllic week spent at a resort on Young Island, a tiny islet reached by a very short water taxi from the south shore of St. Vincent, one of the Windward Islands. The resort consisted of a cluster of simple thatched cottages hidden in tropical vegetation next to a sheltered beach shaded by coconut palms and serviced by a dining facility and bar. Close off shore were coral reefs alive with colorful fish. This was my first real snorkeling experience.

The main island was teeming with people — mostly black. As we drove around, we saw families with eight or nine children standing in their yards. The ecosystem was clearly becoming over stressed. Esther noted a birth control clinic next to the hospital, but alas it appeared to be another case of too little, too late. A foray up the steep volcanic slopes of Mt. Soufriere rewarded us with glimpses of bamboo forests at least eighty feet tall, huge tree ferns, and other species of native plants already eliminated by cultivation from most of the Island.

Next, in 1974, my friend and Harvard classmate Andy Fiske, invited us to accompany him and his wife and two other couples on an eight-day cruise on the schooner *Freelance* from Fort-de-France, Martinique, north to Antigua, British West Indies. There were exciting stops ashore, including St. Pierre, the city on Martinique that was incinerated by the 1902 eruption of Mount Pelee, and the rain forests of Dominica. One interesting observation made at one of the ports on that island were the piles of disassembled solid mahogany furniture stacked on the docks ready for export. A number of the old colonial mansions on the island were being abandoned, and entrepreneurs were acquiring this material for a song and selling it on the mainland at a huge profit.

When Tim and Karen Reynolds moved into our little house at Dolbia we learned about the Point Pleasant Resort on St. Thomas in the Virgin Islands. It was run by Karen's parents. So in the winter of 1979 we flew down there for the first time. Point Pleasant is situated on the steep northeastern facing slope of a limestone knob near the eastern end of the island with a magnificent view toward St. John and Tortola in the British Virgin Islands. The swimming was delightful in this sheltered bay, but the coral was moribund, already showing the effect of pollution from development.

While we were there we had the good fortune to be invited to fly in a small plane completely around the rugged island chain from St. Thomas on the west to Virgin Gorda on the east, with a northward loop over the extensive colorful reefs of Anagada, which has a maximum elevation of only a few feet above high tide. We later heard an amusing story about a woman tourist staying on Anagada. She was snorkeling on the reefs when she encountered a ten foot barracuda, a fish which sports a mean mouthful of sharp teeth. She levitated out of the water exclaiming, "My God! What do you have in there!" The local comment was, "Oh, that's just old Andy. He's always around."

The next day we had a yacht's eye view of the nearer islands with swims on surf-swirled beaches and lunch at a remote retreat on the almost uninhabited Jost van Dyke, an island now becoming thoroughly developed.

Two other days were spent on St. John, a half-hour ferry ride from the eastern tip of St. Thomas, exploring the National Park, a gift of the Rockefeller family. The head ranger took us to visit Mrs. William Callahan, whose home and magnificent gardens were being acquired by the Park Service. The living collection of orchids assembled by her late husband was outstanding.

We returned to St. Thomas five more times in the next ten years, the last three as guests of Karen's mother, Ruth Pfanner.

*Peru*

One of the scientists serving on the board of TNC, whom I came to admire was Mildred Mathias, a botanist on the faculty at the University of California, Los Angeles. In June 1977, she was leading a U.C.L.A. summer extension course on the ecology of the Peruvian Amazon, so I enrolled. Mildred was assisted by a zoologist, Hugh Rowell. The class consisted of a congenial group of thirty students with quite an assortment of ages and backgrounds. We flew to Lima, and thence over the Andes to Iquitos, 2,300 miles up the Amazon from its mouth, but still navigable by ocean-going freighters. Indeed Iquitos serves as Peru's Atlantic port. For twelve days we descended the river in various types of craft, ranging from large power-driven dugouts to a flat-bottomed steamboat with overnight accommodations, stopping off at four different camps along the way for forays into the forest. We terminated 500 miles down stream at Leticia, Colombia's Atlantic Port at the Brazilian frontier.

It was total immersion! This is not to say we capsized or got swept away by unexpected floods; but rather that we felt the pulse of the great river and the jungle throbbing day and night, smelt the exotic smells, saw the strange shapes and colors of the plants and animals, and met the native inhabitants, constantly interpreted by experts, from early dawn until we collapsed into bed. At the end of the day we would have sessions of "show and tell" when experiences and information would be shared. For a botanist who had already visited rain forests in tropical Africa, Cuba, and Panama, there were familiar features — gigantic buttressed tree trunks and tangled lianas festooned with orchids, bromeliads and other epiphytes, tall palms bristling with black spines, feathery tree ferns, and strange non-green parasitic flowering plants on the forest floor. But previous exposures only enhance ones capacity to appreciate the enormous diversity and complexity of the ecosystem and the subtleties of the pathways of energy flow and nutrient recycling.

The size and power of the Amazon has to be experienced to be appreciated. The river, brown with silt, writhes through the flood plain like a gigantic snake, eroding the outer edges of its bends and depositing sheets of rich mud on the opposite banks. Eventually adjacent meanders widen until they meet and break through, leaving behind crescent-shaped oxbow lakes. As one descends the river the presence of these clear bodies of water can be detected by flocks of terns diving for fish. On them we found masses of floating water hyacinth (*Eichornia crassipes*), water lettuce (*Pistia stratioides*) and the enormous round floating pads of *Victoria regia* with raised rims and undersides beset with protective spines.

Thirty-six foot flood crests periodically inundate the adjacent forest. In Brazil this may be as much as 150 miles back from the main stem of the river, so when in flood it is a 300 mile trip by boat from one side to the other. Many species of fish have evolved the habit of migrating into the flooded forest to graze on invertebrates and the seeds and nuts that have fallen to the floor. As the flood subsides they return to the river by way of small streams, the mouths of which the natives have found rewarding places to fish. We paddled up some of these mysterious, sinuous, clear water tributaries overhung by trees and vines. At night they were alive with glowing eyes in the beam of a flashlight — caiman from the water, and the huge orange eyes of the potoo, a relative of our common nighthawk, from high dead snags. This strange bird incubates its single egg upon the top of a stump, a fifteen-inch continuation of which it perfectly simulates. In daylight one would never detect it.

For weather we had showers almost every half hour. In the field the most useful equipment was an umbrella. I wore a long-sleeved cotton shirt that was wet most of the time either from the rain or from sweat. I only needed one shirt, as I washed it each evening and hung it out. In the morning it was still damp, but soon dried out from body heat.

Our second stop on the river was Yanamono Lodge, an attractive facility on a substantial tongue of land lying between the Amazon and a major tributary, the Rio Napo. When flood crests descend the Amazon, the flow of the Napo is temporarily reversed, the up-stream current becoming too strong for safe navigation. At the confluence of these two rivers stands a monument to Francisco de Orellana, the per-fidious Spanish explorer who accompanied Gonzalo Pizarro in 1538 on a military expedition into the Amazon basin. Progress through the rain forest along the Napo being extremely difficult, they built a sub-stantial boat and sent it downstream with a contingent under Orellana's command to investigate. When Orellana reached the Amazon, he abandoned Pizarro and took off down the big river to its mouth and thence across the Atlantic to Spain, where he was welcomed with acclaim. He left a few dissenters behind, some of whom bred with the Indians, thus founding a settlement of mixed origin. Pizarro, when he finally reached the Amazon, decided to beat a painful retreat west-ward across the Andes to Quito.

At Yanamono Lodge we had an opportunity to observe some of the wildlife at close range. A tame tapir about the color of an eggplant and a capybara, the world's largest rodent, were wandering about the clearing and a gray-winged trumpeter, a large ground bird, followed us faithfully on our hikes through the forest. Raucous blue and yellow and red and green macaws came in to feed on bananas. One of these during a "show and tell" session alighted on my shoulder and, then proceeded to reach down, pluck a pencil from my shirt pocket and crunch it to splinters.

Some of the flowering plants, such as the heliconias, sported spec-tacular colorations. Many of them have spikes of flowers which open one at a time, and the plants are widely scattered through the forest. They are pollinated by hummingbirds that harvest their nectar. There are about 300 species, each with a bill specially shaped to fit the struc-

ture of a flower. These birds
are not territorial, but travel a
trap line from one plant to
another, thus assuring cross
pollination.

A Yagua village was near-
by and the Indians gave us a
blowgun demonstration, hit-
ting a bull's-eye with their
darts at forty feet. The guns
are about six feet long, beautifully constructed of two
strips of wood carefully
grooved and glued together.
Their darts are made of hard

slivers of wood, shaped with a piranha tooth file and wound with a bit
of kapok fiber for a snug fit in the bore of the gun. When hunting
monkeys the tips are dipped in a poison — either curare or an extract
from the skin of a tiny dendrobatid frog — and the darts are weakened
behind the tip by a circumferential groove. If the quarry attempts to
remove the missile, it breaks off leaving the poisoned tip in the animal.

This introduces two Amazonian characters into our story. First, the
piranha, whose jaw is part of the Indian's hunting equipment. The
piranha is a fish famed for its ability to rapidly strip meat from the
bone. Despite their ferocious reputation, we found we could swim with
these fish in the river with impunity. Second, the dendrobatid frogs
which are abundant in the rain forest. They are less than an inch long
and brilliantly colored blue and red.

We visited several Indian villages, studied their small plantations
hewn from the jungle, and observed some of their methods of hunting
and fishing. The native buildings on the flood plane are on stilts, the
floors of which are often reached by a ladder consisting of a notched
log. Fireplaces, located on their wooden platforms, are a dirt hearth
framed by wood. Roofs were thatched with woven palm fronds.

Along the river the natives were exploiting the freshly exposed expanses of mud on the insides of the meanders by planting rice. They were in temporary residence nearby to protect their crop from depredation. Little children were playing around on the river in tiny dugouts.

Two years later it was Peru revisited. I repeated the course at the same time of year, down the same stretch of river, with the same leader. Again we had a congenial group with three repeaters. The participants included four professional zoologists, who greatly enriched the whole learning experience with their trained eyes and insights. This trip was notable on several counts. Instead of a succession of heavy daily showers, only a few were experienced during our twelve days on the river and the river was low. During this two year interval amazing changes had taken place. Mud flats formerly planted to rice were now young Cecropia forests, the trees being at least thirty feet tall and several inches in diameter. Oxbow lakes previously showing open water were now completely choked with vegetation. Tracts of mature forest were now native plantations, and we observed slash/burn agriculture, where the natives were cutting down the trees and burning the debris.

For our last night on the river an evening flashlight walk was scheduled. We were at Monkey Island Lodge, about an hours run by boat above Leticia. That afternoon we had been sitting around on the boardwalk that runs down to the bank of the river, reading and working on our notes. Shortly before setting out our ornithologist, Lloyd Kiff, stepped off the walk and was struck at, and most happily missed by a five-foot fer-de-lance, one of the world's most poisonous snakes. Our

Peruvian guide, Hugo, stick in one hand and flashlight in the other, shooed the snake down the steep thirty-foot bank onto an exposed mud flat and there, after some thrashing around, captured it alive. For some strange reason, this excitement was substituted for the walk. The snake was packed into a plastic water cooler

and taken down to the zoo at Leticia that evening. The next day we visited the zoo and the snake was brought forth for us to view. I was able to take a close-up photo of the snake's wide open mouth with inch-long fangs exposed. In December I enclosed a print of this shot in a Christmas letter to Lloyd. His response was that it caused him once again to break into a sweat.

On our second Peruvian trip the group also made an excursion into the high country of the Andes. We first flew up to Cuzco, the famed capital of the Incas, at an altitude of over 11,000 feet, and then by train down the Urubamba River to the lost city of Machu Picchu.

The Incas were amazing craftsmen. In building their structures they were able to shape huge stones so perfectly that one cannot insert a knife between them, and this without the use of iron. The monolithic outer bastion of Sacsayhuaman, the fortress overlooking Cuzco, is constructed of rocks weighing up to 300 tons which had been moved miles from the quarries. They also constructed aqueducts to service their gardens in the arid western valleys. Despite earthquakes and the ravages of five centuries, some of these water works are still functional today.

Our train to Machu Picchu backed and filled up a series of switchbacks to the alto plano at an elevation of 12,000 feet and then descended into the valley of the Urubamba, a tributary of the Amazon, which it followed deeper and deeper into a canyon. From the window, torrent ducks, looking very much like grebes, were observed swimming in the river. As we proceeded into the canyon, its spectacular, near-vertical walls were clothed with gray bromeliads. Finally the gorge enters a couple of great entrenched meanders. Machu Picchu, sitting high on a ridge jutting into the second meander, is now reached from the railroad station by a road that climbs 1,500 feet to the ruin by a series of switchbacks. Constructed in 1948, it is named in honor of the late politician and explorer Hiram Bingham, whose visit to the site in 1911 revealed its great historic significance.

We were fortunate in being able to stay overnight in the little inn adjacent to the ruins. After the tourist crowds had left, we had time to really explore the site and savor the spectacular scenery. On both sides

Mildred Mathias at Machu Picchu.

of the ridge the land drops off precipitously to the river, which winds like a ribbon at the bottom of the gorge. To the east and west snow-capped peaks rise to over 20,000 feet.

To me one of the most interesting features within the ruins, some of which have been well excavated and restored, is the observatory. There, on the crest of the ridge, may be found a large stone serving as a sundial. Its faces are aligned with the points of the compass. Directions of importance and other data are also indicated. Among the agricultural terraces were some that have been interpreted as being experimental gardens that had differing microclimates. That evening we took a walk on the road, lit only by an incredible display of stars, a sight we no longer enjoy back home in our polluted air. Early the next morning, before breakfast, we climbed Huayna Picchu — the rocky pinnacle at the very end of the ridge, which also supports ruins.

After breakfast I took a solo walk on a trail which led through fascinating vegetation to the hanging bridge situated on a vertical cliff. Massive stonework permits its traverse, at places even under an overhang, to an abrupt stop at a gap. This used to be spanned by a log which could be removed at will by the former inhabitants. For me this quiet stroll was a spiritual experience.

## Central America

My first "sunset ramble" in Central America took place in 1973 in connection with a board meeting of The Institute of Ecology, held in Monterrey, Mexico. After the meeting, the participants made a foray into the arid country west of the city to visit the Cuatro Cienegas, a complex of wetlands supporting what is perhaps the highest concentration of unique aquatic species in the world. It is encouraging to learn that TNC and its Mexican partner Pronatura have now acquired the 7,000-acre Rancho Pozas Azules, which will permanently protect the best of these desert springs.

What I remember particularly about this trip to Mexico, however, was being entertained by a wealthy lady living in the city. We were all invited to a sumptuous dinner at her home, after which we retired to her spacious living room where stood a matching pair of Chinese vases at least four feet tall, all beautifully decorated with little figures in red and gold. I screwed up my courage to ask our hostess where she had obtained these magnificent objects. She told me that they had been removed from China by Chiang Kai-chek and that they had been purchased in Taiwan, which was raising money for military purposes. Tensions between this island and mainland China are still festering today.

The following year Esther and I joined a Connecticut College alumni tour of Guatemala and the Yucatan. My impression of Guatemala was of an unstable countryside. Steep, deforested hillsides, composed of soft materials, were being eroded. Volcanos were everywhere in evidence and one that was smoking close to Guatemala City erupted shortly after we left. We visited colorful markets, including one at Chichicastenango, and were impressed by the small stature of the Mayans, some of whom we passed along the roads bearing incredible loads.

From Guatemala City we flew in an aged DC-3 to Tikal for a day's tour of the Mayan ruins, buried in the jungles of Peten. There, an estimated 400 square miles of city have been all but obliterated, yet at its heart huge temples, some well restored, rear their altars steeply above the 200-foot canopy. While most of the party returned to the airport for lunch, our leader, June Macklin, and I remained to take a walk in the forest. Tantalizing glimpses of toucans, with their fantastically oversized bills, motmots, hummingbirds, begonias, orchids, bromeliads, palms and strangling figs, all strengthened a resolve to return for more. At one point a slender mammal about three feet in length with a long tail leapt across the trail right in front of us. We later learned that it was a tayra — the largest member of the mink family.

In 1976 we joined seventeen members of New London's Lyman-Allyn Art Museum on a two week cruise on the Argonaut, at one time the largest private yacht afloat, which was operated by a Greek enterprise. Embarking at Montego Bay, Jamaica, we labored through stormy seas to the Island of Cozumel, off the east coast of Yucatan, stopping for a snorkel on the sheltered side of Grand Cayman. Under the enthusiastic leadership of Edith "Fuzzy" Giptein we undertook excursions to Mayan ruins, as our floating base of operations churned southward at a leisurely pace along the coast of Belize as far as the Honduran city of Puerto Barrios.

For me the high point of the trip was an expedition down the Rio Dulce, the outlet to Lake Isobel, a huge body of water at the base of the Yucatan peninsula, on the boundary between Honduras and Guatemala. We were scheduled to go by bus to the Mayan ruins of

Quirigua, then by boat down the river to its mouth and thence by sea to Puerto Barrios. After leaving the interesting ruins we then had a very hot and bumpy drive on a badly washed-out road to the Rio Dulce. Just before we left the bus our local tour guide addressed us. "Sorry to inform you ladies and gentlemen, but no way can we take you down the Rio Dulce. One of the boats is sunk and the other is out of commission." We then were ferried in large dugouts, powered by outboards, to the Catamaran Club, an "Hawaiian village" resort, located on an island a short distance down stream, where we were to have lunch. Most of us were fuming at being deprived of our anticipated boat trip and at the prospect of repeating that unpleasant bus ride back to the Argonaut. As we disembarked we asked the native boys who were running the dugouts if they could take us down the Rio Dulce. They responded with enthusiasm and took off upstream to gas up. After a delicious lunch, most of us hopped aboard the waiting dugouts and swished off down the river at full throttle.

At this point I should mention that only a portion of our tour were on this expedition. The rest of the group, under Fuzzy's leadership, had flown to the ruins at Palenque. We had several on our trip who did not care for the prospect of flights in a small chartered plane. These included Fuzzy's husband, Ed, a heart specialist, as well as our own dentist, Ivor Hunter, and his wife. These folks, rather sensibly, also did not opt to accompany us in this hair-brained adventure down the river.

After several bends the river opened up into a six-mile-long lake whipped by a stiff head wind. As we cut through choppy seas we were soaked by spray and were busy bailing with our sneakers or whatever else was at hand. In the middle of the lake we hove to to allow the slowest dugout to catch up with us. Just at this point we noticed a large boat pursuing us, a man standing on the top of the wheelhouse waving his arms. He materialized into our tour guide on one of those excursion boats he had "miraculously rehabilitated." We were all taken aboard and the tour guide and bus driver roared off upstream in one of the dugouts. Just at that point a sinister looking vessel bore down on us from the opposite direction. It was a gunboat with machine guns at the ready fore and aft, manned by scowling Guatemalans. It proceeded to board us. Happily this turned out to be only a routine inspection, and we were permitted to continue down the magnificent meandering jungle-clad gorge to the ocean. One of the memorable sights was a white hawk, which sailed across the river just above us. The tropical night fell as we reached the mouth of the river, still wet, but fortunately fortified with whisky, which had been provided. It was another hour through three-foot choppy seas before we reached Puerto Barrios. We were all grateful we were not still in the dugouts, as in no way would we have made it in them through the open ocean to our destination.

This was not the end of the story. The less adventuresome, who had opted to return by bus, came back to find it empty. Thinking themselves deserted by the driver and guide, they returned to the Catamaran Club for help. The proprietor, an American retired from the navy, agreed to fly them in two installments to Puerto Barrios in his small private plane. When the Hunters were delivered at the airport, they hired a taxi to get to the ship. On the way the driver had a slight fender bender and an incipient gunfight ensued. They might have done much better to have flown to Palenque.

Our next trip to Central America was to Costa Rica. My friend Lucie Strayer, whom I had known for years as an enthusiastic member of TNC, contacted me and proposed that we promote a tour of that lovely country. She was very familiar with it having recently traveled there. Arrangements were made in February 1982. through Costa Rica Expeditions, an organization headquartered in San Jose, which provided Jim Lewis as our guide and naturalist. Our party of twelve consisted of Lucie, Esther and me, my colleague in the Zoology Department at Connecticut College, Bernice Wheeler, Ruth Pfanner, two other couples, and a younger contingent, which Esther and I referred to as the three musketeers. This consisted of my son Dick, Allen Carroll, and Julie Zickefoose.

Costa Rica is a small country, about the size of Vermont and New Hampshire combined, but it has dedicated over ten percent of its land to National Parks. Living conditions there are unusually healthy for a tropical country. We went prepared to protect ourselves against malaria, but were assured, when we got there, that that was unnecessary.

During our sixteen-day visit we managed to get glimpses of the rich biodiversity of the country—the Poas Volcano and cloud forest of Monteverde on the continental divide, the dry tropical forest of the Pacific slope at Santa Rosa, the palm swamps and Caribbean beaches at Tortuguero, and the wet tropical forests of Corcovado on the Osa Peninsula. Birds were a special focus for our group and, under the leadership of Jim Lewis, we were able see 278 different species. At the Monteverde Cloud Forest Reserve we caught glimpses of the rare Respelendent Quetzal and a Black Guan. We inspected the new headquarters facility, the construction of which had been partly funded by the Conservation and Research Foundation. There a pair of golden toads was on display, the male bright orange and the female multicolored. Alas, this species has now apparently become extinct, despite the protection of its habitat. Amphibia appear to be especially vulnerable to radiation and atmospheric pollution.

In the area around Santa Rosa, situated on the Pacific coast at the western end of the country close to the Nicaraguan border, the dry tropical forest is being destroyed by fires set to convert them to cattle pasture. Dr. Daniel Janzen of the University of Pennsylvania, who has been studying the rich biodiversity of the area, has come to the realization that in order not to lose the forest one must use it. So he has been attempting to educate the local people on the importance of maintaining their water supply by preserving the watershed and in imaginative and sustainable ways of harvesting the forest's resources. One of these, of course, is by exploiting ecotourism.

While in Santa Rosa National Park we put up a herd of peccaries, saw large boa constrictors and rattlesnakes, had fine views of howler monkeys, and observed a white-faced monkey catching and eating a mouse. Santa Rosa was an old colonial hacienda. We visited the Big House, which we discovered was not only a museum, but also a national shrine. According to plaques mounted on the walls, it was there in

1856 that a hastily conscripted army of Costa Ricans routed an invading force from Nicaragua assembled under the leadership of an American adventurer by the name of William Walker. This incursion was reportedly bent on subjugating the Costa Ricans to slavery. The statement sufficiently piqued my interest so that, upon my return to the States, I spent some time researching this incident.

Walker turned out to be an extraordinary character. By the time he was twenty-four he had obtained a medical degree from the University of Pennsylvania, studied medicine abroad, obtained a law degree, was admitted to the bar in Louisiana and then had become foreign editor of a newspaper. He became bethrothed to a young woman who, as a result of an early illness had lost her powers of speech and hearing. Upon her untimely death he migrated to the West Coast. In the 1850s Nicaragua was being torn by civil strife. Walker was invited to assist the democratic government of Nicaragua stabilize the country and thereby resist British expansion in Central America. He soon set sail for Nicaragua from San Francisco, accompanied by fifty-eight men. During the next two years he became commander-in-chief of the democratic army, defeated the opposition, unified the country, and shortly afterward was elected president of the Republic.

Then Walker made a blunder that was fatal to his cause, an ill-advised takeover of Cornelius Vanderbilt's Accessory Transit Company, which was not fulfilling its financial obligations to Nicaragua. Vanderbilt had developed what was then the quickest route to the West, taking passengers from the East Coast to the mouth of the San Juan River, thence by smaller boats up the river to Lake Nicaragua, from the western end of which it was only eight miles to the Pacific. The fabulously wealthy tycoon retaliated. He stirred up neighboring countries and financially aided them both directly and through the intervention of foreign powers. With Vanderbilt's encouragement and with the support of the British fleet, President Mora of Costa Rica mobilized an army of 9,000 men "to take up arms for the Republic of Nicaragua" against what he maintained was an American invasion. Without waiting for a declaration of war the Costa Rican army, advanced into Nicaragua. It was in response to this action that Walker's men counter-attacked at Santa Rosa.[1] Thus economic forces, international intrigue and power politics are omitted, truth is bent, and national myths become perpetuated. Today Costa Rica is an exceptionally peaceful country with no army — only a local police force.

From Santa Rosa we returned to San Jose and then descended the east slope to Puerto Limon by train — a journey not without its excitements. At one point our carriage became derailed, which took about half an hour to get back on track, and twice, portions of the train became uncoupled. Later, we discovered that when ascending the slope a second engine follows the train to assure that an uncoupled section doesn't take off on a wild ride down the mountain. We had been warned to watch out for thieves at stations — but our son Dick, at one stop, got out on the platform between the cars and narrowly escaped having his binoculars yanked off his neck.

The following day we travelled for six hours by motorized dugout to Tortuguero National Park near the Nicaraguan border on an inland waterway consisting of the mouths of rivers, protected by barrier beaches, interconnected by artificial canals. The shores were mostly heavily vegetated by forests, including stands of raffia palms. It was a great place to see herons, kingfishers, and sloths hanging in overarching branches. We stayed at Tortuga Lodge, overlooking a protected lagoon, and in the evening observed the large, reddish fish-eating bats skimming the surface of the water. The park is named for the sea turtles which come there to lay their eggs. It was not the nesting season, but a walk along the outer beach revealed the shallow depressions of old nests and the remains of egg shells. Research on the turtles is being carried out there and the area is being patrolled to protect the nests from poachers.

The final episode of our trip was a three-day stay in Corcovado National Park located at the northwestern end of the Osa Peninsula, which projects into the Pacific Ocean not far from the Panamanian border. Three shuttle flights took our party at low altitude across steep forested hills being denuded by clear-cuts before reaching the park.

After flying for some time over a dense forested wilderness, we touched down on a grassy strip just behind the shore. Here we met up with a U.C.L.A. group led by my old friend, Mildred Mathias. This was most fortunate for us as they had with them, as guest, the ornithologist, Dr. Alexander Skutch, who described for us conditions in Costa Rica when he first came to the country in the 1930s. Annie Simpson de Gamboa and another young woman in their party also told us about their research on the biology of heliconid butterflies.

Corcovado is preserving a great remnant of the low altitude, moist forest ecosystem of Central America. It is large enough to support predators such as jaguars, one of which had severely mauled a horse shortly before we arrived, and the rare harpy eagle, which feeds on monkeys, of which there are four species in the park. Since our visit, efforts, which have been given support from the Conservation and Research Foundation, are being made to protect large stretches of forest adjacent to the park through ecotourism and sustainable management practices.

As the sleeping facility at the park was already occupied, we were quartered in tents at the edge of the clearing. At dusk, as we were eating supper, Esther spotted a spectacled owl. It stayed around and later, after we had gone to bed, was screaming right over our tent. Forays during the next two days were filled with fascinating experiences. The weather was hot and humid. We did not venture into the ocean off the beach, which was being patrolled by sharks, but over the ridge in the next valley we had a most refreshing swim in a large, crystal-clear pool on the Rio Claro.

Back in San Jose our party held a farewell banquet at which we were told about the program of the newly formed Fundacion de Parques Nacionales by Geoffrey Barnard who was on the staff of TNC. The following day we visited the National Museum and met Luis Diego Gomez, who was then the director of the museum. He invited us to his home for dinner. About a month later Luis paid us a three day visit at Dolbia in connection with a fund raising trip in behalf of the fundacion, financed by the Conservation and Research Foundation.

The following year we made a second trip to Costa Rica. The first half, sponsored by TNC, was a cruise along the Pacific Coast on the *Baja Explorador*, which accommodated our party of eighteen. We landed at various national parks along the shore from Corcovado at the southeast to Santa Rosa at the northwest. This gave us fine opportunities to snorkel off the boat, to visit red mangrove swamps at the mouths of rivers, and to see turtle beaches in action. The second half of the trip was with Mildred Mathias for a portion of her extension course, which started out at the research facility run by the Organization for Tropical Studies (OTS) at La Selva in the eastern lowlands. The excellent trails and well-equipped laboratories make this is a splendid place to study the biology of the rain forest.

We spent some time observing the activities of leaf-cutting ants carrying pieces of leaves along their well-beaten trails to a huge underground nest. And a memorable demonstration was a six-foot vine snake, light brown and about the diameter of a pencil. When released into a thicket it virtually vanished, the body appearing just like the tangled stems of the vines.

Our third trip was in 1991 — a Christmas gathering for the entire family. Minda, her husband Ted, Dick, his wife Judith, the four grandchildren and ourselves made a party of ten. As we were all widely scattered around the country, we made a covenant to give each other no presents, but to convene in San Jose for a week's tour of the country.

Esther and I departed a few days early to visit the Wilson Botanical Garden at Las Cruces Biological Station, owned and operated by OTS. Its director was our friend Luis Diego Gomez. We were joined there by Dick and Judith. The station is a lovely spot at mid-elevation on the Pacific slope, not far from the Panamanian border. It protects a significant remnant of undisturbed forest. While there, we learned of the availability of an adjacent forested tract, the only other one left in the valley. We encouraged Luis to acquire it for the garden. Later a grant from the Conservation and Research Foundation underwrote the expense of a successful fund raising trip to the West Coast, which enabled OTS to close the deal.

Back in San Jose we met the rest of the family. Through Costa Rica

Mildred Mathias, hand on the spathe of *Dracontium pittieri*, a tropical relative of
the Jack-in-the-pulpit. Its single leaf rises at least seven feet above
the members of her ecology class at the
La Selva Station of the Organization for Tropical Studies, Costa Rica in 1983.

Expeditions we chartered a small van with driver and a naturalist guide, which took us for overnight stays to La Selva, Monteverde, and La Pacifica. In driving down to La Selva from San Jose, I was horrified to see the extent of deforestation that had taken place just in the eight years since my last visit. It was a relief to know that a significant strip of unbroken forest, the Zona Protectora, connecting La Selva with Braulio Carrillo National Park, had been saved from destruction.

When we got to Monteverde we were told that the crowds attempting to enter the preserve were so great that the administration had found it necessary to limit the number of visitors. Despite making a very early start, we were informed, when we arrived at the entrance, that the days quota had already been filled. I am not accustomed to throwing my weight around, but in this instance I informed the attendant in charge that our party included three trustees of the foundation that had provided funds for the construction of the facility from which he was operating. Fortunately he was willing to make an exception for us. It was obvious that something further needed to be done to relieve the traffic congestion at the entrance to the preserve. It was serviced by a narrow dirt road with almost no space at the end for parking. What needed to be done was to control access by providing bus service from a parking lot near the town.

Since my earlier visit the preserve had been greatly enlarged by acquisitions on the east slope known as the Bosque del Ninos (Children's Forest). Funding for this had been initiated by school children in Scandinavia and augmented by similar activity in the United States.

My last venture in Central America was a trip to Panama in 1996, sponsored by TNC and hosted by the Asociacion National para la Conservacion de la Natura (ANCON), the Panamanian organization promoting the establishment of national parks and the preservation of nature. Our first night was spent at the Rio Chagres Environmental Center, located in the buffer zone of the Soberania National Park, which protects the watershed of the Rio Chagres. This river is the principal source of water feeding Gatun Lake, which constitutes the major portion of the Panama Canal. Its flow is vital to the operation of the locks. During the week we visited two National Parks: the first, Bastimentos National Marine Park at the northwestern corner of the country on the Caribbean coast near the Costa Rican border; the second, Darien National Park at the eastern end, next to Colombia. On our first day a flight from Panama City took us to Bocas del Toro on the island of Colon. There we were housed at ANCON's Education Center, constructed on piles extending out from the shore. The next day we were taken in outboard craft through an amazing archipelago of small red mangrove islets to Bastimentos Island where we had lunch and an opportunity to swim. Unfortunately the sea was too rough to permit snorkelling on the reef. The following day we had to leave Colon by a small open boat to catch a plane on the mainland. It was a rough trip in three-foot seas and we all got soaked. Luckily we were given the privilege of changing into dry clothes in the back office at the airport before our flight to Panama City.

We then flew in to Cana, situated within the 1.5 million-acre Darien National Park, a mountainous, forest-clad wilderness lying on the Colombian border. Still roadless, it is the one break in the PanAmerican highway, and thus far the Panamanian government has successfully resisted pressures to complete its construction. Highways spell disaster to wilderness, and ANCON has been promoting an efficient ferry service to bypass this critical section of the isthmus. Cana, is the site of an old Spanish gold mine operated in the sixteenth and seventeenth centuries. It was briefly exploited by the British at the end of the nineteenth century, but abandoned since 1900. At Cana we landed on a small grassy airstrip to find another of ANCON's Environmental Education Centers. The immediate area, a disturbed one, is recovering from the mining operation, which, we were told, had at one time employed 20,000 workers. There were remains of an old railroad, including a locomotive, a mine pit about 100 feet deep, two large furnaces, and machinery, all now being swallowed up by the encroaching jungle. It was a wonderful place to observe birds at the forest edge. Our most spectacular experience was seeing a herd of about 200 white-lipped peccaries foraging right next to the clearing. On our second day Juan Carlos Navarro, the Executive Director of ANCON, flew in and told us more about the status of the park. His organization has bought up almost all of the mineral rights in the park and was working to acquire more land and to strengthen administration of its buffer zones.

## China

The People's Republic of China, which was established in 1946, was really opened up for visitation by tourists for the first time in 1980. In March of that year my friend Charles Chu, Professor of Chinese and Chairman of the Chinese Department at Connecticut College, led a trip to that country under the auspices of the College Alumni Association. It was his first return to his native land in thirty-five years.

Charles Chu, artist and leader on our trip to China.

Esther and I signed up to go. Our party of forty-five included people with widely divergent ages and professional backgrounds, their interests and insights enriching the experience. Our itinerary included two days in Hong Kong, followed by twelve in China, with visits to Kwangchow (Canton), Shanghai, Chenchiang, Nanjing, and Beijing (Peking), and three in Japan, with stops in Kyoto and Tokyo.

Hong Kong, still under British rule at that time, was a fascinating city, throbbing with modern technology, but presenting a frightening glimpse of a standing-room-only scenario — a population that has escaped growth restraints. Massive twenty to thirty story apartment complexes separated by very narrow streets lined the shores of Victoria Island for mile after mile and crept up the steep, wooded mountainsides. Similar crowding was visible across the busy harbor in Kowloon, on the mainland. Sheltered bays were completely choked by barges and junks, providing living quarters for the water people.

A short train ride from Kowloon took us to Lo Wu at the Chinese border, where we went through the usual international formalities in a station adorned with large oriental paintings on the walls. Upon entering the People's Republic one has the impression of stepping back into the nineteenth century and sometimes into the fifteenth. The train ride to Kwangchow was in a comfortable coach provided with tables between facing seats. A female attendant brought us hot tea in a large aluminum kettle as we whirled through a fertile southern Chinese countryside.

Women with shovels over their shoulders were trudging out from their compact little villages to work in the fields, where water buffalo were plowing or grazing in the ditches. Crops were being cultivated along the edges of the roads and canals. Here, no suburban sprawl or encroachment onto precious soil. The ride terminated in a large station adorned with a huge painting of Chairman Mao.

Facilities at Kwangchow were crowded by a convention meeting there. So after sightseeing we were bussed out of town to the Nanhu Hotel, a resort designed for Chinese dignitaries. The buildings, located in a rural setting, were substantial stone structures with very high ceilings. At that time of year the marble floors were wet with condensation. A notable feature were the huge bathtubs, constructed of ceramic tiles.

Our accommodations in the other cities we visited each had its special flavor. At our modest nine-story hotel in Shanghai most of the staff lined up outside to greet us and clapped as we descended from the bus. In Chenchiang we were housed in a brand new facility — a low two-story stucture, of which the Chinese were very proud. For us it might just as well have been a motel in Fargo, North Dakota. It was furnished with curtains from Australia adorned with wallabies. The heating fixtures came from the United States. There we participated in a good-will tree-planting ceremony in the muddy courtyard. In Nanjing we were housed in buildings that formerly served as the British Embassy. In Beijing it was a huge hotel, the reception hall occupying most of the ground floor and serviced by an elevator at each end. There, an event occurred that amazed us. We were all bundled up as the weather was cold and damp. After reaching our rooms, Esther discovered that her coat, under pressure, had popped a large red button. We went down to the bus to see whether she might have lost it there. Returning from a fruitless search, the woman operating the elevator pointed to Esther's gaping coat. She then pointed up and held up seven fingers. Ascending to the seventh floor, there, on a little stand next to the elevator door, sat the missing button, which she proudly presented to Esther.

Our Chinese tour guides were most friendly and anxious to arrange the trip to suit our particular interests. The doctors among us wanted to visit a hospital. Others were interested in educational enterprises. I expressed a desire to see an agricultural commune.

Our visit to a hospital included attending an operation on a deviated nasal septum and removal of a polyp. As observers we were all covered with sterile robes and allowed to stand around the edges of the operating room. The patient walked in and sat in the operating chair. Four acupuncture needles were inserted, one in each cheek and one in each hand between the thumb and forefinger. The needles, lightly wired

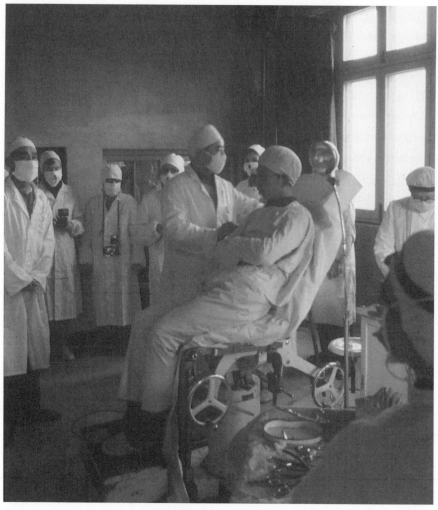

Acupuncture operation.

to a small rheostat on a table behind the patient, were activated by a technician. The man's face was swathed with sterile cloths and the operation commenced. As observers we could detect no evidence that the patient was experiencing pain. In the middle of the procedure the surgeon held up the misplaced piece of bone before replacing it in the proper position. At the end of the operation, which took about half an hour, the needles were removed and the patient walked away unassisted. We understood that he would remain in the hospital for a day before being dismissed.

At many of our special stops we would be invited to sit down at a table, served a mug of hot tea and given what was called a "brief introduction." They weren't always brief. The weather was cold, the rooms unheated, and we wrapped our hands around the hot mugs to warm our fingers. At a primary school we observed the children being taught art, singing, dancing, and arithmatic. Each room was furnished with a small foot-activated organ or piano. Photos of Chairman Mao were on the walls and in one room a little boy was depicted riding on a goldfish and shooting a rocket at a gold "2000." Later, at a children's palace, a place to which gifted youngsters were invited for special training, we were entertained by a chorus of small children, led by the teacher. One of the songs, proudly presented for our special benefit, was "Jingle Bells," the English words well pronounced. Older children were playing in an orchestra and constructing electrical equipment. In Nanjing we were entertained at the Nanjing Teachers College. There each of us had an opportunity to have a half-hour conversation with a student studying English. My partner started off by asking about marriage customs in the United States. He probably found my responses a bit shocking in view of the strong marital commitments in place in China. Other members of our party reported students expressing resentment at their repressive regime.

We were taken to an agricultural commune, where we were shown extensive fields of truck crops and given a sumptuous meal as a sample of its produce. We also visited a dairy operation, one which we were informed was rather rare in China, as they cannot afford the inefficiency of beef as a source of food. Animal protein, when available, is pretty much confined to fish, seafood, pork and poultry. A third stop was at an experiment station devoted to silk production. There special dwarf mulberry trees were grown for the efficient harvesting of leaves for the silk worms, which were being raised under controlled conditions. The cocoons are collected and their delicate threads unwound. I was astonished to learn that the insects were being bred to produce silk of various colors.

We visited two industries. One was a factory manufacturing art objects — oil paintings, decorated marble slabs, silk toys (Santa Clauses and small animals), and objects carved from jade. This was a labor-intensive operation requiring highly skilled workers and relatively small amounts of energy from fossil fuel. The other was a large textile mill making cotton and synthetic fabrics requiring substantial inputs of energy. Most of the raw materials were coming from China with exception of some of the synthetics that were being imported from the United States and West Germany. This was an example of the "Leap Forward" efforts of the Republic to modernize the economy. Since our visit, success with this program, largely powered by coal combusion, has blanketed much of the country with a pall of polluted air that is posing a serious threat to human health.[2]

As a botanist I was interested in the native flora that has close affinities with that of eastern North America. The woody plants I was able to observe were mostly under cultivation, along the streets, in parks, temple grounds, and palace gardens. In the southern portions of the country the city streets were predominately lined with sycamores. These had been decapitated at a height of about twelve feet. The spreading branches are carefully pruned and saved as a source of fuel. To the north, the streets were mostly planted with locusts and willows.

Factories in Chenchiang: *Left*: A room in a labor intensive art factory.
*Right*: A floor in an energy expensive cotton mill — an early example of
China's "great leap forward."

The Great Wall of China.

The maiden-hair tree (*Ginkgo biloba*) has never been discovered growing in the wild, but was originally reported as growing only in temple grounds. We saw two huge specimens in front of the Jiao Shan Buddhist temple on an island in the Yangtze River. Fragments of native vegetation were encountered there and at the memorial to Sun Yat Sen outside Nanjing. Familiar genera included oak, chestnut, cherry, peach, apple, sweet gum, pine, fir, and cedar. One of the most extraordinary finds was in a shop in the Beijing airport. It consisted of two bifurcated ginseng roots (*Panax quinquefolia*), reputed to be an aphrodisiac. They were neatly packaged in a box with a cellophane window, the weight about five ounces. The item was priced at $2,000. No wonder this plant has been nearly extirpated from our Appalachian woodlands!

Of course, as tourists, we had an opportunity to enjoy the art and architecture of a rich oriental civilization. One of the most remarkable structures we visited was the Great Wall, originally constructed more than 2,000 years ago. It extends for over fifteen hundred miles along the Mongolian border. We reached a restored section of it on a three hour bus ride from Beijing. We ascended the twnty-five foot wall and walked for about a mile along the ramparts, which wound up and down through the mountains as far as the eye could see. The walkway at the top, accessed at intervals by stairs on the southern side, was about twelve feet wide. Where it ascended the sides of the mountain, it consisted of flights of stairs. We were in luck. It was a beautiful sunny day. For the first time in over a week it was warm enough for us to take off our coats. The following day the road was impassable, closed by a blizzard.

Wherever we went in China our contacts with the people were warm and friendly. They gave the appearance of being healthy, purposeful, disciplined people and well adjusted to a solar economy. Padded jackets, blue for men and often colored-prints for women, gave protection from a cold climate and unheated living quarters. At an evening concert we attended in Nanjing the temperature in the hall was 45°F. Street lights were scarce and dim; but the traveller could walk abroad at night without fear. A private apartment we vistited had but one small fluorescent light in the ceiling of a room. Most of the people in the cities were travelling by foot. There were lots of bicycles, but these were evidently in short supply. In Kwangchow our bus driver begged Charles Chu to use his passport to buy one for him as he had been trying unsuccesfully to purchase one for three years. Very heavy loads were being moved along the streets on simple two-wheeled carts drawn by toiling individuals. There were virtually no private cars. Transportation on land was by bus, electric bus, and train; by boat on the rivers and canals. On the Yangtze we saw tugs pulling chains of twelve or more barges. Air travel was pretty much limited to diplomats and wealthy tourists. When we arrived at the Nanjing airport, we had to knock on the door. It was specially unlocked for us. The attendants were having tea in one corner of it. At that time there were only ten to fifteen flights a day out of Beijing.

The city streets were teeming with people. China was obviously suffering from overpopulation. We were told about the draconian measures the government was taking to curb population growth. At least in the cities married couples were being limited to a single child and were under constant surveillance. Severe penalties were being imposed for infractions of this policy. We also learned that men were frequently being required to work in places far removed from their wives for months at a time. This should give us pause to consider how population might effectively be stabilized in a free society.

Our brief glimpse of Japan was in striking contrast to that of China. In Kyoto and Tokyo a brilliantly lit technological society had filled the highways with cars and trucks, sometimes to the point of gridlock, and smothering itself with pollutants. Temples were crowded, the bushes adjacent to them covered with little paper chits, which we presumed to be votive offerings. It was a frenetic occidental pace in an oriental setting.

Nowhere during our brief stay in China were we aware of serious air pollution, although we were mostly under cloudy skies. It is disturbing to read how rapidly the situation is changing. Mark Hertsgaard in his remarkable book *Earth Odyssey*, published in 1999,[2] describes how, just in the last decade, the increase in industrial and domestic consumption of coal in China has been not only blanketing the country with toxic fumes that are creating a severe hazard to human health, but also causing destructive acid rain and making a huge contribution to the problem of global warming by its production of $CO_2$ into the atmosphere.

### South Africa

In 1984 the United States was debating various controversial issues with South Africa. In the spring of that year I received an invitation to join a team of American botanists to visit their professional counterparts in South Africa on a private citizen mission designed to promote peace between the two countries through friendly cultural exchange. This was under the auspices of People to People International, an organization founded in 1956 by President Dwight D. Eisenhower to foster goodwill and understanding between Americans and the citizens of other countries. In September our delegation met in Washington, D.C. for briefings in advance of its three week trip, which included visits to universities in Johannesburg, Pretoria, Bloemfontein, Port Elizabeth, and Cape Town; to botanical institutions; to outstanding botanical gardens; and to a private game reserve. Each of the scientific participants gave at least one presentation within his or her field of expertese at one of the institutions visited and contributed to the journal published by the delegation.

The scientific participants came from twenty-six institutions located in nineteen different states. Eight were accompanied by their wives. Four were friends of mine. Ralph Erickson, who replaced me at the University of Rochester, had used some of my data for an analysis of root growth. Charles Heimsch had been one of Ralph Wetmore's students. Reed Rollins had recently retired as Professor of Systematic Botany at Harvard, and I had known William Hiesey from the days when I had been at the Carnegie Laboratory on the Stanford University campus. One of our group, Jim Henderson, Professor of Biology at the Tuskegee Institute, was black. In those days of apartheid it took courage for a black to travel with a white group in South Africa. I was pleased that he was everywhere courteously treated in white facilities, at least as far as I could tell.

The only stop on our seventeen hour flight from New York to Johannesburg was on the desolate, arid Isle de Sol, in the Cape Verdes off the west coast of Africa. The last two hours were over the Kalahari Desert. We arrived at our destination in a shower and began to adjust to new time, a new out-of-sync spring, a sun rising and setting to the north, a sky full of strange stars and a land clothed with unfamiliar plants and still governed by repressive regulations.

After four days of professional contacts, a visit to a gold mine and sightseeing in Johannesburg and nearby Pretoria, we flew northeast, dropping down over the Drakensburg escarpment, to Mala Mala. This is a 60,000-acre private game reserve at the western edge of 4.7 million acre Kruger National Park, which extends for over 400 miles along the border of Mozambique. The terrain is semi-open bush country clothed with low trees and threaded by sandy river beds edged by tall reeds. From a luxurious tourist facility we were driven on early morning and late afternoon forays in land rovers, from which we had very close-up views of big game. These included elephant, white rhino, giraffe, cape buffalo, hippopotamus, lion, impala, greater kudu, bushbuck, waterbuck, and baboon. The animals appeared quite accustomed to these vehicular incursions on their turf. The first afternoon we passed two male lions following a lioness. After dark we encountered them again in the beam of a spotlight. One of the males was lying disconsolately beside the track, while a short way off the other was copulating with the lioness. At one point we approached very close to a rhino in rather thick brush through which it would have been difficult to beat a hasty retreat. At another, we backed up to a tree on the far side of which an elephant was feeding. Later on, when we were in Port Elizabeth, one of my companions and I were having lunch with a woman who had recently been to Mala Mala. She reported that when she had been on one of those forays, her driver had pulled off a similar maneuver. When the elephant started to become aggressive, the driver took off, but in the excitement of the moment still had the vehicle in reverse! She was there to tell the tale, but had been scared out of a year's growth.

In Bloemfontein I had a very pleasant contact with Choet Visser, a sports enthusiast who was in the rug business. He invited me and another friend to his home to meet his family. Later he took us to his store where he presented me with two antelope skins and a rug designed to commemorate the twentieth anniversary of the establishment of the Republic of South Africa.

The southern portion of the African continent has experienced a long and complex human history beginning with occupation by our hominoid ancestors, as attested by recent discoveries of prehistoric remains. European colonization both by the Dutch, referred to as Boers, and the English commenced in the seventeenth century. Between them there was political and military contention until it was finally peacefully resolved in 1961 with the formation of the Republic. The white establishment continues bilingual, speaking both English and Afrikaans, the modified Dutch spoken by the Boers.

The last two cities we visited were situated on the southernmost shores of the continent, Port Elizabeth to the east, facing the Indian Ocean and Cape Town on the west, facing the Atlantic. The tip of South Africa lies at a latitude south of the equator equivalent to what northern Florida is to the north of it. The vegetation at the southern end of the continent has always been isolated from that of the northern hemisphere by the tropics, and its climate has apparently been continuously more or less temperate. The result has been the development of a unique flora of great beauty and diversity. It was here, on the hills and mountainsides, that I encountered the fynbos, a low shrub-land community dominated by heaths, reeds, and leathery-leaved Proteas, the last two belonging to families of plants endemic to South Africa. This ecosystem is naturally maintained by fires, occurring at intervals of fifteen or more years. Here there is a profusion of bulbous wildflowers whose underground parts escape the fires. We are familiar with some of these as garden introductions belonging to such genera as gladiolus, amaryllis, and freesia. The shrubby species reproduce by seeds which require fire for germination. Among my surprises was encountering the stiff sword-shaped leaved *Sansevieria,* a tough plant often used for decoration in public buildings and other difficult places.

At Cape Town we visited the Kirstenbosch Botanical Garden, established to preserve and display the spectacular flora of South Africa. One of the world's most beautiful gardens, it is situated on the slopes of Table Mountain, which dominates the city. Among the garden's spectacular displays is its collection of cycads, surviving representatives of a very ancient group of gymnosperms.

I later learned a story about two plants of a very rare species of cycad planted on either side of the entrance to a public building in Durban, a coastal city on the Indian Ocean, which we did not visit. One day the inhabitants awoke to find a hole where one of these had been. The missing plant was eventually found in the garden of a wealthy Californian, who had financed this extraordinary theft. The plant had been dug up at night, trucked to an airport, loaded on a private plane and smuggled into the States. Because it was so special it had a small radioactive tag attached to it, which permitted its positive identification.

Our group made a number of field trips in the Cape Town area. One of these was to the top of Table Mountain, one to the Cape of Good Hope Nature Reserve and a third was an excursion about sixty miles inland, over a mountain pass, to Worcester, which lies in a rain shadow. On these trips we were privileged to have as our leader Professor E. Ted Schelpe, president of the Botanical Society of South Africa, who was a wonderful fount of information.

In Worcester we visited the Karoo National Botanic Garden. Karoo means stony plains and is applied to dry areas. This garden displays a remarkable collection of desert shrubs and succulents assembled from the deserts of the region. Notable among these are the stone and window plants. Their succulent leaves are almost entirely below ground, the portions at the surface resembling stones. The exposed tips of the cylindrical leaves of the genus *Fenestraria* are translucent and refract the light down to the protected underground photosynthetic tissues. Another genus, *Lithops,* has leaves the exposed tips of which resemble stones. They had a healthy young specimen of *Welwitschia banesii,* an endemic, found only in the Namibian desert. This rare gymnosperm produces only two elongated, leathery leaves from a woody crown. These continually grow at the base and lie on the surface of the ground. Growth is extremely slow. It has been estimated that large specimens may be over a thousand years old.

When we reached Cape Town our delegation hosted a banquet for the botanists of the area. My dinner partner was Danielle Law, the Executive Secretary of the Botanical Society of South Africa. This contact with her developed into an international exchange, which turned out to be my most significant contribution of the trip.

The following day at the Kirstenbosch Botanical Garden I made a presentation on our experiences in the preservation of natural diversity in the United States. The talk was well received.

Shortly after I returned home I received a letter from Ms. Law asking me a series of questions relating to our successes in preservation in the States. These included: what motivates people to contribute money and land for conservation, how natural areas are managed, what tax benefits we enjoy, and how suitable natural areas are identified. I answered them at length and sent her a copy of *Land Saving Action*. In a letter of thanks she wrote:

> We have been working on memoranda for the Minister of Environmental Affairs and Tourism, under whose aegis any legislative proposals will fall. The advice you have given personally on the whole question of the motivation of donations of land to the State have been invaluable. We in fact quoted in full the answers you gave to the questions we posed, in the final memorandum to the Minister, as well as passing over the copy of *Land Saving Action* you generously sent me. So I can doubly reassure you that your input of considered thought has been of immense benefit, both in clarifying our own thoughts on the subject as well as being able to quote someone with such extensive experience in this matter.

Later on I helped Ms. Law and Mr. Dale Parker, chair of the Flora Conservation Committee of the Botanical Society, plan a trip to the United States to learn more about how we go about land preservation. Mr. Parker had already established three private game and nature reserves totalling over 66,000 acres in various parts of South Africa. Unfortunately this trip had to be cancelled.

I wrote in my impressions of our trip that it was sad to observe the familiar pattern of habitat destruction in the South African countryside resulting from exploitation, too frequent burning, and the introduction of aggressive exotics. In a country where essentially all the land, with the exception of the national parks, is in private ownership, opportunities to preserve natural diversity lie in private action. It would be great if our successes might inspire the people in South Africa to develop a natural heritage program of habitat preservation.

## Nepal

When my friend Tim Rhodes was visiting us at the time of the annual meeting of The Nature Conservancy held at Dolbia in the fall of 1985, his parting shot was, "I would like to see some mountains before I die. How about going to Nepal?" I thought this was a great idea, so the old boys laid plans for a departure in late February of the next year. The trip involved an eight-day trek to the crest of the Himalayan foothills below Annapurna and Dhaulagiri, three days of rafting down the Trisuli River and two days observing wildlife in Chitwan National Park. In preparation for the venture I started to get in shape by vigorous walking up and down hills.

The final leg of our flight, from New Delhi to Kathmandu gave us a dramatic view of the northern section of the subcontinent of India, once upon a time attached to southern Africa, colliding with the southern edge of Asia. As far as the eye could see the flat plain of the Ganges was plunging under the Asian plate to push up an endless escarpment of lofty, snow-clad peaks. We were soon to experience the biological evidence of this phenomenon, the somewhat modified African fauna of the lowlands adjacent to the holarctic flora of the mountains.

Kathmandu, the capitol of Nepal, is a fascinating old city located in a broad valley — the site of an ancient lake — surrounded by the Himalayan foothills. We put up at an attractive modern hotel, the Yak and Yeti, which we found had been covered by a mesh net to prevent the large flocks of rock doves from occupying every available window sill and niche sheltered by the the overhanging roof.

At the headquarters of Mountain Travel, the organization which arranged our tour, we met the eight others with whom we would trek. Our party had an international flavor, consisting of a Swiss couple, a Canadian couple working at a hospital in Saudi Arabia, a mother and daughter from California, an Australian woman, and our leader, Warwick Deacock. Originally English, Warwick had served in the British army and subsequently moved to Australia, where he was running a travel enterprise. Support for the expedition consisted of six Sherpas, who served as guides, established the camps, and prepared the meals, and about ten porters, who carried the tents, bedding, gear and provisions. This left us with nothing to carry but light day packs for photographic equipment, binoculars, a day's water supply and supplementary clothing. The Sherpas were Buddhist people of Tibetan stock, who migrated into the mountains of Nepal around 1530. The porters were Hindus, recruited from the valley communities. At our briefing Warwick assured us that our trek would proceed at a leisurely pace and that we would "float through the country."

The trek began at Pokhara, about an hour's flight west of Kathmandu at an altitude of 2,700 feet. Being about the latitude of Miami, the vegetation, with its clumps of bamboo and occasional palm trees, had a semitropical aspect. For the first four days, our trek followed a major trade route into Tibet as far as a 9,600-foot pass that led down to the Kali Gandaki, a river that runs out of one of the deepest gorges in the world. Its headwaters are in the fascinating little feudal Kingdom of Mustang, perched between Nepal and Tibet, that has been under the rule of a single family for at least twenty-five generations. The average altitude of the country is 15,000 feet.

The track was rocky, many steep portions paved with interminable stone steps. At frequent intervals there were nicely constructed resting places consisting of a stone seat with shelf behind, just the right height for easing a heavy load. We were amazed to encounter numerous pack trains of from four to thirty donkeys laden with burlap bags of produce or equipment. They were accompanied by one or two drivers, adept at throwing stones. The lead animal was adorned with head plumes, a forehead plate with mirror, an anti-browse muzzle, and a bell.

In the valley just above Pokhara there had been recent robberies by Nepalese youths, so our route circumvented this section of the track by leaving it immediately north of the city to climb steeply to a ridge with a magnificent view of Machapucchare, the nearest of the great peaks. There we made our first camp. Shortly before supper we were hit by a violent thunderstorm. One of our tents was blown down, another ripped. We were lashed by several inches of sleet, which turned to slush the following morning.

During the storm a thief stole Warwick's camera from his tent. When tourists to the third world carry equipment hanging from their necks worth more than a years wages, this kind of gear must present a very tempting target. For the remainder of the trek our camps were guarded at night by a Sherpa. We were also advised to stay together as we traversed tracts of uninhabited forest. Otherwise we were allowed to straggle. A Sherpa always brought up the rear to assure that no one went astray.

The steep lower slopes of the hills had been endlessly terraced with rock retaining walls, behind some of which winter grains were being harvested. Others were ablaze with yellow mustard. Most of the houses were solidly constructed of stone with roofs of thatch or slabs of slate, and were often clustered into compact little villages.

As a retired school teacher, Tim struck up an acquaintance with some of the youngsters we encountered on the way, who were learning English. He made a point of visiting some of their schools, which he found extremely primitive. School starts at ten o'clock, and one of my vivid memories was seeing three little girls in floppy sandals happily skipping past us down stony stairs that it had taken us an hour to ascend. Their daily trip to school was down 1,500 vertical feet to the bottom of the valley and then 800 feet up the other side. No school buses here.

On our fourth day, we ascended above the cultivated land into the relatively undisturbed forest. Familiar genera included birch (*Betula*), maple (*Acer*) and whitebeam (*Sorbus*). In places the dominant tree was a rhododendron. Its clusters of deep crimson flowers were just coming into bloom. This tree becomes at least sixty feet tall and one or more feet in diameter. In fact we saw one at least three feet thick. Here and

Rhododendron being harvested for firewood in Nepal.

there on the forest floor several species of primrose were in flower. Higher up we climbed through stands of silver fir and Himalayan spruce two to three feet in diameter.

On the fifth day, we awoke to find it had snowed during the night. Leaving the trade route at Ghoropani, we waded through snow, the porters with bare feet, to the crest of a ridge at 10,600 feet where we could look up another 16,000 feet to the shining peak of Annapurna. Later, dropping to a somewhat lower elevation, we traversed cloud forests with weird contorted trunks, thickly festooned with golden-brown mosses that supported small epiphytic orchids — a terrain that is said to have inspired Tolkein to write about Hobbits.

It was sad to observe that the tourist traffic was accelerating the destruction of this magnificent forest. The Nepalese were building tea houses and inns in this high country to accommodate trekkers. The rhododendrons were being harvested for firewood, the conifers for timbers and roofing, and land was being cleared for cattle pasture.

Our return to Pokhara was via a less travelled route, passing through the fascinating old Ghurka town of Gandrung. We were told we would be "contouring" around. It was an interesting use of the word, as the walk would take us down several thousand feet across a valley, up over a high ridge, and then down into the next valley. At the end of the trek, Tim and I were ready for the luxury of a hotel.

The following day we were driven east about fifty miles to the bank of the Trisuli River, where we boarded a rubber raft manned by a couple of Nepalese. From there we were swept down stream for three days. It was a welcomed change of pace for tired limbs, but by no means devoid of excitement. The vertical drop was some 1,200 feet. One of our rowers was a good naturalist, who was able to identify the many birds we saw along the way, most of them new to us. The first two days

A one-horned rhino.

we were in a canyon, where we camped at night on the banks of the river. On the third day, we left the hills behind and floated on a more placid course along the boundary of Chitwan National Park, which protects a precious remnant of sal (*Shorea robusta*) forest with its great diversity of wildlife. At the shore of the park we were met by a Land Rover and driven to Tiger Tops, a tourist facility with luxurious accommodations.

We arrived in mid-afternoon, just in time for an elephant ride. Stepping off a balcony onto a pad mounted on the animal's back we took off at a stately pace into the park. The mahout sat in front on the elephant's neck. Armed with a stiff two-foot stick, he communicated with the elephant from time to time by giving it a resounding whack on the head. In places we were in "elephant grass" growing up to twenty-five feet tall. There we were able to photograph the Indian one-horned rhinos at close range. They were very little disturbed by the elephants. In sloughs along the river we saw crocodiles and their rare relative the gavial.

Just before dinner it was announced that a tiger had made its kill. This was a well orchestrated affair. Everyone crept barefoot by flashlight to a blind at the brink of a gully. There, right below, the great orange-striped cat could be observed under a floodlight feeding on a carcass.

At dinner one of the guests told us about a British dowager who had been taken on an elephant ride. She was an animal rights activist. When she saw the mahout whack the poor animal on the head with his stick, her adrenalin began to surge. She took her handbag and swung it at the head of the mahout, nearly knocking him off his perch. It was reported that the party returned to Tiger Tops "rather perturbed."

On the following two days we went on nature walks with naturalist guides. Some of these were at Tiger Tops and some at the Tented Camp, where we spent the second night. Wildlife was all about. Among the birds were hornbills, storks, and parakeets, while in the dust we saw signs of where a pair of leopards had spent the night and fresh tracks of tiger and crocodile. At one point, as we were walking in open wood-land we came upon a fresh rhino turd. These are about the size and shape of a child's football. I asked our guide what we should do if we came upon one of these creatures. He said, "Oh, just get behind the largest tree." I looked around. The largest I could see was only eight inches in diameter. Fairly soon we reached a blind on a bank of the river. Upstream I saw a floating log on which were two strange looking birds. A look through the binoculars resolved them into ears and, just beyond them, a horn. The log was the back of a rhino that was escaping the heat of the afternoon.

The establishment of national parks is a most important step toward the preservation of biodiversity, but pressures from a growing human population and increasing tourism create problems for their administration. At Chitwan competition between people and big game for limited resources is involved. Fortunately mountainous sections of Nepal are also getting protection. One of these is the 443 square mile Sagarmatha National Park in the northeastern part of the country, which includes Mt. Everest and the upper catchment of the Dudh Kosi River system. Adjacent to it is an incredibly rich ecosystem, the proposed Makalu-Barun National Park and Conservation Area. Hopefully this 900 square mile easterly extension will also receive national park status.

## The Pacific

In February of 1984, we joined a natural history tour of the Hawaiian Islands led by our friend Joe Van Os with whom we had previously made fall migration forays to Monhegan Island in Maine and Block Island off the Rhode Island coast. Our party of fourteen included our son, and our friends Ruth Pfanner and Ann Gaylord. Since the major objective of the trip was ornithological, we spent most of the time in exciting, out-of-the-way places.

The island chain, which is of relatively recent volcanic origin, started forming far to the west, where the earliest islands have been completely eroded to sea level and are now present mainly as coral reefs. The process of island building is still going on at the southeastern end of the chain on the island of Hawaii and, beyond that, under the sea. Our trip began on the oldest of the large islands, Kauai. Our most memorable experience there was a helicopter ride around its largest volcano, Mt. Waialeale, which has been eroded in a most fantastic way into colorful canyons, vertical cliffs, and razor-sharp ridges. The thirteen miles of the Pali Coast, frequently shrouded by mysterious curtains of mist, is so precipitous that it can only be reached by a frighteningly narrow foot path high above the pounding surf. Our flight took us up several of the uninhabited valleys along this coast. Later we drove to the crest of a ridge overlooking the Alakai Swamp in the heart of the mountain, one of the wettest spots on earth with an annual rainfall of about 600 inches a year. There, in the mist, we saw and heard some of the endemic honey-creepers — the amakihi, the anianiau, the akepa, the apapane, and the iiwi.

On the island of Hawaii, after a long day of birding, we arrived at Hilo on the very day Kilauea started to erupt again. That evening we chartered a small plane to fly us at low altitude back and forth past a thousand-foot fiery fountain that fed a glowing flow spreading over the mountainside. The advancing edges of the flow were outlined in brilliant orange as the molten lava continually broke through the darkening crust. We were close enough to feel heat through the windows of the plane.

On the island of Maui we had an unforgettable walk through an ohia and tree-fern forest on the slopes of Mt. Haleakala. It was along a wooden thirty-inch-wide aqueduct. Crossing ninety-foot deep ravines on this narrow walkway, supported by almost invisible wooden trestles, added a special flavor of adventure. We were advised to cross one at a time in order to avoid putting undue strain on the structure, and each of us made loving use of the single handrail.

Four years later Ruth and Ian Berendsen invited us to accompany them on a trip the New Zealand. Ian, whose father had been the New Zealand ambassador to the United Nations, had been brought up in that country. He subsequently became a member of the United Nations staff and married my friend Ruth. Ian was returning to New

Crossing an aqueduct on Maui.

Zealand to visit relatives and favorite haunts.

We left in January. It is a very long flight, so we stopped off for a couple of days in the Hawaiian Islands and took our friends over to Kauai for the spectacular helicopter circuit of Mt. Waialeale. Then leaving Honolulu on Air New Zealand a little after midnight, we arrived in Auckland about eight in the morning of the following day, having lost a day by crossing the dateline. It was a bit of a surprise to find that so much of that leg of the journey was south. In nine hours we had only crossed one more time zone, and had just plunged from midwinter into midsummer. The North Island is warm — almost semitropical; the South Island, cool and temperate.

New Zealand has about the same land surface as the state of Colorado and was supporting about seventy million sheep and three million people. Auckland, the largest city, lying about as far south of the equator as Norfolk, Virginia, does to the north of it, is situated at a narrow constriction in the North Island that nearly cuts it in two. One bay opens east on the Pacific; the other west on the Tasman Sea. There are huge marinas on these bays. We were told that there was a boat for every four inhabitants in the entire country. It would be hard to find a spot more that seventy-five miles from water.

Our stay on the North Island was brief. Immediately upon arrival we flew in a small unpressurized plane to Rotarua, situated near the middle of the island on a lake occupying a large volcanic crater. This is the center of the Maori culture. At the edge of town an area of thermal activity, with hot springs and geysers is owned and operated as a tourist attraction by these Polynesian people. We spent a delightful day driving into the country to visit some of the remaining untouched forests that have been preserved through the generosity of the Maoris, who have given a portion of their heritage to the government as a national park. Within the park is Okataina, another crater lake. The walkway along its eastern shore traverses a forest notable for its magnificent stands of tree ferns, some over sixty feet tall.

From Rotarua we flew directly to the foot of Mt. Cook. The flight took us past large volcanic peaks on the North Island and lands that are being rapidly deforested; then half way down the snow-capped and glacier-hung mountains that run along the western edge of the South Island. This range is being slowly subducted under the Tasman Sea, which now drowns great glacier-scoured valleys to form spectacular fiords. On the eastern slopes braided streams have filled wide valleys with gravel. To the south, where the pleistocene glaciation has been more severe, the valleys have been dammed with morainal deposits to form large lakes, just as the Finger Lakes have been in New York State. The prevailing westerly, moisture-laden winds from the Tasman Sea dump 300 inches of annual precipitation on the mountains, which are clothed at the lower elevation with a lush rain forest dominated by silver and mountain beech (*Nothofagus*) and carpeted with mosses and ferns.

Mt. Cook is in the middle of one of a series on national parks established along the mountain chain. It is a formidable mountain, rising to a height of 12,350 feet. While we were there several climbers lost their lives attempting to scale it. Ian and I hiked up the Hooker Valley over a series of recessional moraines to the foot of its gravel-covered glacier, while Ruth and Esther explored the flora in the beech forest of Governor's Bush.

From Mt. Cook we went south by bus through the open, east-slope foothills to Queenstown, situated on Lake Wakatipu. Being in the rain-shadow of the mountains this is sheep country, covered with grasses burned dry by the summer sun — a Californian landscape. To protect the livestock from the winter winds, exotic evergreens and Lombardy poplars have been planted as windbreaks in the flat, more open situations. A chairlift on a vast open mountainside only needed a blanket of winter snow to provide transportation to wonderful skiing.

We visited a large sheep station where we had a demonstration of their sheepdogs. There are two breeds that look very much alike, but have very different behaviors. One barks loudly and serves to scatter the sheep on the extensive mountain pastures; the other is silent and rounds up the animals into a tight flock by threatening to nip their heels. They are both beautifully trained to obey whistled commands.

For me the high point of the trip was walking the famous thirty-four mile Milford Track which threads its way across the mountain range from east to west through pristine country. The trek is organized as a five-day package, and it is necessary to make reservations months in advance. As it is normally limited to people aged between ten and seventy, I had to obtain special medical permission. It turned out that I was the senior member of the party of forty by about eight years. Participants enjoy the luxury of light packs, as food and sleeping accommodations are provided. It was a congenial international group with people from Australia, England, Japan, Canada, and the United States in addition to the local "kiwis."

The first day consists of a twenty-mile boat ride to the north end of Lake Te Anau, followed by a short walk to the first lodge. The second day is an easy ten-mile walk up a steep-walled, forested valley along the Clinton River to the second hut. The third day takes one up a head wall to MacKinnon Pass at 3,800 feet and then down 3,000 feet to the third lodge — a hard day for old knees. The fourth day is an almost level thirteen miles down to Milford Sound, where the party is met by a launch that takes it to the hotel in Milford for a banquet. The final day includes a boat trip down Milford Sound to the Tasman Sea and return to Te Anau by motor coach. Special memories of this trek include glimpses of large trout in the crystal clear waters of the Clinton River. Fishermen may feel that the whole trip is wasted by not having pulled at least one out, but it was a great feeling to know that they were there, enjoying the unpolluted environment. There were close-up glimpses of birds — the flightless weka, a brown bird about the size of a chicken; the gray New Zealand robin that almost ran over our boots as we stood in the trail; the large aggressive keas, parrots that were ready to scavenge any unattended snack or other object. A huge landslide had dammed the river at one point and numerous rocky streams had to be crossed. Incredibly we had three days with no rain! After a downpour the streams would have been formidable. Wires were stretched across some of them to provide hand holds to keep the hiker from being swept away.

The boat trip down Milford Sound was spectacular. The moun-

View looking westward down Milford Sound from Milford.

tains plunge vertically for thousands of feet into a sea livened by
friendly bottle-nosed dolphins which ride the bow wave and occasionally roll to get a good look at the passengers. It was there that I was
introduced to the fiordland crested penguins. I took this excursion
twice, first with the trekkers and then with Esther and the Berendsens,
who had driven over to pick me up. On the second run there were some
really avid birders, and I got a chuckle out of suggesting just at the right
point that they should take in the penguins.

On the east coast at Dunedin we enjoyed the hospitality of Ian's
brother's family before leaving for home. We broke the return flight
with a stop-off for five lazy days in Fiji, putting up at the Fijian Resort.
This was a luxurious hotel complex on the south shore of Viti Levu,
the largest of the islands in the archipelago. We were astonished to learn
that it has a greater land surface than that of the Hawaiian Islands.
Being right on the equator, it was hot and we spent much of our
time snorkeling behind the barrier reef, where ten-foot breakers were
thundering on the coral about 400 yards across the lagoon. It was a
wonderful winter break and Ian's guidance made it a quality experience.

# 12

# PHILOSOPHY AND MOTIVATION

As a preamble I must acknowledge a great debt to my father, who, as a scientist, was dedicated to the search for truth. As a student at MIT he had gone through an exhaustive exercise with his friend George Hale, who had been brought up in a strict fundamentalist tradition in which the Bible was the last word. Dad read the Bible very carefully in order to be able to discuss the text with his friend and analyze its many interesting discrepancies. To a certain extent I believe he was able to modify Hale's outlook. He told me of his heavy sessions with Uncle George and encouraged me to think things through for myself. I did.

After college I didn't see my friend Tim Rhodes very often. He became a schoolteacher, first in private schools in the Midwest and in the suburbs of Boston, then later, by choice, in public schools. He ended his professional career as principal of a school in Lincoln, Massachusetts. After retirement he moved to Camden, Maine. But through all these years we kept in touch. In 1950 he acquired a half interest in Beach Island in Penobscot Bay, about an hour by boat from Camden. Esther and I had the privilege of joining him and his wife Janet from time to time at this heavenly spot.

It was during one those last visits, when we might have been about seventy, that Tim and I started discussing religion. We both had been brought up in the Unitarian atmosphere of the First Parish Church in Brookline. We had attended its Sunday school, participated in its youth activities and were members of the scout troop which met in the basement of its parish hall. Tim and I were standing together at the wheel of his little lobster boat while chugging around the island when I made the remark that I really hadn't changed my basic religious beliefs since we were in college. Tim growled a response to the effect that I must have been intellectually dead during all those intervening years. This put an end to the subject and we went on to other interests and concerns; but his remark had an impact. I began to wonder whether my statement had been correct and his comment justified.

The twentieth century has been an extraordinary period of discovery. As a scientist I had been following these developments with great fascination. New observations were revealing ever greater depths to the expanding universe, now thought to have started off with the "Big Bang." These inspire awe and humility as I contemplate the minute size of our precious little planet in the cosmos. During this time not only had the double helical structure of DNA been established, but also the entire human genome had been mapped. Genetic engineering was posing serious environmental and bioethical problems for our society.

So what were my positions on some of the great questions — creation, the nature of God, the origin of life, organic evolution, immortality? Had they changed?

Creation: To me this remains a mystery which continues to be explored. Evidence accumulates indicating that the big bang may have occurred billions of years ago. But if so, this leaves us with even more fascinating questions. Why the big bang and what preceeded it? These were not questions I was asking in college.

The nature of God: God has taken many forms in different societies — sometimes multiple personalities, sometimes a single father figure, sometimes malevolent, and sometimes benevolent. For some it embraces the mysterious and unexplained. To me there appears to be order in the universe governed by physical laws. Our understanding of them has been undergoing constant revision and refinement. At the present time the creator and maintainer of this system fits my conception of God.

The origin of life: As a student I read a number of provocative scenarios as to how life might have originated on the Earth. One was the advent of a "divine spark" from which more complex organisms evolved. Another, which essentially side-stepped the issue, was that the initial organism on the planet drifted in from outer space. The possibility that has appeared increasingly attractive to me through the years is that life arose on Earth through the gradual build up of complex molecules that finally produced a self-replicating unit from which more elaborate organisms were evolved.

Organic evolution: Evolution is becoming more and more completely revealed by studies of the geologic record, and its inexorable methods of operation are being demonstrated by present day observations and experiments. The many elegant studies that have been published have helped me develop an understanding of this complex process. It is hard to believe that so many people in our society have been brainwashed to the point that they are unwilling to examine the evidence. Homo sapiens is a species that has evolved from its animal ancestors with which it shares most of its DNA, its nutritional requirements, and reproductive drives. However, it has evolved physical and mental capacities that permit it to exploit the environment, first through more effective methods of hunting, followed by the development of animal husbandry, agriculture, written language, and finally methods of tapping sources of energy. And now our species has become the most destructive biological force operating on the planet.

Immortality: There are several possibilities. One kind we can be sure of. We live on after death in the memories of those with whom we have been in contact — family, friends, neighbors, associates — and those who may have been influenced by our actions or by our ideas propagated by written word or other media. The size of the circle and the length of time involved will vary enormously with the quality of our life and our accomplishments. Great religious leaders, writers, scientists, musicians, artists, and philosophers enjoy the longest afterlife of this sort. Then if we have children, a small part of us lives on in them. Lastly, there is the immortality promised by various religions and sometimes described in detail to fit the circumstances. Thus far, I have seen no convincing evidence that such a condition exists after death. The alternative that I imagine is a deep and dreamless sleep.

Esther and I were married by my old scoutmaster, Robert Schacht, who had by then become a Unitarian minister. Esther had been brought up an Episcopalian, but during college had abandoned that sect. During the early years of our marriage we remained essentially unchurched. It wasn't until after my father died in 1949 and Bob Schacht had officiated at his memorial service, that Esther and I realized that if we expected the performance of satisfying rites of passage we should be supporting an institution that supplied such services. So we joined All Souls Unitarian Universalist Church in New London. This church had at that time reached an all-time low in its history. It had no minister, and at our first meeting only ten members were in attendance. Very shortly after joining, I was elected president, a position I held for a couple of years.

Almost immediately All Souls was fortunate enough to be able to call John C. Fuller as its new minister. It was his first church assignment and he turned out to be an inspiring leader. The congregation grew rapidly during his three years with us and began again to serve a helpful role in the life of the community. Esther and I found ourselves in the midst of a new circle of congenial friends beyond the college walls. After two more ministers, who were with us briefly, the church continued for a period of seventeen years without one. During that period of lay leadership it enjoyed visiting preachers in the pulpit. Today All Souls is a flourishing institution playing a useful role in the greater New London community. Through the years Esther and I have taken great satisfaction in supporting an organization that provides a comfortable home for those like ourselves, who wish to play a helpful role in the community while developing their own religious convictions.

What I have done in this life has not been motivated by an effort to save myself from unpleasant experiences in the next, but rather, at least in part, by a desire to preserve the beauty and biological integrity of the earth we have inherited. Esther and I heard a poem written and read by Robert J. Lurtsema to introduce Paul Winter's Earth Mass (*Missa Gaia*) at Symphony Hall in Boston. It is a lovely blueprint for action. We were so delighted with it that we asked him to send us a copy. Here it is.

## THE EARTH IS OURS

In an outer arm
   of the galaxy
safe from harm, —
   save for you and me
a gem-like sphere
   of blue and white
shines bright and clear
   in space black night,
spins 'round the sun
   that gave it birth, —
the marbled one
   our home, — the Earth.

From ground and granite
   it takes its name
this water planet with
   heart of flame,
its soul ablaze.

\* \* \*

We raise our voice
    in song of praise
as we rejoice
    in our land of dreams
with lakes and seas
    and hills and streams
with rocks and trees
    and grass and flowers
and clean fresh air.

The Earth is ours,
    but just to share
with wolf and whale
    and hunting fox
and garden snail
    and geese in flocks
with moray eels
    and dragon-flies
and baby seals
    with soft wet eyes
with birds and bees
    and stalking cat
algae and fleas
    and water rat
with nesting hen
    and busy ant
and canyon wren
    and elephant
with eagle, frog
    and nursing sow
gorilla, dog
    giraffe and cow
with lion, loon
    and sharks and minks

the masked racoon
　　the snail the lynx
with bulls and bears
　　with hound and hare.
The Earth is theirs
　　as well to share.
Along with leaf
　　and bud and plants
we are but brief
　　inhabitants
dependent all
　　on Earth — our mother
and great and small
　　on one another.

From single cell
　　to human kind
we must use well
　　all that we find
for earth is still
　　a finite source.
We have the will
　　to set the course
to share, each day,
　　with all our kin
that "fullness" for all
　　that dwell therein
and heed the call
　　of love and peace
as if we'd all
　　co-signed a lease
for sun and showers
　　and food and air.
The Earth is ours,
　　but just to share.

Troop 4, Brookline. All left to right. *Front row*: Osborn, Robert Whitemore, John M. Morse, Robert C. Vose, Jr., Richard H. Goodwin, Edward W. Robinson, Delano Wight, Crocker Wight. *Second row*: Robert H. Schacht, Scoutmaster, Lindsey Brigham, Richard Bent, Richard Pentecost, S. Morton Vose III, Charles S. Denny, Timothy Rhodes, Russell Hasting (in front), Herbert Vose, Assistant Scout Master Henry Bigelow. *Third row*: Richard Prouty, Andrew Marshall, Minot Shepard, Cranford Rogers, Edward F. Andrews, Wendell Hastings, Anthony. *Fourth row*: Robert Ralston, Cortland Hubbard, Richard Harding.

# APPENDIX

Round-robin letters circulated among members of Troop 4, Brookline, Massachusetts, between September 4, 1944 and December 10, 1945.

Richard Bent
3 Cedar St.
Worcester, Mass.
Sept. 4, 1944

Dear fellow Boogies, Anti-macks, etc:--

I certainly am highly in favor of Goodwatt's brainstorm, and hasten to add my bit, and send it along.

As most of you know, the Bents deserted the Conn. countryside in June 1943, and moved here to Worcester. We like it, but are glad to hear the Goodwins are taking up their abode near Norwich as there is a lot to be said for that part of the country.

The biggest event of our life recently was the birth of a son and heir, Edward Stuart, on Jan. 6th of this year. He has thrived ever since he arrived, and now weighs over twenty pounds. Has two teeth only which showed up three months ago. Yesterday he decided he had taken it easy long enough, so began to crawl madly all around the apartment. He has been going strong ever since. He gets his name from his two grandfathers.

His mother has had a hell of a time since shortly after his arrival. She developed "Non-tropical Sprue", which is a deficiency disease (or

rather ailment), and had to spend four months in the M.G.H. in
Boston. She lost thirty pounds, and had to live for a couple of months
on blood transfusions and intravenous feedings. Charlotte was able to
come back to Worcester about the first of August, and, altho she has a
long way to go, seems to be making some satisfactory progress now.

As result of Ted's birth and Charlotte's sickness, our activities
have been very limited for the past year, but we hope for better days
ahead. Since we left Norwich, I have been working at the lumber business here in the Worcester office. We converted to war business early
in 1942, and have been doing that type of business nearly 100% since.
It has consisted of shipping lumber to the Army, Navy and Maritime
Commission, and their contractors--both prime and sub. In the early
days of the war, the lumber was used chiefly for construction of Army
and Navy bases and Government housing projects, etc. This type of
work was largely completed a year ago, and since then practically all
lumber we've shipped has gone for boxing and crating for overseas
shipment. Today nearly 75% of all the lumber purchased in N.S. and
Canada goes into boxing and crating. The whole industry has been
under increasing tight W.P.B. controls, so that now no lumber yard can
sell more than one truckload of lumber, in any quarter of a year, with
a certified WPB order.

It has been a real job to get the right lumber to the right place at
the right time in spite of the rules and regulations, which, while necessary, have been a bit cumbersome at times (to put it mildly).

Let's take Vose up on his idea of weekend in Dover. I hereby
appoint him a Committee of One to procure the food and drink.

The Bents send their very best to all of you and your families.

As ever,
Dick


Edward W. Robinson
UNITED STATES ARMY
Camp Cooke, California
November 3, 1944.

Dear Chums:

No, this novel chain letter hasn't been stalled in the hands of
S.M.V., as Rich suggests, nor has it even been to Dooney yet--rather it
has been lying dormant in Binson's foot locker. A thousand pardons,
fellers; it seems I've been most horribly on the go lately, and my correspondence has suffered accordingly. Don't anyone think for a moment,
I've been registering complaint by using the silent treatment, because
like those who have written before me, I consider Rich's idea an

extremely novel one. I have already asked him to let me see the letter when it has completed the rounds--and I believe you will all approve my action of adding his name to the end, so that he may be the first beneficiary of his own efforts.

Enough of the drivel: good evening, Mr. and Mrs. America; let's go to press!--

Yours truly has seen eleven months of service in this man's army, all in the Continental confines of the U.S. I tried on four occasions to land a commission in the Navy before the draft caught up with me a year ago. Then, being partly fed up with the Navy for passing up such excellent talent (?), I chose the Army when I had cleared the mill at the induction center; since then I have regretted my decision on a number of occasions, for it seems I entered the Army too late to land any of the plums. From the reception center at Fort Devens, I was shipped to Fort Eustis, near Williamsburg and Newport News on the Peninsula of Virginia, where I took my basic training with a search-light battery, specializing in Radar, a subject which proved more inter-esting. Alas! at the completion of basic, I was doomed to leave desir-able Anti-Aircraft for the drudgery of the Infantry. Our group was transferred in toto to the 97th Division, then training at Fort Leonard Wood in Missouri. In July the outfit was transferred to Camp San Luis Obispo, a nice little camp near a town of the same name in California, about halfway between Los Angeles and San Francisco. We remained till the end of September. For the next month we went through amphibious training involving a brief stay at Camp Callan, near San Diego, where we had "dry runs", followed by a two-day cruise aboard LCI's, then a ten-day affair on transports in the Pacific, including a number of practice landings. Now the Division is assembled at Camp Cooke, about 40 miles south of San Luis, for squad, platoon, company, battalion, and regimental combat team problems. Running comment indicates it's the old Banana Boat for us soon, and I wouldn't be at all surprised one of these days to land in the western Pacific--already Eddie Andrews seems to believe his D.E. may escort us to shore some day!

Having reconciled myself to the Infantry about as much as I could with all its uninteresting details, I resolved to make the best of a poor situation. The physical requirements are rugged for a man who is con-sidered old, according to Army standards, but I've stuck it out so far. All but made Infantry O.C.S. two months ago, but found out at the beginning of this week that my eyes didn't quite make the grade. Luckily I attained the position of assistant squad leader, about a month ago, having toted around a B.A.R. for some four months, and a buck sergeancy is on the way now. In case the question was in anyone's mind, I have found three years of service in the Mass. State Guard, as non-comm. and officer, valuable.

I sure miss being at home with my vivacious wife and 1-1/2 year-old son, Ned. He has advanced so rapidly, because he _is_ at that age where naturally he would, that I'm unable to relate all his accomplishments, but he is quite a talker and has a phenomenal memory. Fortunately Barby and Ned were able to move in with the Gliddens for the Duration, so I know they are getting good care. If I could feel my time in the service will spare my son a similar experience twenty years hence, I shall consider it time well spent. Not much space left, so brief, but fond regards to all.

ED.

P.S. I made buck sergeant today, (11-13-44), so at least rose above the rank of private, even if not officer material. The attached clipping may hand you a laugh! EWR.

Edward Andrews
11 February 1945

Let's mill on Vose!
(Above should be as good a greeting as any. Wish to hell I was near enough to do just that, too.) No doubt about it. Goodbun certainly has a fine thought here. My only news of the gang has been through the mighty Vose, for the most part. The rest of you rather lost contact with me. Don't know as I blame you so much at that. After all, I have been away on active duty since November 1940, with almost all of it at sea. Before that I did remain more or less in the same place, in New Jersey. Now and again I did see one of you when passing through, but our own lives and interests kept contacts down to a minimum, to say the least. Believe the last time of any consequence that I saw most of you was at 'Binson's wedding.

Much water has passed under the dam for me during the past four years. First, I cannot make much of a report on home life, as I have none to speak of. After returning from twenty months working out of Panama, I did manage to have my wife and daughter (will be eight in May) with me in Miami for two months, while I attended school and skippered a school ship. Managed to locate a lovely home, large enough to have Pappa and Mother Andrews down as house guests for several weeks. Daughter Barbara had a time chasing around the winter play spot, but image that in another ten years she might have more of a time.

After leaving Miami, went directly to South America, almost. No sooner arrived that ship was ordered to New York making me most unhappy (don't you believe it!). Arrived just in time to lose a daughter, and sailed again with a convoy (to be gone a month) not knowing whether Peggy would be alive upon my return or not. We also lost a son the Spring before I reported for active duty. For you medical students, we are victims of the "RH Factor", which is another way of saying that we will never have any more children of our own.

Enjoyed working out of New York for about five months, during which time being able to get home once a month for four or five days. That was a welcome change. It was too good to last, for next I found myself assigned to a destroyer escort. Training the crew, commissioning the ship plus shakedown took until Jan. 4, 1944 when we left for the Pacific, where we have been ever since.

As a whole, the duty has not been too bad, but the time passes so quickly that I sometimes wonder if I'll ever get back before turning into an old man. We have had many experiences, some altogether too close calls, as well as seeing most of the islands in the South and Southwest Pacific. Right now it might almost be easier for me to start home over the Burma Road, if I could be relieved to go home, which is impossible, of course! Sure wish I could though. I never was cut out to remain away from home so long, war or no war.

I hope my contribution to this chain does not take as long as did 'Binson's efforts. Poor fellow, he can't be expected to know the trials of overseas mail, not having sailed the last I have heard. However, should he ever see this, he might be interested to learn that the letter took better than three months to reach me, because he forwarded it as "Free" postage. The only possible way to have a letter reach this neck of the woods is by airmail. Then it has been known to make it all the way in as little as seven days--a far cry from three months!

As previously stated earlier in this letter, I have no idea when or if I'll be on my way back. Should any of you happen to be passing through New York City and care to look me up, my home remains at 747 Kimball Avenue, Westfield, N. J. Peggy and daughter Barbara are there and would certainly welcome a call from any or all of you. Poor girls! They have had rather a tough assignment, trying to make a go of it alone for over four years. Just think, I have known my daughter but half the years she has been alive! Robbery I calls it. You can easily imagine that there is no love lost between me and the little yellow men or European supermen.

If anybody has waded through all of this, good for you. That is the story, anyway. Wouldn't mind a letter from any or all of you if you can spare the time. Mail is all we have to live for out here--there is no liberty and no place to go.

                              As Ever,
                              EDDIE

Andrew Marshall
HW 497th ARMD FA BN,
APO 263, c/o Postmaster, New York, N. Y.

May 4, 1945.

Dear Guys:

I got this round robin letter almost a month ago now, and with the
best of good intentions sat down to answer it in a hurry, resolving not
to let it lie around for a month like Robinson. But just about then this
13th Armored Division took of, as they say around here, like a big
bird, and travelled a censored but ungodly number of miles, sometimes
fighting Jerry and sometimes not. Without going into the details, I
think we are allowed now to say that we landed in France early this
year, fooled around in Normandy for a while, went to work for the first
time for pay in the Saar basin cleanup, then helped chop up the Ruhr,
and are now on another mission in another part of Germany. What we
are running into now is unpredictable and a little unnerving at times,
because in one town they will welcome you as though they had been
waiting for the Americans for the last ten years, and in the next they
will pop at you with flak and 88's. My particular slot is alternating
between exec and CO of an armored artillery battalion, depending on
how many lieutenant colonels there are around. I have commanded it
for a total of about eight months, and at the moment am exec. I've
changed back and forth so many times that it is now practically pain-
less. All I do is turn my hat the other way and go to work on the other
job. As it is a particularly hot outfit, the job is pretty good fun either
way.

Since I haven't laid eyes on any of you for the last five years at
least, I'll go back that far, briefly. The job selling Stevens products in
New England which I took shortly after college was turning out fairly
well, and I stayed there until the National Guard was called out in
January 1941. From then it was just as it has been for every one else
- a lot of different schools and jobs in different parts of the country.
North Carolina, Oklahoma, a tour on ROTC duty at Harvard, California,
Oklahoma again, Texas, Georgia, Texas again, and finally overseas. Lee
went with me to Oklahoma the first time, but a little later the calamity
hit us, and she died in December 43, after being sick for two years.
Our two children, Andrew 3rd and Lee Jr., are living now with my sister Blanch in Manchester, N. H., with four of her own. She claims it is
easier to take care of six than four, and proves it by looking and
acting younger all the time. Brother Mac is at home at last on sick
leave, recovering from a leg wound he got from a German antiperson-
nel mine in the Siegfried line. He has been with the 1st Inf Div in all
its actions, has been wounded twice, and sports a Silver Star. I hope he
is in the US for good now. Jamie lives in Jamaica Plain near the

family; her husband is a Lt. in the Navy, stationed in Philly. That about completes the Marshall dope. After the war, it's anybody's guess. Looks a little on the empty side right now, but the war being over is enough to look forward to in itself. I don't see how the Germans would ever dare to start another war again, after the impact of the hundreds of tanks thundering through all these little German towns, and the thousands of people getting bounced out of their houses to let the soldiers in there. We will be terrible suckers if we ever let it happen to the US. At any rate, the next few years can't help being better than the last few.

It was a hell of a lot of fun reading about all of you. Apologies again for the lateness of the letter, and good luck until I see you all.

As ever,
ANDY M.

Richard Prouty
July 18th, 45.

Hi Boys--

The round robin letter reached me yesterday--and a darn interesting group of case histories. Being in the U. S. C. G.--I guess I got the biggest kick out of hearing Penty bitch and gripe about his service with the Coast Guard at Curtis Bay.

A brief summary of my activities include marrying a lovely girl (if I do say so myself) from Chicago--Ann Jenkins. Her mother was married in our church and was Elio "Bud" Rictchie's aunt. Ann has given us twins--a boy, Jonathan, and a girl, Hilary, born Jan. 20th, 1944. We were married in March '43, just after I received a commission from the Coast Guard Academy Reserve Officers' training school in New London, Conn. We skiied on our honeymoon in Colorado and she is also a good woodsman, tennis and golf enthusiast.

While I was overseas mostly in the Mediterranean theater pursuing the "Champagne campaign"--she has been skimping on gas and meat at 12 Cotlin Rd., Brookline. Before my 15 months in the Mediterranean which included the Southern France invasion--I put in 6 months as skipper of an "83 footer", convoying and antisubmarine patrol in the 6th Naval District. I also had a few months in the Caribbean--which was a garden spot. All of my service, with the exception of the 6 months 83 footer training, has been on the U. S. S. DUANE, formerly Admiral Lawry's flag ship.

At the moment of writing I am again in the U. S. A.--Ann is with me,--and if I get leave I'll see the children before going to the Pacific. I sure hope the Japs will cave in by Dec. 45!

Good luck to all of you --
DICK PROUTY


Richard H. Goodwin
New London, Conn.
August 11, 1945

Dear Gang:

On August 8, 1944 Goodberry stuck a slug in the slot and 366 days later out came the jackpot, a damn fine set of letters. Dooney got missed, and I am sending everything to him with the suggestion that he keep the ball rolling: Denny, Vose (T.G.), Bent, Vose (S.M.), Binson, Andrews, Rhodes, Penty, Marshall, Prouty & Goodberry. Remove the repeat material and carry on! Suggestions: put on air-mail to the unlucky guys still overseas and correct the address list as best you can.

With the atomic bomb and Russia closing in, Dick Prouty's hope of peace by December '45 seems overly probably. This is doubtless a joyful prospect to all, and here's a hope that all the boys are back soon with nothing worse than Binson's nick on the hip. The atomic bomb, however, brings sobering reflections! What if the Jerries had beat us out in the production of atomic power? And what if this power falls into the wrong hands in the years to come? Anyone who has thought on what we can do toward maintenance of peace, in a personal way, should air them in this round robin. We may be pawns in a complex community, but this doesn't preclude our taking positive action in the right direction.

I second the nomination of T. G. Vose as chairman extraordinary and permanent member of the CFBBAD (Committee for better binges at Dover), leaving to his able lack of discretion such things the setting of dates, publicity, commissary, procurement of lubricant, B.W.B. and/or whatever else he may deem appropriate. There should be plenty of catching up to do!

The Goodberries weathered a civilian winter in New London and have enjoyed their new environment. My office at the College is situation in a small greenhouse on the north side of the science building, known locally as the gold-fish bowl. This position in the public eye has kept me on the straight and narrow (at least on campus) and I still hold my job. The student body is easy on the eyes and is exploited with great frequency and, I gather, with some success by the Coast

Guard (at times this relation should be put in reverse). Perhaps Dick Prouty could give us the inside story on this.

The summer is being spent in two places--a camp on Squam Lake, N. H., for the month of July and a house at the mouth of the Thames River, New London, on a fine beach. Subs, freighters, L.S.T.s, D.E.s and numerous other craft of all descriptions put in and out every day reminding us that the war is still on. Flights of 50 or more fighter planes from Groton and Westerly are also a daily occurrence. The campus is relatively peaceful now. During regular session the buildings get buzzed until the girl-friends come out and wave (or until the sun-bathers get under cover--I'm not sure which). We have little of great moment to report. We consider ourselves among the lucky few who have been enjoying an intact family unit. The kids have been learning to row and paddle and swim and climb on mountain trails, and Esther and I made the most of our first real vacation in three years. I can still enjoy paddling to a wooded island, frying ham and eggs over a smoky fire, watching a fiery sunset over the purple hills, a cool moon-lit dip, and a bed of balsam boughs. I dare say Andy and Binson will be more appreciative of Simmons Beauty-Rest mattresses (etc.?) by the time they get mustered out.

Enough of this, and best of luck to each and every one. Some of you guys have had more than your fair share of troubles. Let's hope that better times lie ahead! Keep the letter circulating, and see if you can make the round in less than a year.

As ever,
GOODBERRY.

P.S. It looks as tho the Jap accordion is just about folded up! 8/12/45

Charles S. Denny
c/o U. S. Geological Survey
Military Geology Unit
Washington, 25, D. C.
Sept. 3, 1945 (V-J day plus 1)

Dear Gang,

Recently the Dooneys have been at Wesleyan University in Middletown, Conn. Then a year ago we came down here to Washington to work for Uncle. At Wesleyan I was teaching everything from Geology to aircraft engines, in which subject I became an expert in 4 easy lessons. Down here I have been working for the Corps of Engineers writing terrain intelligence reports, chiefly on the Pacific Islands and

China, although we did do some work in Europe. Ann has been chiefly occupied taking care of Nancy (5) and Betsey (3).

In the summer of '43 I spent three months on the Alaska Highway with Hugh Raup, a botanist from the Arnold Arboretum. In late July of this year we spent two weeks in Sunapee, New Hampshire, and another week in Cambridge and Duxbury, where we saw TG and Pete and Barbie Robinson, missing Eddie by only a few days.

Our future plans are indefinite, but we expect we shall be in Washington for some time. At the moment I am going to Fort Knox, Kentucky, for 3 months.

If any of you mugs come to Washington be sure and look us up. At the moment we are living in Arlington (addressed listed in the telephone book). I can think of no other great news except that I have lost some hair on top and gained something about the middle.

I look forward to this mill at Dover. A good idea! I should like to hear first hand about some of the places that Andy, Eddie, Eddie and Dick have seen.

Best regards,
DOOONEEY

Robert C. Vose, Jr.
Robert C. Vose Galleries
559 Boylston Street
Boston

Sept 6 1945

Dear Mugs:

So the letter made its rounds in a year almost to the day! I'll bet this next trip takes less than 6 months. Somehow Old Mousehouse got left out on the last round, but all the original letters are still included and he didn't miss anything.

Things are on the way back now as proven by the fact that my eyes have been subject to the strain of viewing the oafish Dooney, hot-air Bent, and round-the-world Robinson all within the past few weeks. Of these worthies I would make the following comment: to the casual glance there is absolutely no outward change in large Denny, but the inner man is developing slowly and, surprising as it may seem to those who have know him, someday, I believe that he will amount to something! Bent, on the other hand, hasn't changed inwardly or outwardly. He will gladly sell you anything you don't want for more than you want to pay. The Sarge (EWR) has changed in every respect. No longer is he the stolid banker from Boston, contented and soft in the midsection. Physically he looks to be about in the same condition that Pentecost <u>claims</u> to have attained. Furthermore, he has been around and has a lot of new ideas. Whether or not all of them are good, Barby is as yet unconvinced, but it remains to be seen.

Delighted to hear that most of you endorse the Dover bender. I shall take it upon myself to attempt to organize it when the time comes.

As of yesterday I am back at the Gallery! Thing really are changed. No more grunting and groaning with second hand machinery for me.

Congratulations to <u>Cmdr</u> E. F. Andrews USNR. If anyone ever deserved the rank he does after 5 years away from home.

So Rhodes is going to liven up the dangerously conservative A F of L. I'll bet he has been waiting for the reaction he hoped that remark would make. Maybe you have something there, Rhodes, but no matter how long the argument, there will always be a sizable gap between the practical point of view of a man in business, depending on it for his living, and the theoretical, idealistic point of view of the professional man. Of course, I don't know what we are arguing about yet, but that is at least a start for one.

I'd like to get a look in at Pentecost, Waterboy in the second grade, teaching his hill-billies to play the harmonica or something.

Within the year we ought to be able to get together, but this should take another round before then.

Best,
BOB


S. Morton Vose
Robert C. Vose Galleries
559 Boylston Street
Boston

September 11th, 1945.

Dear Gang:

Reading a crop of letters which has accumulated during the travels of this round-robin has certainly been a most interesting experience. The contents add up to quite a document!

I found myself woefully out of date with most of you fellows, and am certainly glad to catch up. Reading the experiences which the war has brought to a good many of you makes me realize how lucky I am that my cranky digestion has kept me at home with my family. On the other hand, I must confess to a bit of envy for you who have had a hand in the good work, and have been seeing the action of the past few years.

My own report shows only one important change in twelve months' the addition of a second daughter, Virginia Williams, born June 21st. The family has been at Sunapee, N. H. during most of the summer, where I've managed to join them for a week and a couple of weekends.

I'm still at the Galleries, where Bob has now rejoined me. Most of my spare time still is spent with the Mass. State Guard, from which I'll now probably resign as soon as I can gracefully do so. Two kick-backs from my bad tempered stomach have given me a total of a couple of months of enforced leisure this season, so I'll have to start behaving myself, as training for the proposed Dover get-together!

During the year I've had the good luck of seeing a few of you mugs; Binson, Big Dooney, Bent, Goodwatch--and lets see, I guess Penty was in Boston within that period,--and Tim. Must say I'm not quite as much impressed by changes in character as Bob seems to be. I think most of us, by this time, are predictable and incorrigible. Of course, I must qualify that by admitting of those I have seen, only Binson and Penty have been doing anything violently different from their previous pursuits.

Well, the next few years should certainly be interesting and important ones. Wonder if we can do anything about them?--Good luck, Gang.

MORT.


John M. Morse
5038 Nicklas Pl NE
Seattle 5, WN.
Sept. 19, 1945.

Fellows!--

TGV condescended to ask me in for the second round! A very good idea this bringing all up-to-date: especially since I haven't contacted my college roommate for umpty years! Having finally recovered from Penty's rough epistle, I'll add a little temperance:

Family history: married 1941; arch. work in Wash. D. C. 1941-2; Boeing Aircraft Co. (Seattle) as aeronautical engineer (ha-ha!) 1943-Aug. 1945; since then working with small arch. office here doing contemporary work ("modern')--mostly residential and small commercial. Am registered architect in this State--now all I need is some business (come on out and settle down!--the weather's fine says the ch. of commerce--I say there are 2 seasons: the rainy season and August.)

As you see, I've been lots luckier than many--I hope I appreciate it. We have two kids: David is 3, Kitsy 8 months. Lots of fun. Also own a house. Guess we'll at least give this part of the country a good try.

Bent and Robinson have been thru here and it sure cheered us up to see "Easterners". I'm often taken for an Englishman! Such provinces! Maybe you'd like a brief report on the Northwest:

In the first place it's sparsely populated: only 2 good sized cities, Portland and Seattle (the latter some 450,000, owing to war mfgr.) Wide spaces and great variety of landscape: the "wonders" are (1) the isolated mountains such as Mt. Rainier (an ice-cream cone, rising 14,000 ft. from plain--3 hours drive from Seattle--good open-slope skiing and summer hiking), (2) the protected waters of Puget Sound and its many harbors and islands--sailing galore, ferries galore, et., (3) the large and greatly unspoiled Nat. Park comprising the Olympic Mts.--on a peninsula across Sound from Seattle, (4) the quite genuine English vacationland on Vancouver Island--5 hrs. by ferry from Seattle, (5) Lake Washington--fresh water 30 mis. long, bounding Seattle on east and connected with ocean via canal and locks--sailor's heaven. (Of course Col. Basin and Grand Coulee which I haven't yet seen.)

As a city Seattle is a small town--no public bards for hard liquor (N. B. Penty and Bent!), poor burlesque (N. B Robinson), few modern buildings, startling paucity of downtown parks (appreciate Boston, NYC and Wash, DC if you don't already), poor transportation to outside world: Navy took away its big ship piers and it had better hustle to replace 'em. Many small businesses and industries--Boeing and shipyards are only large ones and they look as though they'll be pretty small soon. Mild climate, some nat. resources, and very cheap elec. power are the drawing cards. It is a city of homes--people work hard to keep up appearances, and most social life centers around private clubs. Money is a very big talking point--but few have much of it. Capitalism is strong' a "planned" democracy looks red, but also unions are in full control.--in building they will hold back possible advance (N. B. Tim). In business, people appear conservative, lacking in confidence, and ready to play only a sure winner. I guess the East has them buffaloed. Everything it seems, is made in the East--way across the mts!

This all sounds grim--but everyone's hopeful here, and after all, the first settler landed here in about 1850!

This has turned out to be a pretty serious bit of stuff. Sorry! Hope we can lighten up our lives (and heaps) with a big mill on D___y, B__son, and ____. We're hoping to all get East somehow next summer (1946). Sure mill the old mugs and jernts.

And here's hoping the boys in uniforms get free soon. They deserve it!

Goodwatt's thoughts on atomic what-have-you were interesting. I

was very depressed at the news of the bomb and since then haven't
been able to grasp whole significance, I'm sure. It certainly is time we
all stopped being selfish and too lazy to <u>work</u> for good times. I shudder
when I feel myself settling back to "normalcy". 'Snuff!

MOOSEY, MOUSE, JACK . . . . .


Edward W. Robinson
Maebashi, Honshu, Japan
18 October, 1945.

Hi, Pals:

After all the insulting remarks directed at me for all the time it
took me to add my installment a year ago, I'm put on my mettle to do
better this time. Sooooo, here I am, writing the very day the robin
reached me. Oh, yes, Eddie A., I can't use the air mail method this
year, either, because we simply can't get hold of the stamps here and,
anyway, there would probably be less time differential from Free Mail,
because we are in the same theatre (or have you left by now?)

Whoever said that a lot of water can pass under the dam, or over
the bridge, in a year or so, wasn't just a-clicking his gums! The 97th
Infantry Division is probably the most-traveled outfit in the U. S. Army
today. Last December we were within two days of leaving for a Pacific
Coast POE, when our orders were canceled, and I was fortunate enough
to be home for Christmas on furlough. I returned to California just in
time to be alerted for an Atlantic Coast POE, and by March we were in
France. Our outfit remained in the rear area, training, for about a
month, and was rushed onto the "line" the last day of March. Like
Andy Marshall, I was in on the Battle of the Ruhr Pocket in fact, we
were close to the 13th Armored a number of times.

Hardly had that campaign ended than we were off for
Czechoslovakia and the Army of Old Blood-and-Guts. The division made
three thrusts across the old boundary from Germany and on V.E. Day
was in the neighborhood of Pilsen (You know, Pilsener Beer!) Once
before Eger, the capitol of Sudetenland, we received plenty of opposition from Jerry snipers, who were well dug-in, and I received a graze
wound across the fanny. Fortunately, it was an easy way to earn the
Purple Heart, as I wasn't even stopped and our roughest action was
later in the day. Another time, near a small town called Ronsperg, five
of us shot it out in the darkness with a Heinie night patrol, drawing a
beltful (25 rounds) of machine gun fire over our heads. Luckily we
had the drop on them, and although one of our men received a shallow
shoulder wound, we drove the enemy away.

We saw .88 fire at times, and found it deadly accurate, but I thank my lucky stars that we joined in the Battle of Germany late enough to see relatively little enemy artillery action and no Luftwaffe planes. My experience was broadening and, now that it is all over, I wouldn't exchange it for the world. Still, I've seen enough action, with my limited experience, to have a bellyfull. You boys who saw it a lot tougher, like Eddie Andrews last Thanksgiving Day, sure had it hot and heavy.

After V.E. Day, our division began to sweat it out, wondering what was in the cards for us, but the answer wasn't long in coming. We were soon alerted for a westward journey, being one of the first divisions to redeploy to the Pacific. A month at home with the family on furlough in July, was a wonderful experience, but over all too soon. Supposedly we were to have had two months of advanced training at Fort Bragg, N. C., but by the end of August we had crossed the continent and were on our way across the Pacific. I spent a delightful evening with Emily and Jack Morse in Seattle on the only pass I received on the West Coast.

I've gone on at great length and must begin to think about the wind-up. To make the story short, I am now in a camp, formerly occupied by Japanese O.C.S., near Maebashi, a silk manufacturing center, 60 miles northwest of Tokyo. The division is part of the army of occupation and, of course, our duties are policing areas that are potential military targets in event of any uprisings. So far the Nips have been behaving well. I'm a squad leader, with the rank of Staff Sergeant, but tomorrow leave my company to serve on a detached assignment of some kind with the Division Finance Office. One thing I don't want to do is become the indispensable man, for on November 10th, second anniversary of my induction, I am eligible to apply for discharge, because the Army considers a man of 35 too old for its purposes. I'm glad it does, for I'm anxious to "reconvert", like Bob, Mussy and maybe others have already done. Let's do as Rich Goodwin suggests: work our fingers to the bone to prevent recurrence of these terrible wars. Maybe some of you didn't actually serve the colors in uniform, but I bet none of you can say that you didn't find your lives vastly changed. We don't want our children to be in on the next fracas, which will be a real nightmare.

Family notes: never seen Barby looking better. She does a lot of entertaining at the Officer's Club and Buddies' Club in Boston, and right now is teaching, part-time, at the nursery school in West Newton, where our Ned, aged 3 1/2, started his scholastic career October 1st. He's husky enough to take on the Vose Twins, and then some!

Maybe the Dover Bender will be a reality soon--I hope.

> Always affectionately,
> EDDIE.

Edward Andrews
United States Navy
Camp Elliott
San Diego, Calif.
November 12, 1945

Hello gang!

Having just received one half of the chain letter from Ed in Japan,
I'll not delay its progress any longer than I can help. However, the half
containing the route slip still has not arrived so this will have to be
held until it does. There may be considerable delay in receiving my
mail for several weeks now too.

As you can see from the address, I am no longer a sea-going sailor.
After two years, plus a few days, I was relieved of command of my
destroyer escort. Together we steamed one hundred and fifteen thousand miles or so, through every hazard the Pacific Ocean has to offer,
including many additional the Japs threw in for good measure. We
earned four battle stars, and came home without the loss of a man.
Now the ship is going into inactive status, and, being no longer of any
use to her, so am I!

My present location is a so-called "Intake Station" where all hands
being discharged from the naval service are gathered while awaiting
transportation. There is a four day delay here, doubtless a demand of
the railroads. However, my time is up tomorrow, when I entrain for
New York and the Separation Center. The latter takes about eight
hours, so I am told, and then my naval career is all over but for the
Tall Tales.

It has been a long one--almost <u>five</u> years to the day--and, in a great
many ways, an interesting one too. I have seen plenty of the world,
which is supposed to be broadening, so you educators say (Now I'll
have to engage in some kind of lengthening process to keep from being
one-sided). For my money I have seen just about all of travel I care to
for many years to come.

I have visited Panama, Costa Rica, Cuba, Jamaica, Trinidad,
Bermuda, Bahamas, Perlas Islands, Galapagos Island, Bora Bora, New
Hebrides, Solomons, New Guinea, Admiralty Islands, Easter and
Western Carolines, Philippines, Treasure Islands, Marshalls, Hawaii,
and many others too numerous to mention. Considerable time was
spent around New Guinea where we engaged in shore bombardments,
initial landings, and naval warfare in general. We also saw considerable of the Philippine campaign, making a small bid for fame while
doing our bit to remain alive last Thanksgiving time.

We were caught directly in the paths of two typhoons, the first of
which, south of the Fijis, we survived by divine providence alone. The
second caught me as commanding officer of a convoy from Manila to
Okinawa to Tokyo, The storm hit us between Luzon and Okinawa and

scattered the convoy over ten thousand square miles of ocean. That was a real mess, but no lives were lost, and I was awarded a letter of commendation for my efforts. This all happened only last September.

So much for the war.--Now as far as the future is concerned I have many dreams and some indefinite plans. There is a good possibility that I may engage in business more or less for myself, as a manufacturer's agent, with offices in New York. That is what I would like to do, but I'll have to study the situation at close hand before deciding. Barbara Elizabeth, our daughter, is now eight and she and Peggy have been keeping things running during my long absence. They have done a wonderful job and I can hardly wait to be with them again.

When I see you all at Dover, I'll have a million yarns to spin. By then they should be magnified to interesting proportions. See you then. As ever,

EDDIE


Timothy Rhodes
768 Foxdale Ave.
Winnetka, Ill.
Dec. 10, 1945.

Dear Gang:

It sure was interesting to read all the letters. I wonder if the Eddies and Andy realize how interested we all are in the fighting we missed. I only get an idea of it when some one I know is telling of it. Is it modesty or some new-fangled mental hygiene that keeps your comments so brief?

As some of you know, I have moved out to Winnetka, a North Shore suburb of Chicago, to teach in the local Country Day School. As I enjoyed Jack Morse's report on the Northwest, I'll submit mine on Chicago. Like Mussey's neighbors, mine are preoccupied with money. Unlike his, however, they have lots of it. In this difference, I think Jack has the best of it, for not only do I have to struggle with very high prices, but the morale of money makers, their money made, is rather contemptible; ostentation and social nonsense rule their lives. The struggles of people to get money they lack is not exalting but is at least perfectly decent. I feel rather strongly about this, as I find that the children are victims. Winnetka provides everything for children except homes. Adult contacts of children out of school are often largely with superstitious or at least uneducated maids. One mother, whose son is a boarder, raised Hell with the school when she found that Thanksgiving was a 4-day, not a 1-day holiday. For the first time in many years, I have found discipline a problem. I have it pretty well

licked now, as a result of getting sometimes so tough I hardly recognize myself. The other day in a study hall where you could have heard
a pin drop I found myself gloating like a bully. Oh well, it may not
always be so. Perhaps the war has upset them.

We found some very nice people in a singing group here who
turned out mostly to be eastern. Jimmy Dennison's sister, Ed Yeoman's
uncle, and several from Brookline.

There is no scenery to please the outer eye and to cheer the inner
soul has been made at best difficult by the dominance hereabouts of
the WCTU. I have to borrow a car and drive 15 miles to Chicago's city
limits to buy the heartwarming brew.

It annoys me that out here in the free and easy west one is
expected to cooperate with the police. Picked up the other night for
lacking a light on my bike I was exhorted to set a good example to the
children. The cop took it for granted that I was on his side.

As for the family news, we have another child since I last wrote
and have lost our car to an irresponsible telephone pole.

Here is my 10¢ worth on the atomic bomb: The only countries in
danger of say 40% destruction--100% would profit no one--are the U. S.
and Russia. If one of them is mauled, then there will be only one great
power, which will run things, not democratically, to be sure, but perhaps with some success. None of the sensible proposals will be adopt-
ed, but you cannot tell the future. Fear alone may restrain an aggres-
sor till we grow up.

>                    Yours truly till we're atomized,
>                    TIM.

# NOTES

CHAPTER 1

1. Linder & Company, 1948: *The First Hundred Years, 1848–1948: Being a brief history of Linder & Company, Inc. and its antecedent firm of Linder and Meyer, Boston.* The Barta Press, Boston, Massachusetts.

2. Letters addressed to Mrs. George Linder on file at the Francis A. Countway Library of Medicine at the Harvard Medical School.

CHAPTER 3

1. Goodwin, R. H. 1937. "The role of auxin in leaf development in *Solidago* species." *Amer. Jour. Botany* 24(1): 43–51; "The cytogenetics of two species of *Solidago* and its bearing on their polymorphy in nature." *Amer. Jour. Botany* 24(7): 423–432; "Studies on the seedling development of *Solidago rugosa* Mill. *S. sempervirens* L. and the reciprocal hybrids between them." *Amer.*

*Jour. Botany* 24(9): 627–640; "Notes on the distribution and hybrid origin of X *Solidgo asperula." Rhodora* 39: 22–28.

CHAPTER 5

1. Goodwin, R. H. 1939. Evidence for the presence in certain ether extracts of substances partially masking the activity of auxin. *Amer. Jour. Botany* 26(3): 130–135.

2. Goodwin, R. H., and D. R. Goddard. 1940. "The oxygen consumption of isolated woody tissues." *Amer. Jour. Botany* 27(4): 234–237.

3. Charles, D. R., and R. H. Goodwin. 1943. "An estimate of the minimum number of genes differentiating two species of goldenrod with respect to their morphological characters." *Amer. Naturalist* 27: 53–60.

4. Goodwin, R. H. 1944. "The inheritance of flowering time in a short-day species, *Solidago sempervirens* L." *Genetics* 29: 503–519.

5. Goodwin, R. H. 1941. "On the inhibition of the first internode of *Avena* by light." *Amer. Jour. Botany* 28(4): 325–332.

6. Goodwin, R. H. 1942. "On the development of xylary elements in the first internode of *Avena* in dark and light." *Amer. Jour. Botany* 29(10): 818–828.

7. Goodwin, R. H., and Royal E. Shanks. 1943. "Notes on the flora of Monroe County, N.Y." *Proc. Rochester Acad. Sci.* 8(6): 299–331.

8. Goodwin, R. H. 1943. "The flora of Mendon Ponds Park." *Proc. Rochester Acad. Sci.* 8(5): 233–289.

9. Rodgers, D. 1942. *John Torrey: A Story of North American Botany.* Princeton: Princeton Univ. Press, p. 352.

10. Goodwin, R. H., and W. Stepka. 1945. "Growth and differentiation in the root tip of *Phleum pratense." Amer. Jour. Botany* 32(1): 36–46.

11. Goodwin, R. H., and O. vH. Owens. 1947. "The formation of chlorophyll a in etiolated oat seedlings." *Plant Physiology* 22(2): 197–200.

12. Stafford, H. 1948. "Studies on the growth and xylary development of *Phleum pratense* seedlings in darkness and in light." *Amer. Jour. Botany* 35(1): 706–715.

13. Goodwin, R. H., and F. Kavanagh. 1949. "The isolation of scopoletin, a blue-fluorescing compound from oat roots." *Bull. Torrey Botanical Club*

76(4): 255–265.

14. Kavanagh, F., and R. H. Goodwin 1949. "The relationship between pH and fluorescence of several organic compounds." *Arch. Biochem.* 20(2): 315-324; Goodwin, R. H., and F. Kavanagh. 1950. "Fluorescence of coumarin derivatives as a function of pH." *Arch. Biochem.* 27(1): 152–173, and 1952. *Arch. Biochem.* 36(2) 442–455; Goodwin, R. H., and B. M. Pollock. 1954. "Ultraviolet absorption spectra of coumarin derivatives." *Arch. Biochem & Biophysics* 49(1): 1–6, and *Arch. Biochem.* 49(1): 1–6.

15. Goodwin, R. H., and C. Taves. 1950. "The effect of coumarin derivatives on the growth of *Avena* roots." *Amer. Jour. Botany* 37(3): 224–231.

16. Goodwin, R. H., V. Koski, and O. vH. Owens. 1951. "The distribution and properties of a porphyrin from the epidermis of *Vicia* shoots." *Amer. Jour. Botany* 38(8): 629–635.

17. Goodwin, R. H., and O. vH. Owens. 1951. "The effectiveness of the spectrum in *Avena* internode inhibition." *Bull. Torrey Botanical Club* 78(1) 11–21.

18. Goodwin, R. H., and B. M. Pollock. 1954. "Studies on roots. I. Properties and distribution of fluorescent constituents in *Avena* roots." *Amer. Jour. Botany* 41(6): 516–520; Pollock, B. M., R. H. Goodwin, and S. Green. 1954. "Studies on roots. II. Effects of coumarin, scopoletin and other substances on growth." *Amer. Jour. Botany* 41(6): 521–529.

19. Goodwin, R. H., and C. J. Avers. 1956. "Studies on roots. III. An analysis of root growth in *Phleum pratense* using photomicrographic records." *Amer. Jour. Botany* 43(7): 479–487; "Studies on roots. IV. Effects of coumarin and scopoletin on the standard root growth pattern on *Phleum pratense.*" *Amer. Jour. Botany* 43(8): 612–620.

20. Goodwin, R. H. 1972. "Studies on roots. V. Effects of indoleacetic acid on the standard growth pattern of *Phleum pratense.*" *Botanical Gazette* 133(3): 224–229.

CHAPTER 6

1. Christiansen, Gordon S. Undated. *Survival in Nuclear War: A Vanishing Possibility.* New London, Connecticut. Privately printed.

2. D'Muhala, Thomas F., Richard H. Goodwin, Paul Haake, and Gifford

B. Pinchot. 1978. *Nuclear Power in Connecticut: A Scientific Evaluation.* New London, Connecticut. Mimeographed Report.

3. Hertsgaard, Mark. 1999. *Earth Odyssey: Around the World in Search of Our Environmental Future.* Random House, Inc.: New York, N.Y., p. 372.

4. Ehrlich, Paul R., Carl Sagan, Donald Kennedy, and Walter Orr Roberts. 1984. *The Cold and the Dark: The World After Nuclear War.* New York: W. W. Norton, p. 229.

CHAPTER 8

I. Niering, William A., and Richard H. Goodwin. 1962. "Ecological studies in the Connecticut Arboretum Natural Area. I. Introduction and a survey of vegetation types." *Ecology* 43(1): 41–54.

2. Goslee, Sarah C. 1998. "The effects of environmental factors and land-use history on the long-term vegetation dynamics of the Bolleswood Natural Area, Connecticut College Arboretum." Ph.D. Dissertation, Duke University, Durham, N.C.

3. Mitchell, Carolyn C., and William A. Niering. 1993. "Vegetation change in a topogenic bog following beaver flooding." *Bulletin Torrey Botanical Club* 120(2): 136–147.

4. American Association for Advancement of Science Council Study Committee on Natural Areas as Research Facilities, Report. F. Raymond Fosberg, Ed. 1961. Symposium on College Natural Areas. Robert Allerton Park, University of Illinois, Proceedings. June 1, 1962.

CHAPTER 9

I. Goodwin, Richard H., "A Biological Inventory of the Burnham Brook Preserve." Ecological Studies Leaflet No. 9, The Nature Conservancy, Washington, D.C., 1966. pp. 25–39.

2. Cooley, Susan D., *Country Walks in Connecticut: A Guide to The Nature Conservancy Preserves.* Boston: Appalachian Mountain Club, 1982. p. 213.

3. Carey, Andrew B., et al. 1981. Trans. Northeast Sect. Wildlife Soc. 38: 90–104; Carey, Marion G., et al. 1981. *Jour. Medical Entomology* 18 (2): 175–176: Main, Andrew J., et al. 1982. *Jour. Medical Entomology* 19 (6): 655–664.

4. Hemingson, Joyce. 1986. "The Pollen Biology of *Clethra alnifolia* L. (Clethraceae)." Doctoral Dissertation, University of Connecticut. pp. 1–57.

5. Lee, Deborah. 1991. "The Feeding Ecology of *Xylopus par* (Cocquillet) (Diptera: Chionomidae), a Wood-eating Midge." Doctoral Dissertation, University of Connecticut.

6. Askins, Robert A., M. J. Philbrick, and D. S. Sugueno. 1987. *Biol. Conservation* 34: 129–152; Askins, Robert A., J. F. Lynch, and R. Greenberg. 1990, in *Current Ornithology*, Dennis M. Power, Ed., vol. 7, chap. 1, pp. 1–57.

7. Pierce, Benjamin A., and J. M. Harvey. 1987. *Copeia* 1987 (1): 94–103.

8. Orwig, David A., and D. R. Foster. 1998. "Forest Response to the Introduced Woolly Adelgid in Southern New England." *Jour. Torrey Bot. Soc.* 125 (1): 60–73.

9. McDonnell, Mark. 1974. "The Vegetation and Microclimate of a Small Valley Located in East Haddam, Connecticut." Undergrad. Independent Study Report, Conn. College. p. 32; White, Bill. 1975. "A Study in the Environmental Factors Determining Vegetation Type along Burnham Brook." Student Report, Conn. College. p, 18; Attai, Linnette J., and Wenley Ferguson. 1987. "Relationship between Small Mammal Populations and the Size of Isolated Forest Tracts." Undergrad. Independent Study Report, Conn. College. p.9; Hartvigesen, Gregg. 1987. "The Impact of Browsing by White-tailed Deer (*Odocoilus virginianus*) on Forest Strusture in Connecticut." Masters Thesis, Conn. College. p. 29; Markow, Joseph. 1995. "Territorial Behavior in Three Species of Plethedontid Salamanders (*Plethedon cinerius, Euricea bislineata, and Hemidactylium scutatum*)." Honors Thesis, Conn. College. p. 50; Brawley, A. Hunter. 1993. "The Effects of Soils in RainWater Chemistry." Limnology Class Report, Conn. College. p. 6.

10. Goodwin, Richard H. "The Flora of the Burnham Brook Preserve of The Nature Conservancy." *Studies in Human Ecology*, Connecticut College, New London, CT. No. 13, 1985, p 56; No. 13a,1987, p. 63; No. 13b, 1991, p. 69.

11. Goodwin, Richard H. "Vertebrates of the Burnham Brook Preserve of The Nature Conservancy. *Studies in Human Ecology*, Connecticut College, New London, CT. No. 14, 1985, p. 20; No. 14a, 1991, p. 21.

12. Breeding Bird Census Reports: 1964 *Audubon Field Notes* 18 (6):

568–569; 1965 Idem. 19 (6): 592-593; 1967 Idem. 21(6): 669–670; 1981 American Birds 36(I): 75–76; 1989 *J. Field Ornithology* 61:1 Suppl.; 1990 Idem. 62 (I): Suppl.; 1991 Idem. 63(I) Suppl.; 1992 Idem.64(I) Suppl.; 1993 Idem. 65(2) Suppl.; 1994 Idem, 66 (4) Suppl.; 1995 Idem. 67(4) Suppl.

13. Pado, Kerry S., and Richard H. Goodwin. 1987. "Butterflies of the Burnham Brook Preserve." Typed Report. p. 2.

14. Gephard, Stephen. 1995. "Fishes of Burnham Brook Preserve, East Haddam, Connecticut." Typed Report. p. 9.

15. Mason, Christopher O. 1977. "A Vegetation Inventory of the Burnham Brook Preserve, East Haddam, Connecticut." *Studies in Human Ecology* No. 9, Connecticut College. p. 46; Johnson, Loretta. 1984. "Natural Resource Inventory of Burnham Brook Preserve: Nodding Fern Tract." TNC Internship Report; Fike, B. Jean. 1994. "Inventory of Plant Communities in the Burnham Brook Preserve, East Haddam, Connecticut." Masters Thesis, Connecticut College. p. 72.

16. Goodwin, Richard H. 1996. "Burnham Brook Preserve and Acid Rain." *Conn. Botanical Society Newsletter* 24(2): 7–9.

CHAPTER 10

1. James, Frances C., and Charles E. McCullouch. 1995. "The Strength of Inferences about Causes and Trends in Population." In: *Ecology and Management of Neotropical Birds: A Synthesis and Review of Cricitcal Issues.* T. E. Martin and D. M. Finch, eds. New York: Oxford University Press, pp. 40–51.

CHAPTER 11

1. Carr, Albert Z. *The World of William Walker.* New York: Harper & Row, 1963, p. 289.

2. Hertsgaard, Mark. *Earth Odyssey: Around the World in Search of Our Environmental Future.* New York: Broadway Books, 1998, p. 372.

# INDEX OF NAMES

Adams, Alexander B., 176, 177, 180, 181

Adams, John C., 148

Ahlgren, Clifford, 140

Akeley, Mary L. Jobe, 177

Albizzi, Marquis degli, 34

Alitiz, Maria Buchinger de, 225

Ames, Blanche, 5

Ames, Oakes, 5

Ames, Oakes (*Grandson of Oakes and Blanche*), 6

Anable, Gloria, 176

Andrews, Edward F., 19, 125, 310, 322

Angelo, Heath, 163, 165

Ardwin, Margaret, 204

Arnold, Elting, 168, 225

Askins, Robert A., 202

Atkins, Edwin A., 44

Atkins, Mrs. Edwin A., 45

Avers, Charlotte J., 120

Avery, George S., Jr., 99, 113, 155, 156

Bailey, Irving W., 39, 104

Baker, John H., 166

Baldwin, Malcolm F., 219

Barbour, Thomas, 45, 50

Barnard, Geoffrey S., 266

Baxter, Milton S., 153

Belardo, Joseph, 197

Bemis, Grosvenor, 215

Bennink, Richard E., 173
Bent, Richard, 125, 307
Berendsen, Ian, 292
Berendsen, Ruth, 292
Bingham, Hiram, 257
Bird, Mary, 34, 47
Bishop, Sherman C., 109, 110
Blair, William D., Jr., 195, 197
Blanchard, Nancy Wight, 13
Blunt, Katharine, 156
Boardman, Walter S., 180, 225
Bolan, Richard S., 227
Bosa, Mario A., 226
Bowman, Wallace D., 141, 217, 238
Boyer, Homer, 19
Boysen-Jensen, P., 99, 100, 101
Brainerd, John, 173
Braunfield, Robert A., 192
Breasted, James H., 22
Brenneman, Russell L., 219
Briggs, L. Cabot, 172
Briggs, Winslow R., 217
Brooks, Ernest, Jr., 162
Brown, Allen, 136
Bryan, Kirk, 35
Buck, Elizabeth, 116
Buck, John B., 116
Burke, Roger M., 197
Butler, Eva L., 171
Butler, Sewall, 172
Butler, Sylvester B., 171

Caldicott, Helen, 228
Caldwell, Lynton K., 220
Callahan, Mrs. William, 252
Calvin, Melvin, 113
Carroll, Allen T., 192, 262
Chapin, Melville, 217, 222
Chapman, Conrad, 166, 225
Charles, Donald R., 105, 125

Chen, Bo-Quan, 205
Childs, Edward C., 159
Christiansen, Gordon S., 126
Chu, Charles J., 271, 278
Chute, Austin, 18
Clark, Mrs. Bill, 195
Clausen, Jens, 104
Collins, George, 178
Conklin, Marilyn J., 194
Cooke, Todd J., 221
Cooley, George R., 170
Cooley, Susan D., 192, 200
Copp, Belton A., 141, 157, 175, 177, 215, 217
Cosenza, Benjamin, 200
Councilman, W., 11
Crozier, William J., 32

D'Muhala, Thomas F., 129
Damman, Antoni W. H., 204
Dana, Mrs. Albro, 172
Darling, Louis, 174, 210
Darling, Sir Frank, 217
Day, Ernie, 180
Dayton, Wallace D., 183
Deacock, Warwick, 286
Delisle, Albert, 44
Denny, Charles S., 35, 125, 315
Densmore, Roseanne, 150
Dent, Charles E. , 112
DeSante, David F., 234
Dewey, Chester, 108
Dinsmore, Ruth, 2
Duer, Leland B., 194

East, E. M., 39
Edison, Theodore M., 162
Egler, Frank E., 158, 175
Emerson, Ralph, 40
Emerson, Robert, 104

Eplan, Leon, 227
Erickson, Ralph O., 280
Esau, Katherine, 118

Farlow, John Smith, 9
Farlow, Lilian Horseford, 9
Farlow, William Gilson, 9, 10
Feldman, Lewis J., 221
Fell, Barbara, 160, 162, 169
Fell, George B., 160, 162, 163, 167, 169
Fernald, Merritt L., 30, 32, 104
Fiske, Andrew, 250
Fosberg, F. Raymond, 166, 173, 181, 225
Foster, Charles H. W., 181
Foster, David R., 238
Foster, Edwin C., 154
Foster, H. Lincoln, 159
Fowler, Charles, 28
French, C. Stacy, 118
Fuller, John C., 215, 302

Gamboa, Annie Simpson de, 266
Garceau, Oliver, 18
Gauci, V. J., 233
Gaylord, Ann, 291
Gephard, Stephen, 204, 206
Giptein, Edith E., 260
Giptein, Edward, 261
Goddard, David R., 103, 109, 110, 125
Goddard, Doris, 125
Gofman, John W., 127
Gomez, Luis Diego, 266, 267
Goodwin, Harry Manley, 1, 3, 299
Goodwin, Mary Blanchard Linder, 1, 4, 5, 15, 215
Goodwin, Mary Linder. *See* Wetzel
Goodwin, Richard D., 4

Goodwin, Richard H., 314
Goodwin, Richard Hale, Jr., 105, 137, 140, 146, 148, 262, 265, 267, 291
Goodwin, Samuel D., 4
Goodwin, Sarah C., 4
Goslee, Sarah, 158
Gough, Allen, 141
Grace, Charles M., 225
Grasso, Ella T., 128
Green, Paul B., 221
Greene, Susan, 119
Griffin, Jeffrey F., 238
Gunning, Brian E. S., 221

Haake, Paul, 129
Hake, Sarah, 222
Hale, George Ellery, 20, 23, 24, 299
Hall, Henry S., Jr., 50
Hammerschlag, Robert J., 168
Hancock, John, 13
Hand, Chauncey H., 198
Harrison, Gordon, 180
Harte, John, 132
Harvey, John M., 203
Hawkes, Al, 172
Heimsch, Charles, 280
Heisey, William, 104
Heller, Alfred E., 184
Hemingson, Joyce C., 202
Henderson, James H. M., 280
Henkle, Edward, 216
Henry, Sarah Bates, 222, 229
Hepler, Peter K., 221
Hertsgaard, Mark, 130, 279
Hervey, Annette, 220
Hiesey, William M., 280
Hill, James D., 209
Hoagland, D. R., 113
Hofgaard, William, 100

Hopson, Myra, 175
Hruska, Allan J., 232
Hunt, Kenneth W. , 165
Hunter, Mr. and Mrs. Ivor E. G., 261
Huntington, Henry E., 24

Ide, John M., 170, 185, 187
Ide, Margaret, 170, 185

James, Frances C., 244
Janzen, Daniel H., 263
Jeffrey, Edward C., 30, 32
Jenkins, Robert E., 182
Johnson, Huey D., 181, 227
Johnson, Lucy Baines, 179
Jones, Franklin, 179
Jordan, Philip H., Jr., 194
Jordan, Sheila, 194
Jorling, Thomas C., 227

Kaplan, Donald R., 222
Kashanski, Barbara R., 196
Kashanski, John, 196
Kavanagh, Frederick, 107, 114, 119,
     215, 220, 221, 229
Keck, David D., 104
Kendall, Henry W., 128
Kiff, Lloyd F., 256
Killip, Ellsworth P., 153
Kirkpatrick, Jay, 236
Klemens, Michael W., 204
Knight, Samuel H., 32
Koski, Violet M., 118
Krause, Mary Lou, 235

Lanham, Sandra, 230
Lariviere, Carol, 192
Law, Danielle, 283
Lee, Deborah, 202, 204
Lefebvre, Edith, 194

Lefebvre, Gertrude, 194
Lehmann, Ernst, 123
Lemmon, Carol, 204
Leuchtenberg, Duke Dmitri von, 34
Linder, A. Hosmer, 11
Linder, Captin William, 6
Linder, David H., 11
Linder, Elinor Alberts, 11
Linder, George, 11
Linder, George A., 7
Linder, George II, 6
Linder, John F., 11
Linder, Mary F. *See* Putnam, Mary
Linder, Mary Frances, 7, 8, 11, 17
Linder, Muriel, 11
Lintilhac, Crea S., 238
Little, Charles E., 227, 243
Lord, Elizabeth M., 221
Loucks, Orie L., 244
Loveridge, Arthur, 50, 97
Lubart, Joseph, 209
Lurtsema, Robert J., 303
Lutz, Harold S., 158

Macklin, June B., 260
Magrath, George B., 11
Malone, Thomas F., 224
Marcy, Florence E., 2
Marcy, Richard, 3
Mark, Cyrus, 180
Marquette, Cindy, 148
Marshall, Andrew, 125, 312
Marvin, James W., 213, 215, 222
Mason, Charles N., 225
Mathias, Mildred E., 252, 266, 267
Mathieson, Helen Fricke, 250
Matthews, Warren, 153
Meadows, Donella H., 227
Metzler, Kenneth, 204
Meyerowitz, Elliot M., 222

Miller, Gerry, 204
Miller, Richard G., 225
Miller, Sid, 157
Moreau, R. E., 54
Morse, John M., 125, 318
Munns, Edward N., 167

Navarro, Juan Carlos, 271
Netting,  M. Graham, 181
Nichols, Robert L., 41
Niering, William A., 158, 162, 169,
     216, 250
Noonan, Patrick F., 183

Olson, W. Kent, 195
Orellana, Francisco de, 254
Os, Joe Van, 291
Owens, Olga von H., 114, 118

Pado, Kerry S., 204
Page, James K., Jr., 219
Parker, Dale, 284
Parker, George H., 27
Parnall, Ruth, 155
Pattison, Ethel E., 194
Pentecost, Richard, 125
Perkins, Frank E., 2
Perkins, Major, 57
Perkins, Robert, Jr., 166
Perkins, Timothy, 245
Pfanner, Karen L. *See* Reynolds
Pfanner, Ruth , 252, 262, 291
Phillips, Roger, 205
Phillips, Walter, 153
Pierce, Benjamin A., 203
Pinchot, Gifford B., 129
Pindar, Patricia M., 195
Pizarro, Gonzalo, 254
Poethig, Richard Scott, 222
Pollock, Bruce M., 115, 119

Pough, Richard H., 161
Pratt, Albert, 18
Proctor, Noble S., 204
Prouty, Dwight, 11
Prouty, Dwight, Jr., 11
Prouty, Ethie B., 11
Prouty, Lewis I, 17
Prouty, Richard, 16, 125, 313
Putnam, Mary Linder, 49
Putnam, Patrick Tracy Lowell, 49

Ratcliff, Jack, 18
Rawles, Mary, 109
Reid, Christine, 34, 47
Reynolds, Karen, 192, 251
Reynolds, Timothy, 192, 251
Rhodes, Timothy, 16, 17, 20, 28, 125,
     197, 235, 285, 287, 299, 323
Ripley, George K., 173
Robbins, William J., 114, 220
Robinson, Edward W., 125, 308, 320
Rollins, Reed C., 280
Rosenthal, Jack, 156
Ross, James B., 167, 170
Ross, Malcolm, 53
Rossbach, George, 104
Rossbach, Ruth Peabody, 104
Rowell, Hugh, 252
Russell, Scott D., 221
Ryerson, William N., 241

Sabido, Miguel, 240
Sachs, Tsvi, 221
Sax, Karl, 240
Schacht, Robert H., 19, 302
Scheffey, Andrew J. W., 227
Schelpe, E. Ted, 283
Scheres, Ben J. G., 222
Sears, Paul B., 158, 166
Shanks, Betty, 116

Shanks, Royal E., 108, 116
Sharpe, Richard, 190
Shelford, Victor E., 161
Sigman, Marilyn, 150
Siver, Peter A., 208
Skutch, Alexander F., 266
Slawson, Marguerite, 186
Smiley, Daniel, 166
Smith, Eleanor, 225
Smith, Harold T. U., 41
Smith, Martin, 236
Spoehr, Hermann A., 104
Stafford, Helen A., 114
Stebbins, G. Ledyard, 28
Steever, E. Zell, 174
Stepka, William, 111, 118, 119, 126, 192
Stern, Curt, 109
Steward, F. C., 112
Stocking, Patricia, 173
Stoiber, Richard, 33
Storey, H. H., 55
Strayer, Lucie M., 262
Strong, Edward G., 187, 190, 197
Swan, Walter A., 154

Tarpill, Andrew, 186
Tarpill, Dorothy, 186
Taves, Carolyn, 115
Thimann, Kenneth V., 39, 99
Thomas, Lewis, 132
Torrey, John, 108
Tritton, Louise M., 238
Tyree, Melvin T., 231

Ugalde, Alvaro F., 226
Ulyate, Ray, 72
Ungerer, Mr., 58

Vestal, Paul A., 41, 44

Vine, Craig O., 71
Visser, Choet, 281
Vogelmann, Hubert W., 220, 222
Vose, Robert C., Jr., 125, 197, 316
Vose, S. Morton II, 125, 197, 317

Wadleigh, Kenneth R., 2
Wahle, Richard, 192
Walker, William, 264
Wardlaw, Claude W., 221
Weston, William H., 40
Wetmore, Ralph H., 28, 37, 39, 104, 121, 221
Wetzel, Mary Goodwin, 105, 120, 137, 217, 267
Wheeler, Bernice M., 262
Willier, Benjamin H., 109
Wilson, Alexander T., 223
Wintsch, Robert P., 203
Wright, Inga-Lisa, 149

Zickefoose, Julie, 192, 204, 262